Wild Flower Habitats
of
Hertfordshire
Past, Present and Future (?)

Wild Flower Habitats

of

Hertfordshire

Past, Present and Future (?)

by

BRIAN SAWFORD

Photographs by the Author

Wild Flower Illustrations by Peter Walton

Includes

Comprehensive Checklists of Wild Flowers

for all Major Habitats

Castlemead
PUBLICATIONS
WARE

First published in 1990

CASTLEMEAD PUBLICATIONS
Swains Mill, 4A Crane Mead, Ware
Herts., SG12 9PY

Proprietors: Wards's Publishing Services

ISBN 0 948555 09 2

British Library Cataloguing in Publication Data
Sawford, Brian
Wild flower habitats in Hertfordshire.
1. Hertfordshire. Flowering plants
I. Title
582. 13094258

ISBN 0–948555–09–2

Typeset by Hertcom (formerly Prefis) Ltd

Printed in Great Britain in 10 pt. Century Type by
The Bath Press, Avon

To
Gavin, Laura, Daniel
Emma, Darryn and Kevin

' – O precious days, O happy hours,
How mem'ry backward lingers,
To pluck again the dewy flowers,
With childhood's rosy fingers!'

ANON

Foreword

One day in late June, 1855, two correspondents from the *Phytologist* journal went on 'a day's Botanising about Tring, Herts'. They had an enjoyable excursion, travelling up from London by train and returning in time for dinner. They rambled about the local woods and fields, and remarked on the diversity of the Herts landscape: 'the crowned heights' of the beechwoods, 'the canals, reservoirs, and last, not least, the railways, formed a picture not easily forgotten'. It was an account of a day out in west Herts that could have been written tod ay.

But the flowers were a huge disappointment. There were almost no orchids on the downs and few cornfield weeds, and the editors of the *Phytologist* published an appeal for more information about what was happening to Hertfordshire's wild flower habitats. Nearly a century and a half later Brian Sawford's elegant and comprehensive book has provided an answer. Surveying the history and ecology of the county's woodlands, heaths, fields and wasteland he has coloured in what our frustrated 19th century explorers had begun to glimpse: that the relationship between wild flowers and their habitats is critical and complex. Subtle changes in the way that grassland and arable is managed, for instance, of a kind that were certainly beginning in the 1850s, can have a dramatic effect on their flora.

We can now count the cost of a century and a half of not just outright habitat loss but habitat degradation: ancient woodlands coniferised, rivers turned into lifeless drains, downland put under the plough, and the relentless impoverishment of the wild flowers of such favourite places.

Hertfordshire's experience of these profound ecological changes has been a mixed one. We have a good range of habitats, with a fair amount of woodland and open space, and have been spared the scale of destruction wreaked in more exclusively agricultural counties. The price we have paid is the inheritance of a landscape of fragments: patches of heathland surviving at the edge of golf courses, marshland flowers finding refuge in the corners of reservoirs. As our 19th century botanisers glimpsed, Hertfordshire is a county where natural and man-made landscapes sit very close together.

There may be some comfort in this, as the author notes in his concluding chapters on the wild flowers of artificial habitats like railway embankments and ponds. But the prospects for the specialised flora of our remaining semi-natural habitats are grim unless their attrition can be halted. Brian Sawford's survey provides an invaluable benchmark to where we stand at present, and with luck a foundation on which future restoration of wild flower habitats can be based.

RICHARD MABEY

September 1990

Acknowledgements

It is impossible to acknowledge all those who have contributed to this book. The many fieldworkers, going right back at least to the early 19th century, must however be mentioned, their thousands of hours of studies and vast accumulations of records provide much of the background to this work. To these, past and present, I express my gratitude and trust that my interpretation will, in its own way, stimulate others to follow in such dedicated and distinguished footsteps for the long-term benefit of Hertfordshire's wild flowers.

In particular I must thank my wife, Terri, and our children, to whom this book is dedicated, for their patience and support throughout the production of text. Special thanks are given to Trevor James, my colleague at North Hertfordshire Museums' Natural History Department and co-recorder of botany for the county, for much useful discussion both in the office and during our many hours of field-work together. His detailed approach to the recording of our county and meticulous documentation is a model that more should follow, proving especially valuable for today's much needed wildlife conservation.

To Susan Lee and Alan Ward of Castlemead Publications goes a sincere appreciation for all their assistance in the production of this book and their continuing commitment to quality publications with an important local bias.

Finally, particular thanks to Peter Walton for the superb illustrations which grace the pages of this book and to Richard Mabey for kindly providing the Foreword.

Contents

Contents

List of Illustrations

List of Tables

List of Colour Plates

1

Introduction

With a varied underlying geology and a long history of human occupation, the Hertfordshire landscape contains a surprisingly wide range of semi-natural habitats for wild flowers. However, as these pages will show, although a considerably diverse flora can still be found, there is an increasing concern over the losses and reductions of many, sometimes once common and widespread, species and their habitats. The aim of this book is to provide a better understanding of the complex of physical and biological interactions, particularly the seemingly overwhelming impact of human interference, that is reflected in the status and distribution of the county's wild flowers. Also, and most importantly, it is hoped that readers will be shocked at the current state of affairs and consequently motivated to seek to positively maintain and improve their environmental heritage.

All life depends upon plants. It can be certain that right from very early times and until comparatively recently a significant part of the human population had more than just a passing interest in wild flowers, shrubs and trees of the countryside. Apart from the wider and most profound importance of all green plants in creating and maintaining the atmosphere, many species were vital for everyday life; countless generations of Hertfordshire people were directly dependent upon the plants around them for food, fuel, building materials, cures and remedies. Exploitation and harnessing of the resources of the (now long destroyed) truly natural habitat of the region, coupled with human development and improved technologies, led to modified and entirely new semi-natural habitats, within which different plant communities would form. For many native and, as time passed, introduced plants, knowledge was acquired of their locations, life cycles, uses, methods of care, cultivation and control and this was passed from generation to generation. Sometimes dating back centuries, the extant vernacular names of some of our wild flowers reflect former economic, medicinal or social uses. Place names, including some of Anglo-Saxon origin, may preserve the earliest references to aspects of Hertfordshire's wild flowers and their habitats.

The written record of Hertfordshire's flora really begins in the 16th and 17th centuries when studies of plants and their uses in medicine came to the fore and with the coming of advances in printing and wider literacy. A number of very fine books on plants were produced. Most of these were just herbals but some of the more detailed works attempted to describe the distributions of, mainly medicinally, interesting wild plants and relate them to their surroundings. So began the wider studies of the British flora and the first botanical record for Hertfordshire was provided by William Turner. His *Names of Herbes*, published in 1548, notes the observation of Spindle growing 'in most plentye between Ware and Barkway' (Dony, 1967). Many contemporary herbalists were based in London and parts of, then, very rural southern Hertfordshire at least were within compass of forays to collect wild materials of their trade. Several, including the renowned Gerard and Culpepper published herbals with locations for Hertfordshire plants, sometimes in minute detail.

To date their have been three major works covering the flora of the whole county, Webb and Coleman's *Flora Hertfordiensis* (1848–1849), Pryor's *Flora of Hertfordshire* (1887) and, most importantly, John Dony's *Flora of Hertfordshire* (1967) which includes a most succinct account of the historical study of the county's flora from William Turner to the early 1960s, and which still remains, a quarter of a century later, a cornerstone for wildlife conservation in the county. These three works all contain information upon basic habitat and distribution of wild flowers, including contemporary assessments of status, but particularly valuable, and pioneering in concept, are the habitat studies and species distribution maps contained in Dony's survey. Although many changes had already occurred that allowed comparisons to be drawn with the previous floras, he was nevertheless to a large extent recording much that still remained of an 'older' countryside before the post-World War 2 boom in agriculture, development and pollution crises had gained too much of a hold. His legacy is the provision of an accurate factual basis against which later changes can be monitored.

As indicated above, disturbing losses and significant declines in both habitats and more specialised flora continue to accelerate. Hertfordshire has a poor record for the loss of wild flowers, as is evidenced in the list of extinct species contained in Appendix 2. It should be noted that there have also been gains in both habitats and species, although the majority of cases involve transitory sites, such as gravel pits and waste dumps with alien or casual plants.

Much very good wildlife conservation is taking place in the county but, as will be pointed out, never has there been such an urgent need for more as we approach the 21st century. Sound wildlife conservation can only realistically be undertaken in the light of sound knowledge of habitats and their wildlife and vegetation is the primary basis of all wildlife habitats. It is hoped that this book will encourage the wider study and enjoyment of Hertfordshire's wild flowers in their habitats and promote a fuller understanding of the urgency of the need for increased protection and conservation. Appendix 3 contains details of national and local organisations concerned with wild flower appreciation, recording and conservation to suit all abilities and interests. Particularly important is the County Flora Recording Scheme which, within the next decade, is intended to acquire comprehensive data for the publication of a new *Flora of Hertfordshire*.

Checklists of characteristic wild flowers (including some rarities) will be found for most of the major semi-natural habitats in the Appendices. Most vernacular names used are those recommended by Dony, Jury and Perring (1986) and scientific nomenclature follows that of Clapham, Tutin and Moore (1987); it should be pointed out that both may occasionally differ from names used in some of the older publications and field guides. Also arrangements of several of the checklists do not follow strict taxonomic sequences. Approximate flowering months for most species listed here are indicated in brackets after the scientific name, '(6–9)' for example stands for 'June to September'; where appropriate, brief details of status and current distribution are also included.

Scientific naming of species is based upon Linnaeus's binomial system, using Latin. Each species is allocated two names, the generic name, which has a capital initial, followed by a specific or trivial name, now always with a small initial, for example White Clover is *Trifolium repens*. After first mention, generic names may be abbreviated to their initial, for example Red Clover *T. pratense*. Strictly speaking, trivial names should be followed by the full or abbreviated surname of the person who initiated the present trivial name. If a species is reassigned to another genus, the name of the new classifier is given, with that of the original author (or its abbreviation) prefixed in brackets; for example Early Marsh Orchid *Dactylorhiza incarnata* (L.) Soó was first named by Linnaeus (in genus *Orchis*) and, later, reclassified by Soó to genus *Dactylorhiza*. Such authorisation is not shown here and the reader is referred to Clapham, Tutin and Moore (1987). Sub-species are indicated through the use of a third trivial, prefixed in this book by the abbreviation 'ssp.'. Where the exact identity of species are unknown or uncertain they are indicated thus 'sp.' (plural – 'spp.'). Varieties of a particular named species are suffixed by 'var.' and aggregates of closely related species by 'agg.'. Hybridisation occurs when one species or sub-species is fertilised by another, the resultant hybrid is indicated by the use of '×' in the scientific name, for example the cross between White Campion *S. latifolia* ssp. *alba* and Red Campion *S. dioica* is Pink Campion *S. dioica* × *latifolia*; when two genera are involved hybridisation is indicated by the use of '×' preceding the generic name, for example the cross between Common Spotted-orchid *Dactylorhiza fuchsii* and Fragrant Orchid *Gymnadenia conopsea* is × *Dactylogymnadenia cookei*. Throughout this text, species marked (*) are no longer found in Hertfordshire.

The photographs are intended to show some of the range and beauty of Hertfordshire's wild flowers and their habitats. It is recommended that the reader uses one or more wild flower identification guides as an adjunct to the fuller enjoyment of this book and of Hertfordshire's wild flowers in general. (*See* Appendix 4.)

In the accounts that follow, data up to and including 1987 have been checked against the County Herbarium and botanical records housed in the Natural History Department of North Hertfordshire Museums.

2

The County of Hertford

About forty miles (64 km) from west to east, thirty-three miles (53 km) north to south and landlocked, Hertfordshire is one of England's smaller counties. It encompasses some 630 square miles (163 415 hectares) of mainly undulating but varied countryside, upon soft, easily eroded, geological deposits. Outstanding topographical features are few and mainly confined to the escarpment of the Chalk, which forms much of the north-western boundary of the county. Hastoe Hill near Tring, at 804 feet (245 m) above sea-level, is the highest point. Away from the scarp slope the landscape is gentler. Two plateaux of higher ground stretch from Cuffley to Bushey, and from Redbourn to Hatfield. Most of the population, of just under a million, reside in the southern half of the county. Away from the conurbations much of Hertfordshire remains largely agricultural, with extensive areas of arable and improved grasslands, although, in places, albeit usually small, relicts of formerly widespread and rich wild flower habitats are still to be found.

For the purposes of natural history recording, Hertfordshire is defined as follows: all the area within the administrative boundary established in 1965, including Potters Bar Urban District (formerly in Middlesex), a small area near Holwell (formerly in Bedfordshire), and certain areas now transferred *from* Hertfordshire for administrative purposes – Barnet and East Barnet Districts (now part of the London Borough of Barnet) and parts of Hemel Hempstead Rural District (now transferred to Bedfordshire). In national and local biological recording contexts, this combined area is known as Watsonian Vice County 20, often abbreviated to VC 20.

3

Geology and Landscape

Plant distributions, as will be shown in later chapters, are closely related to the nature of the soils produced from the variety of underlying geological deposits. Hertfordshire's geology (Figure 3.1) is founded on sediments laid beneath the relatively shallow, warm seas of the Cretaceous period. The earliest of these, Gault Clay and Upper Greensand, were deposited over a hundred million years ago, and today form much of the low-lying country at the foot of the Chalk escarpment. Only small outcrops are found within the county, near Ashwell and to the north of Tring. Chalk, a soft, white limestone principally composed of the remains of micro-fossils such as foraminifera, was laid down over the Gault. Its maximum thickness in Hertfordshire is 680 feet (207 m), although much has been removed by erosion, and extensive areas are now obscured by later deposits. On the basis of its nature and included fossils the Chalk is divided into three major horizons, Lower, Middle and Upper Chalk. The upper horizons are particularly characterised by flints, which formed within the sediments after they consolidated.

Figure 3.1 *Map showing surface geology of the County of Hertfordshire*

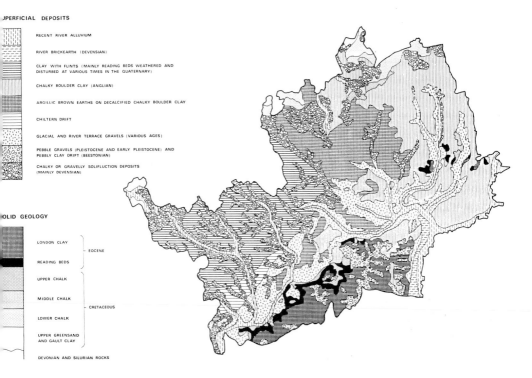

SUPERFICIAL DEPOSITS

RECENT RIVER ALLUVIUM

RIVER BRICKEARTH (DEVENSIAN)

CLAY WITH FLINTS (MAINLY READING BEDS WEATHERED AND DISTURBED AT VARIOUS TIMES IN THE QUATERNARY)

CHALKY BOULDER CLAY (ANGLIAN)

ARGILLIC BROWN EARTHS ON DECALCIFIED CHALKY BOULDER CLAY

CHILTERN DRIFT

GLACIAL AND RIVER TERRACE GRAVELS (VARIOUS AGES)

PEBBLE GRAVELS (PLEISTOCENE AND EARLY PLEISTOCENE) AND PEBBLY CLAY DRIFT (BEESTONIAN)

CHALKY OR GRAVELLY SOLIFLUCTION DEPOSITS (MAINLY DEVENSIAN)

SOLID GEOLOGY

LONDON CLAY
— EOCENE
READING BEDS

UPPER CHALK

MIDDLE CHALK
— CRETACEOUS
LOWER CHALK

UPPER GREENSAND AND GAULT CLAY

DEVONIAN AND SILURIAN ROCKS

5

Having deposited Gault Clay and Chalk over wide areas of Europe, the Cretaceous seas retreated about sixty-five million years ago, when earth movements, which were finally to form the Alpine mountains, uplifted the Earth's crust. For nearly twenty million years the newly created 'chalk' land enjoyed a sub-tropical climate and was eroded by extensive river systems. About fifty million years ago, at the start of the Eocene period, parts of eastern and southern England, including much of Hertfordshire, were again covered by a shallow sea spreading from the east. The effects of this were to erode the surface of the Chalk flat, and lay down over it thirty-to-fifty-feet thick (9 – 15 m) deposits – the Reading Beds. These consist of sands and clays over a basal pebble bed. In places the pebbles are cemented with silica and iron oxide to form a hard conglomerate known as Hertfordshire Puddingstone.

For a period the sea regressed again as further earth movements uplifted and tilted the land. Erosion followed until a further and deeper encroachment of the sea resulted in the deposition of up to 300 feet (91 m) of dark grey, stiff London Clay over the Reading Beds. As the sea finally regressed at the close of the Eocene period, about forty million years ago, beds, up to fifty feet (15 m) thick, of fine sandy clays were laid down. These are the Claygate Beds and are the youngest of Hertfordshire's solid deposits (not shown in Figure 3.1).

During the thirty-five million years or so after Eocene times, erosion removed considerable amounts of the Claygate Beds, London Clay and Reading Beds, particularly from northern and western parts of the county. Much of the Chalk was exposed to further erosion. Outliers of the Reading Beds remained on some of the south-eastern slopes of the newly formed Chiltern Hills. Today, Reading Beds still cap some of the isolated hills in the south and west of the county, although they may be obscured by later superficial deposits. Earth movements which compounded the building of the Alpine mountains of southern Europe compressed Cretaceous and Eocene strata, producing lateral folding, and some faulting across south-east England. The London basin syncline was thus formed, with its northern limb across Hertfordshire, dipping to the south-east.

Clay-with-Flints, a 'foxy reddish brown' clay with many nodular flints from the Upper Chalk, occurs over much of the Upper Chalk in the south-west. This deposit represents Tertiary, and perhaps later, erosion of the Upper Chalk, insoluble flints being left in a matrix of residual clay after dissolution of the calcium component of the Chalk. The Clay-with-Flints outcrops in north-east Hertfordshire are currently being investigated and mapped and seem likely to prove significant. Not indicated in Figure 3.1, they occur on much of the higher ground where later (Pleistocene) deposits were absent or thinner, or have been eroded. It is tentatively suggested (personal communication, Peter Hopson, British Geological Survey) that, in places, the early Tertiary erosion surface of the Chalk is being revealed. Further detailed botanical studies of these areas may show local differences reflected in their flora.

From about one-and-a-half million years ago a steadily deteriorating global climate reached its nadir in the Ice Ages of the Pleistocene period. Most of the superficial deposits were laid down during this period of rapidly fluctuating climate, which ranged form arctic to warm temperate. Glacial episodes of up to 100 000 years' duration were responsible for much erosion and, particularly, the great accumulations of superficial deposits which produced the variety of soil types of Hertfordshire. These glacials were separated by shorter interglacials when the climate was frequently much warmer than today. The nature of these stages has been determined by close examination of deposits, erosion features and fossil assemblages. Pollen remains preserved in contemporary peat and lake sediments have been particularly important in determination of climate and vegetational changes.

In the four most recent glacials, ice sheets spread into lowland Britain from montane areas of Wales, Scotland and Scandinavia. Only in the first two of these (the Beestonian and Anglian) did ice actually reach Hertfordshire. It is estimated that, at times, the moving ice sheets and glaciers may have been up to a kilometre thick. Vast amounts of bedrock were crushed, eroded and transported away by the ice, to create much of the topography we see today. The steep escarpment running south-west to north-east along much of the western margin of the county testifies to this. When climatic conditions ameliorated, meltwaters caused further erosion. In many places the ice-created topography became buried as deposits accumulated from meltwaters, and moraine was left by the retreating ice.

As glaciers and ice sheets move, their undersurfaces rasp over the rocks, grinding them up into fine clays, called *tills*. Larger fragments, often of more obdurate rocks, termed *erratics*, may be plucked off and transported with the tills. Such glacial erratics are very useful in studies of the origins and directions of movement of the glaciers. When the ice melted tills were deposited over a wide area. The Chiltern Drift, found in a narrow belt south of St Albans, and Pebbly Clay Drift of parts of south-east Hertfordshire, date from the effects of several glaciations, the first of which occurred about 500 000 years ago. Chalky Boulder Clay, a till containing abundant Chalk erratics, covers large areas of the north and east of the county, with outliers near St Albans and in the south-east. This resulted from the Anglian glaciation of some 300 000 years ago. At that time ice from noth-eastern Britain covered much of East Anglia, reaching the Chalk escarpment and with lobes penetrating the Vale of St Albans and as far as North London. It is probable that Anglian glaciers only topped and eroded the Chalk escarpment north of a line from Lilley to Whitwell, reducing its height and removing the Clay-with-Flints.

Waters flowing out from the glaciers as they advanced and retreated laid down great quantities of sands and gravels across Hertfordshire, producing a complex series of deposits, especially in the river valleys of the south and east. This situation was further complicated when Anglian ice in the Vale of St Albans blocked the proto-River Thames. Its course, north-eastwards through Hertfordshire, to reach the North Sea off Norfolk or Suffolk, was diverted eastwards through what is now London. Gravel terraces of the proto-Thames form significant deposits sweeping across the south of the county. Some of the Pebble Gravels, related to the proto-Thames and its north-flowing tributary, the proto-River Mole, are almost certainly of pre-Beestonian age and, with the exception of some parts of the Clay-with-Flints, are the oldest superficial deposits found in Hertfordshire.

Although Hertfordshire remained unglaciated during the last two cold stages (the Wolstonian and Devensian), periglacial conditions persisted. Permafrost and summer thaws caused instability in both solid and superficial deposits. With no protective vegetation to speak of, soils were washed or slid down slopes slopes to accumulate as solifluction deposits, notably on the steep-sided hills of the Chalk escarpment. Upper surfaces and thinner deposits of Boulder Clay were, and still are, affected by decalcification and solifluction to form argillic brown earth soils. Cold winds from the north and east blew large amounts of silt (*loess*) over the landscape. Much of this is incorporated within the solifluction deposits. Thin patches occur throughout the county, although a good deal has been removed by more recent drainage and redeposited by rivers. In some places these River Brickearths are quite substantial, as at Hitchin, Hertford, Cheshunt and Rickmansworth. In the last 10 000 years the only significant deposits to accumulate have been alluvium along the courses of the rivers. Forest clearance and agricultural activities, following the Neolithic occupation of Hertfordshire about 5000 years ago, have accelerated this and the build-up of earthy deposits (*colluvium*) on lower valley slopes.

Weathering of the varied geological deposits has produced a diversity of soil types in Hertfordshire, ranging from the highly calcareous rendzinas of the Chalk escarpment to the acid podzols found on the Pebbly Clay Drift. Within these extremes are many more neutral types, whose characteristics are largely related to the availability of ground water. Soils still very much govern the distributions of many plants and consequently those animals which depend upon them, even though the face of Hertfordshire has been greatly modified over the last 5000 years or so.

During the last glaciation the landscape would have been rather bleak with a tundra-like vegetation. As conditions improved, grasses, low scrub and finally mixed deciduous forest clothed the land. The precise nature and full extent of these prehistoric forests are still subject to detailed research. They were probably quite extensive and dense, with the possible exceptions of the chalk hills, which are thought to have supported rather light open forest, and the river valleys, where marshes and open grasslands were maintained by herds of grazing animals. In the centuries of human occupation since Neolithic times, forest clearance, grazing by domesticated stock, drainage, cultivation, urbanisation and industrialisation have eradicated the truly natural habitats of Hertfordshire. Only a few semi-natural sites, mainly woodlands, remain to give some indication of what has been lost.

Today's landscape is very much an artifact of human history, with large areas dominated by buildings and open arable lands. Yet there still remain some corners of the county, also formed by human hand, with ancient woodlands, hedges, fields, lanes and trackways where wildlife still abounds. Throughout history, plants and animals invaded and flourished in newly created and managed habitats, notably coppiced woods, grazed Chalk downs, heaths, commons and meadows. Many species are now restricted to those habitat types which were stable for a

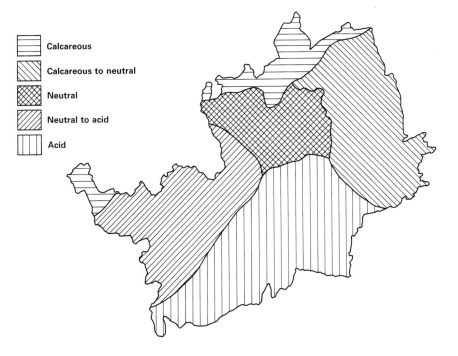

	Calcareous
	Calcareous to neutral
	Neutral
	Neutral to acid
	Acid

Figure 3.2   *Map showing the soil types of Hertfordshire*

very long time and, because of this, are declining as stability through traditional management is removed or habitats are destroyed. In the last two centuries much of the ancient mosaic of the countryside has disappeared. The human population has increased, with consequent rapid growth and changes in agriculture and industry. Much of the former way of life of the countryside has radically changed to the detriment of its wildlife.

Hertfordshire County Council's Analysis of Land Use Allocation, carried out in 1982, showed that 64 per cent of the county was being farmed. Eighty per cent of this farmland was under arable cultivation, the majority of the remainder being improved grassland, that is, grassland that has been subjected to reseeding, drainage, treatment with herbicides and fertilisers or a combination of these. About 20 per cent of the land was allocated to urban and industrial usage. What is left contains rivers, streams, canals, lakes, reservoirs, ponds, parks, commons, unimproved grasslands, scrub and woodlands. About 7 per cent of the county is wooded, but a high proportion consists of relatively recent conifer plantation, although some major areas of semi-natural woodland remain in the west and south. Many of the formerly extensive coppiced woods are now unmanaged, changing important aspects of their wildlife interest. Large tracts of the traditionally open commons and downs in the south and west of the county have been left ungrazed for so long that shrubs and trees have almost obliterated them and to all intents they may now be regarded as woodlands.

It is estimated that less than 5 per cent of Hertfordshire retains important semi-natural habitats of wildlife interest. Most of these have been isolated or fragmented for a long time and few sites are traditionally managed. Some habitats, especially arable and grasslands, are now over-managed and differently treated, for example by the uses of chemicals, to the extent that their intrinsic interest has dramatically waned. For at least a century, naturalists have bemoaned and to some extent catalogued these losses which have seriously affected a great many of our once typical wild flowers. Many of the reductions and some extinctions will be noted in the chapters that follow, and a tabulation of extinct species, dates of their last known occurrences and their former habitats is given in Appendix 2. Ever since botanists started documenting our flora they have continually added new species. This is still true today but now, except very rarely, these are introduced, alien or adventive plants, invariably associated with urban waste and dumps or escapes from cultivation, often of but transient occurrence.

4

Climate

The weather of Hertfordshire, like that of the rest of Britain, is predominantly westerly in origin, but, because of the proximity of the European landmass, is subject at times to considerable variation from the normally relatively warm and moist conditions. Plants need light from sunshine and the amount that any habitat receives through the year has an important influence upon the distribution of many species.

In the chapters that follow, details will be given that illustrate the structure and changes of wild flower habitats, many of which relate to the availability of light. Reductions, extinctions and even increases may occur from short or long term climatic variations. Each species of plant has its own characteristics and tolerances to extremes, for example some continental species found in Hertfordshire at the northern edge of their ranges only grow in warm sheltered localities. Many plants of open habitats have been affected by competition and reduction in sunlight from the overgrowth of taller species. Wider-ranging variations in the amount of sunlight, related to increased cloud cover, and inevitably linked to rainfall and temperature, exact changes, as will prolonged drought. Few data are available for Hertfordshire and widespread habitat destruction and disturbance have probably masked the effects.

From about 1800 there was a general rise in overall temperature and rainfall in Britain. This lasted until the 1870s, when significant declines in annual mean temperatures and decreasing south-westerly winds were experienced, possibly associated with a southerly shift in pressure belts. Other hypotheses have been put forward to explain the reduction in temperature; suggested contributing factors include the approximate 11- or 22-year cycle of sunspot activity and atmospheric pollution. Emissions from distant volcanic eruptions scatter vast quantities of material into the upper atmosphere; for two or three years after the great eruptions of 1883, 1885, 1902 and 1912 monthly solar radiation was reduced by over twenty per cent. Atmospheric pollution was also increased by the uncontrolled wastes of the industrial revolution; the recent links between atmospheric sulphur dioxide pollution and acid rain have almost certainly, had some significant effects on our flora beyond the much publicised damage to northern conifer forests.

By the early 1900s recorders were noting changes in the county's flora, some of which were almost certainly associated with prolonged poor weather. Habitats were neglected or destroyed to meet the exigences of the First World War. By the 1930s winds and pressure belts shifted northward to bring noticeably warmer and drier weather to the British Isles. This coincided with the agricultural depression and social upheavals of the period and resulted in noticeable increases in arable weeds. In the 1940s pressure belts drifted back southwards, with a fall in mean winter temperatures and some exceptionally warm summers.

During the 1950s spring and summer mean temperatures were lowered and wildlife in general decreased, but probably more dramatically than ever before because of the scale of habitat loss as a consequence of wartime ploughing, timber felling, reduction of marginal areas and the widespread introduction of agricultural chemicals. Of particular importance in many wild flower habitats, but notably grasslands, road verges and railway banks, was the almost complete eradication of rabbits through myxomatosis, which swept through the country in 1954 and subsequent years. Numerous sites, including woodlands as well as grasslands, became too overgrown and shady for many of the specialised species and they suffered accordingly. At this time there was probably some decrease in solar radiation from atmospheric pollution related to dust from nuclear explosions, water vapour and gases from high-flying aircraft.

More recently climate has been variable, with some extremes. Summers of the 1960s were erratic but generally cool and wet, with further declines in many wild flowers. Throughout the 1970s spring temperatures remained low, although there was a decrease in the amount of spring and summer rainfall. Widespread plant communities, desiccated by the great drought of 1976, took several years to recover. In the early 1980s the trend was towards colder, wetter, later springs, variable summers, longer autumns and milder winters. The great storm of 16 October 1987 left a legacy of destruction that still defaces many parts of the county and it may take decades before the scars are healed – a salutory warning of the extreme, short-term effects that climate can have. On a more positive note, the winters of 1988-89 and 1989-90 were extremely mild, bringing some of our spring flowers into bloom exceptionally early. As in other hot summers, many flowers had their season curtailed by drought in 1989, whilst others benefitted from the long mild autumn with prolonged flowering.

Some differences in flora are reflected in the facts that the south and west of the county tend to be wetter and warmer than the north and east. Data gathered from the current botanical survey may help to more positively assess vegetational changes in association with climatic variations. As will be shown in subsequent chapters, an important role in the distribution of many wild flowers is played by micro-climates. These can be radically influenced by a wide variety of, sometimes almost imperceptible natural and artificial factors, including soil stability and chemistry, water regimes, altitude, aspect, exposure to wind or sun, associated flora and fauna. With these in mind it can be readily appreciated why modern trends, in farming, forestry, industrialisation, pollution and so on, continue to be so devastating.

5

Prehistoric Hertfordshire and its Wild Flowers

Approximately 18 000 years ago, at the climax of the last or Devensian Ice Age (known as the Weichselian in Europe), an almost continuous sheet of ice fields and glaciers, in places at least 1700 metres thick, covered much of Britain. These extended at least as far as The Wash, South Wales and the Isles of Scilly, including most, if not all, of what is now Hertfordshire. At this time Britain was connected to the European continent and, for some considerable distance south of the ice margins, the land was locked in periglacial, arctic-like, conditions, with vast tracts of relativley sparse tundra vegetation. In the extreme south of Britain there may have been a few sheltered localities that supported some stunted shrubs and trees.

This Devensian Ice Age, which lasted from about 70 000 to 10 000 years ago, removed the vast bulk, if not all, of the previously existing, temperate-adapted wild flowers from the whole of Britain and much of northern Europe. The few parts of Hertfordshire that possibly escaped full cover by ice, at best, would have supported a sparse treeless flora of lichens and mosses with perhaps some arctic sedges, grasses, low-growing herbs and dwarfed shrubs. Some species would now typify parts of the lands close to the ice fields of Greenland, Iceland and arctic Europe. In front of the ice, virtually all the land was locked in permafrost, perhaps hundreds of feet deep, its surface unstable, being subjected to seasonal freezing and thawing. In summers, which because of the southerly latitude may have been longer and warmer than that of the present day arctic, flood waters would have been extensive, causing widespread erosion, changes in drainage patterns and vast accumulations of sand and gravel outwash deposits. Meltwaters, unable to penetrate deep down into the frozen Chalk, flowed over its surface to erode the escarpment and dry valleys that are still such majestic features along the western margin of the county. As the ice fields and glaciers slowly retreated it is difficult to picture the landscape in winter deeply snow-covered and silent, except for the wail of biting winds and cracking of ice; throughout summer a confused network of rivers, streams and small lakes interspersed between morasses by brightly but briefly colourful low-growing tundra flowers; the air probably resounding with the calls of tundra-breeding birds. Lemmings, Reindeer, Elk, Musk Ox, Mammoth, Woolly Rhinoceros, Brown Bear, Arctic Fox, Wolf, Hyena and Lion lived in this wilderness, and here and there, following the great herds of grazing animals, a rare group of nomadic human hunter gatherers may have briefly appeared.

This time, some 15 000 years ago, with ice sheets and glaciers in retreat, is a good starting point to follow the long and changing pattern of

13

Hertfordshire's wild flowers. Early evidence is scanty and comes mainly from microscopic studies of fossilised pollen grains held within contemporary silt and peat deposits laid down in pools and slow-moving rivers, including some excavated in the Lea Valley. These reveal plant communities containing an apparently curious admixture of arctic alpines, weeds and coastal plants; many species were well adapted to the prevailing cold climate and open, largely unstable, soils, including some that no longer occur in Britain and which are now limited to northern continental steppe and arctic regions; but a few species, such as Hoary Rock-rose *Helianthemum canum* (*) and Shrubby Cinquefoil *Potentilla fruticosa* (*) are native to warmer climates. (N.B. Species marked (*) are now extinct in Hertfordshire.)

Periglacial Hertfordshire would, with slowly ameliorating climate, develop extensive stands of dwarf woody shrubs including several prostrate arctic willows *Salix* spp. (*), Dwarf Birch *Betula nana* (*) and a prostrate form of Juniper *Juniperus communis*, probably subspecies *nana* (*). There were many stands of taller herbs which contained species such as Meadowsweet *Filipendula ulmaria*, Common Valerian *Valeriana officinalis*, Dog's Mercury *Mercurialis perennis*, Stinging Nettle *Urtica dioica* and woodrushes *Luzula* spp. Amongst the multitudes of wet flushes, often associated with late lying snow beds, would be found Dwarf Willow *Salix herbacea* (*), Mountain Sorrel *Oxyria digyna* (*), Marsh Marigold *Caltha palustris*, Shrubby Cinquefoil *Potentilla fruticosa* (*), Mossy Saxifrage *Saxifraga hypnoides* (*), Starfruit *Damasonium alisma*, Gipsywort *Lycopus europaeus*, Teesdale Sandwort *Minuartia stricta* (*) and Bird's-eye Primrose *Primula farinosa* (*). There were drier, open areas with unstable and disturbed soils supporting plant communities with species that are now regarded as ruderals and weeds, many of which were distinctly related to the calcareous nature of the underlying Chalk and Boulder Clay soils. In pollen studies some of the most frequently found species include Nipplewort *Lapsana communis*, sandwort *Arenaria* sp., wormwood *Artemesia* sp., plantain *Plantago* sp., Knotgrass *Polygonum aviculare*, Stinging Nettle *Urtica dioica*, knawel *Scleranthus* sp., Silverweed *Potentilla anserina*, Oxeye Daisy *Leucanthemum vulgare*, Perennial Wall-rocket *Diplotaxis tenuifolia* and Treacle Mustard *Erysimum cheiranthoides*. Grasses and sedges abounded to provide lush summer grazings for the herds of tundra herbivores. Other herbs, less abundant but no doubt widespread, added variety and colour to the scene. Many of these, today, are more typical of steppe and arctic-alpine regions, for example Field Mouse-ear *Cerastium arvense*, Perennial Flax *Linum perenne*, Hoary Rock-rose *Helianthemum canum* (*), Alpine Meadow-rue *Thalictrum alpinum* (*), Purple Saxifrage *Saxifraga oppositifolia* (*), Mountain Avens *Dryas octopetala* (*), Spring Sandwort *Minuartia verna* (*), Hoary Whitlow Grass *Draba incana* (*), Arctic Buttercup *Ranunculus hyperboreus* (*), Arctic Poppy *Papaver alpinum* (*) and Snowy Cinquefoil *Potentilla nivea* (*).

In places there flourished stands of salt-tolerant plants, including Annual Sea-blite *Sueda maritima* (*), Sea Milkwort *Glaux maritima* (*), Thrift *Armeria maritima* (*), Sea Arrowgrass *Triglochin maritima* (*),

Saltmarsh Flat-sedge *Blysmus rufus* (*), oraches *Atriplex* spp. (*), Sea Plantain *Plantago maritima* (*), Holly-leaved Naiad *Najas marina* (*), Sea Buckthorn *Hippophae rhamnoides* (*), Sand Sedge *Carex arenaria* (*) and Curved Sedge *C. maritimum* (*). Seas were a considerable distance from Devensian Hertfordshire, particularly since so much water was 'locked up' in the ice fields and glaciers that, world-wide, sea levels were reduced. At the acme of this ice age it is estimated that sea levels may have fallen to 80 metres, or more, below those of today. Research suggests that the saline habitats resulted from an interaction between permafrost in the ground and high rates of evaporation of surface soil water associated with the prevailing continental climate of severe winters and, despite the proximity of ice fronts, relatively warm summers.

With a warming climate, Devensian ice slowly retreated and, about 12 500 years ago, Britain became free of ice. As conditions further ameliorated, successive waves of plants were able to move northwards, both from Europe and from extensive areas of the continental shelf, which had been exposed by lowering of sea levels. The English Channel was yet to form and much of what is now the North Sea was dry land. The initial tundra gave way to 'park-tundra' which, although largely still of an open character, had substantial stands of pioneering trees and shrubs, with birches *Betula* spp., Aspen *Populus tremula*, further species of willows, Rowan *Sorbus aucuparia*, Sea Buckthorn and, especially Juniper *Juniperus communis* which was now of a more upright habit. In places these formed enough shelter for the development of dwarf heath dominated by Crowberry *Empetrum nigrum* (*) and heathers *Erica* and *Calluna* spp. Studies suggest a rich associated flora that contained knapweeds *Centaurea* spp., willowherbs *Epilobium* spp., Devil's-bit Scabious *Succisa pratensis*, Sheep's-bit *Jasione montana* (*), Rock-rose *Helianthemum* sp., bellflowers *Campanula* spp., Thrift *Armeria maritima* (*), Jacob's-ladder *Polemonium caeruleum* (*), Valerian *Valeriana officinalis*, Fir Clubmoss *Lycopodium selago* (*), Moonwort *Botrychium lunaria* (*) and Iceland-purslane *Koenigia islandica* (*). Deposits in the Colne Valley, dated at 12 000 to 13 500 years ago, have yielded some evidence of this variety with a range of ruderals, such as wormwood *Artemesia* sp., plantains *Plantago* spp. and docks *Rumex* spp., and woody shrubs, including Dwarf Birch, willows, Sea Buckthorn and Joint-pine *Ephedra* sp. (*). There is also some indication in the fossil pollen record to suggest that pines *Pinus* spp. might have been fairly close by or possibly even at this site.

Over the next thousand years or so further waves of plant colonisation brought trees into the landscape. First to arrive were birches, with Silver Birch *Betula pendula* more frequent than Downy Birch *B. pubescens*, closely followed by Scots Pine *Pinus sylvestris*. Later oaks moved in but, together with many other species, these were forced out some 11 000 years ago as the climate began to cool. For several hundreds of years, ice sheets were again present in highland parts of Britain from Scotland to North Wales and the Pennines. During this temporary return of cold conditions, known as the Loch Lomond re-advance or Allerød inter-stadial, tundra or 'park-tundra' again covered much of lowland Britain; only in the extreme south did the pine/birch forest survive. A particularly frequent species found in the fossil pollen record of this period is Mountain Avens, which today is limited to basic rocks in mountains from North Wales and Yorkshire to Sutherland and a few very specialised low altitude sites in western Ireland and northern Scotland.

About 10 000 years ago the climate once again improved, with a return to sub-arctic conditions, known as the pre-Boreal period, and Britain was 'finally' free of permanent ice. Only time will tell if indeed the Ice Ages have really ended for, as we have seen, interglacial, like glacial, periods can be very long. Geologists regard this point in time as the start of the Flandrian interglacial, in which we are still living and during which a sequence of climatic and vegetational changes have occurred that are incomplete. Pollen analyses from southern Britain show that climate warmed quite rapidly and 'park-tundra' gave way to a landscape dominated by birch woodland. The light seeds of birch, readily distributed by wind, quickly germinated in the improving soil structures. Scots Pine, with Aspen and Rowan, soon moved in to these woods. The capacity of birches to enhance soils is well known and, with improving climate, many other trees, shrubs and herbs appeared upon the scene to replace the pine/birch forests.

Around 9 000 years ago, at the start of the Boreal period, Hazel *Corylus avellana* became abundant, possibly forming pure stands in some places. In the warmer, drier climate Small-leaved Lime *Tilia cordata* (*), oaks and Wych Elm *Ulmus glabra* became abundant. The developing forests were soon colonised by Beech *Fagus sylvatica*, Ash *Fraxinus excelsior*, Field Maple *Acer campestre* and Hornbeam *Carpinus betulus*. In marshes, along rivers and around lakes, the moisture-loving Alder *Alnus glutinosa* was very common. These warmth-demanding trees, responding to further climatic changes, were to become the dominant vegetation of Britain. Warmer, wetter, oceanic conditions, were to prevail from about 7000 to 5000 years ago – the time known as the Atlantic period.

With ice sheets and glaciers still retreating, tremendous volumes of meltwaters were causing sea levels to rise over the continental shelves, and when about 8600 years ago, what is now the English Channel and considerable areas of the North Sea were inundated, Britain became effectively isolated from further easy colonisation by plants and animals from the continent. Consequently, the bulk of our native flora, and to a large extent of the fauna, was established at this time and has remained less extensive than that of mainland Europe. But although most of lowland Britain was dominated by temperate, mixed deciduous forest there were other habitats to be found, such as sea cliffs, sand dunes, gorges, river valley grasslands, marshes, screes, gravel banks and game trails, and these supported a great variety of plants and animals, many of which, as will be seen later, were to become common and widespread components of our wildlife.

The girdle of seas around Britain and a northward movement of the Gulf Stream compounded the optimum climate of the Atlantic period, which was about 2°C warmer and somewhat wetter than at present, and established the truly natural or climatic climax vegetation, dominated in the bulk of lowland areas of Britain by deciduous forest or *wildwood*. The overall density of the forest at this time is suggested by the relatively

Plate 1 (*Top*) One of Europe's finest bluebell woods (Hitch Wood near Preston; (*Bottom*) Primrose *Primula vulgaris*

low proportions of herbs represented in the fossil pollen record. Forest structure, particularly on the variety of soil types that were found in Hertfordshire, was a complex mosaic of trees, with a great variety of shrubs, forming pure and mixed, dense and more open stands.

Increased forest cover during the early Flandrian period led to dramatic changes in fauna. Most of the large mammals became extinct or moved to more suitable regions of tundra or steppe. Denizens of the forests thrived for a while but there is much evidence to show that these, and other wildlife, were reduced or removed by early human hunters. As this human population increased its impact upon native wildlife became more and more profound and, in a relatively short space of time, the face of the natural landscape would be changed forever.

6

Wildwood to Woods

When Britain was severed from the continent by rising sea levels, about 6500 B.C. virtually all of lowland Britain, including Hertfordshire, was thickly forested, with occasional breaks where river flood plains supported lush grasslands and marshes. It appears that the shallow, nutrient-poor soils of the steep Chalk escarpment were more lightly forested than most of pre-historic Hertfordshire. Pollen studies have shown the wildwood to have been a dense, complicated mosaic of forest trees dominated by Small-leaved Lime, Pedunculate Oak and Hazel, with Wych Elm on base-rich soils and Alder in permanently wet places. There were many other, perhaps fifty or more, species of less common trees and shrubs, plus a great number of herbs and grasses, lichens, mosses, liverworts and ferns in the native wildwood flora. Later, Small-leaved Lime and Wych Elm appeared to have given way to increased cover by oaks and, later still, to invading Hornbeam and Field Maple. Another late invader, Beech, was to extend its range on the free-draining soils of Chalk and gravels. It is possible that a proportion of the decline of Small-leaved Lime and Wych Elm, taking place about 5000 B.C. was associated with some temporary wildwood clearances on more fertile soils by early human colonisers. Examples have been cited in the Lea Valley and dated to the Mesolithic period of human culture.

Overall, the wildwood had characteristics that would be almost un-recognisable in today's woodlands, with trees of widely ranging ages, the oldest of which had huge trunks supporting canopies some 30m or more above the forest floor. Their dense shade may well have inhibited the development of a rich ground flora, although because of the inherently moist microclimate the forest floor would have been lush with mosses, lichens and ferns and herds of mammals would have foraged through the forest, grazing or browsing, groups of wild boar creating considerable soil disturbance as they rooted between the trees.

Here and there, a giant tree would fall, to create open sunlit glades in which a colourful array of 'woodland' flowers, weeds and grasses would flourish until shaded out by shrubs, saplings and eventually trees. Typical species would include many of those found in the more open woods of today, such as Bluebell, Dog's Mercury, Primrose, Wood Anemone and Early Purple Orchid. Browsing deer and grazing wild cattle would have kept some areas more or less permanently open, notably along their major movement routes or *game trails*. Trunks and branches of trees would have been festooned with epiphytic lichens and ferns, well adapted to life in the warm, humid, relatively windless and, as yet, unpolluted conditions that prevailed within the shelter of the forest. Occupying all parts of the forest, from the dim litter-strewn floor to the sunlit extremities of the canopy, would have been an unimaginably rich fauna of invertebrates, birds and small mammals.

Today, because of the long-term effects of man, it is only possible in Hertfordshire, and most of Britain, to snatch brief glimpses of the lost splendour of the wildwood in a few of our 'ancient' woods or 'wooded commons', for example in parts of Wormley and Hoddesdon Park Woods near Broxbourne, Bricket Wood Common near Watford and Hertford Heath. In some places, such as on the Chalk hills near Hexton, fragments of secondary woodland development, following failed attempts at conifer plantation or through natural succession, gives some impression of the nature of the wildwood; although only semi-natural, lacking immense trees, with alien species like Sycamore and Large-leaved Lime and without large mammals, they do have a distinct 'wild feeling' about them.

Before about 4000 B.C., the wildwood of Hertfordshire was, probably, mostly dominated by Small-leaved Lime and Hazel, with oaks and Wych Elm well represented, although on some of the lighter soils of the south Hornbeam may have occurred more frequently than Small-leaved Lime. More acid soils of the southern plateaus supported birches with Hornbeam, Rowan, Aspen, Yew and Holly. Thin, highly calcareous soils on the Chalk favoured a mixed but more open forest of Ash, Wych Elm, Yew, Field Maple and Cherry, and a diversity of such calcicolous, or lime-loving, shrubs as Juniper, Whitebeam and sallows. Although present, Beech was only a relatively minor component; today's extensive Chiltern beechwoods derive largely from plantings of the 19th century to supply the furniture trade.

Significant changes have been detected in the fossil pollen record from sites that are dated from about 4000 B.C. Particularly evident are declines in the amounts of certain tree pollen counts and consequent rises in herbs and grasses. These variations can be closely correlated with the arrival into Hertfordshire of Neolithic settlers, the first farmers, and the beginnings of wildwood clearance. There had been human occupation in Hertfordshire for perhaps four millennia or more before these arrivals, but populations were sparse and their impact on the landscape almost negligible. At most only small glades would have been cleared to facilitate mainly short-term settlement, hunting and gathering before moving on. Studies of Mesolithic sites in the Lea Valley suggest that there may have been a few more permanent sites. The population was small, possibly a few hundred individuals, but there is evidence of the use of flint tools for tree-felling for timber to fabricate canoes and shelters.

About or soon after 4000 B.C., a new wave of human colonisation began when Neolithic peoples crossed into southern Britain from northern France and started to settle. They moved north quite rapidly and entered Hertfordshire via the river valleys of the south, especially the Lea, and, notably, along the more lightly forested Chalk escarpment. The Icknield Way, which traverses parts of the western margins of the county, was probably originally a game trail, but provided an ideal track that was to become an important route for Neolithic and later peoples.

More organised, settled and systematic than their predecessors, these newcomers were essentially farmers, and they began the process that culminated in the complete destruction of the wildwood in Britain. At first small areas were cleared, for living space, for timber to construct long-term dwellings, for fuel, for cultivation of crops especially grain, and to provide open grassy glades for grazing by domesticated sheep and goats. Archaeological remains show that initial settlements were in the more open situations on Chalk, river valley gravels and alluviums. Small trees were probably cut down by hand, larger ones may have been *ring-barked* to be removed later, perhaps by fire, although it is likely that crops were grown and stock grazed amongst dead trees. With clearances on well-drained Chalk, sands and gravels, most of the rich nutrients that were associated with the forest soils soon became depleted by cultivation or leached away by rainfall. Such places began to develop into downland and heathland, especially where long-term grazing was maintained and the return of trees and shrubs was inhibited. Other new semi-natural grasslands and arable fields were also beginning to appear in the landscape.

As they opened up the forest and tilled the land, Neolithic farmers unwittingly encouraged the spread of weeds, ruderals and grassland flowers. They were also responsible for the deliberate or accidental addition of many new and alien plants to the British flora. For, as successive groups moved into or about the countryside they carried stocks of primitive wheat and barley with them. Amongst these were many other seeds, especially arable weeds, which would soon flourish in the newly created fields. As will be shown in later chapters, there were many other plants transported in this way and many formerly restricted to minor habitats by the extent of the wildwood, that would capitalise on the slow but relentless growth of new habitats to become commonplace.

From Neolithic times, but especially in the millennia that followed, some areas carved from the wildwood were maintained for the dual purposes of wood production and livestock grazing. Now known as pasture-woodlands, these frequently became characterised by their large, ancient trees deliberately pollarded, that is regularly cut to produce a rounded head of young branches, to keep upper branches and foliage out of the reach of grazing animals. Eventually, quite extensive areas of southern Hertfordshire were managed in this way until the 18th or early 19th century. Many of the now wooded commons were formerly pasture-woodlands that reverted to secondary woodland when grazing was withdrawn. Examples include parts of Northaw Great Wood, Broxbourne Woods, Frithsden Beeches, Berkhamsted Common, Ashridge and Knebworth Woods.

Particularly evident in the pollen records is the decline in Wych Elm about 3500 B.C. This species favours fertile alluvial soils, which were amongst the first to be cleared and cultivated. Winter elm loppings were a primary source of fodder for stock when grazing was at its poorest. The prehistoric elm decline seems to be associated with developments in Neolithic agriculture (Rackham, 1986). New arable fields and grazing lands allowed a whole range of plants to colonise and similarly animal populations were changing quite dramatically. With human settlement and social development, clearings in the wildwood began to coalesce or become linked by trackways. Certain places, a venerable ancient tree or special grove, acquired ritual (as in May Day festivals, originating in tree worship) or commercial significance.

It has been estimated that our Neolithic ancestors may have removed

Figure 6.1 *Pollarded oak trees at Watery Grove, near Stevenage*

about one-sixth of the wildwood of Britain. How much of Hertfordshire
was cleared by the start of the Bronze Age, about 2000 B.C., is a matter
of conjecture but, by the end of that period, around 600 B.C., it seems
probable that extensive tracts on the Chalk, and to a lesser extent parts
of the Lea Valley and Boulder Clay of eastern Hertfordshire, had been
fairly well deforested. There is ample evidence to suggest open
landscapes, particularly on the Chalk, where many round barrows and
other constructions were sited for visibility on cleared hills and ridges.
An extensive pattern of small arable fields and grazings bounded by
banks or ditches would have covered these areas. On the Chalk escarpment vast open sheepwalks had been created.

Even in these early times, it appears that parts of the wildwood were
being managed in a systematic manner to provide an ongoing natural
resource of timber and brushwood for everyday use. The type of silviculture that was eventually carried out in a great proportion of
Hertfordshire's woods was *coppice with standards*, and this remained the
most significant form of woodland management until the 19th century.
It involved cutting blocks, or *coupes*, of underwood or shrubs in a regular
cycle; typically these cycles were about twelve years in duration, although
latterly these were extended. Standard trees, notably oaks, were left, and
felled for timber when mature or as required. Uses for coppiced materials
were many, often depending on the species involved, and changed as new
techniques and crafts developed. At first, uses would have been quite
basic, for example fencing, handles for primitive tools and weapons,

domestic building and firewood. As the centuries rolled by, Hertfordshire's coppiced woods provided the raw materials for major local industries; Hornbeam was used as firewood for the malting process and to fuel domestic fires, especially those of an ever expanding London, and it seems likely that some, in the form of charcoal, was used in the gunpowder industry; hazel was fashioned into hurdles, fences and poles. Varying soil types and local needs determined the types of trees and shrubs that would be allowed to grow – factors, which over some three thousand years or so, coupled with selective management, have been responsible for the different types of woodland found in Hertfordshire today. (*See* Chapter 7.)

Long-term coppicing had profound effects upon the structure, microclimate, flora and fauna of these developing woods. With regular opening up of parts of the woods, there evolved a rich ground flora and fauna. Hertfordshire's reputation for having some of the finest bluebell woods in Europe owes much to this. A great variety of insects would have flourished in coppiced areas, such as those most beautiful of butterflies, the woodland fritillaries. Pearl-bordered, Small Pearl-bordered, Silver-washed and High Brown Fritillary were all once quite common throughout the county's traditional woods (Sawford, 1987). Some of our remaining woods may have links back to the wildwood, but very few of its prehistoric characteristics remain. From the 19th century onwards,

Figure 6.2 *Coppiced Hornbeam, now over mature (Newton Wood, Knebworth)*

because of declining demands for their resource, most coppiced woods have fallen into disuse and lost much wildlife interest as uncut shrubs have over-shaded and inhibited ground flora.

Throughout the Iron Ages, 600 B.C. to 43 A.D. and, increasingly, during Roman times, 43 A.D. to 450 A.D., settlement and wildwood clearance continued. Equipped with cheap, mass-produced iron tools, the population made significant inroads into forested areas on heavier soils. A network of Roman roads traversed and opened up the bulk of Hertfordshire so that relatively little wilderness remained. More coppices were created to provide fuel for iron smelting, pottery kilns and heating for homes and public buildings. Roman country estates or villas were well distributed and the iron-tipped ploughs, drawn by teams of oxen, were able to cope with cultivation of many of the heavier soils. Increasingly, land was required for crop production and stock rearing to provide for a growing population. Towards the end of the Roman occupation much of Hertfordshire had been settled and the landscape was a patchwork of farmland, woodland and small settlements. Along the Chalk escarpment, the extensive sheepwalks gave way to small arable fields on the deeper soils of valleys and scarp foot. Only on the heaviest or most impoverished soils did much wildwood survive, but even here, because of the great dependence upon timber and underwood, patterns of woods, coppices and pasture-wood were cossetted, developed and managed by increasingly refined techniques and crafts. The east and south of the county probably remained fairly densely tree-ed but there would almost certainly have been some human incursions for hunting, collection of nuts, berries or herbs, timber removal and seasonal herding of stock such as pigs and cattle.

When the Roman occupation of Britain ended in the fifth century, Anglo-Saxon peoples from northern Europe began to colonise, arriving in Hertfordshire mainly by way of the Chalk escarpment from the north east. In places, the new immigrants had conflicts with the declining native British populations, elsewhere the two races seemed to live in harmony. Throughout the five hundred years of the Dark Ages (so named because so little archaeological evidence survives) the countryside of Hertfordshire was probably managed more or less as in Roman times though a few areas may have reverted to woodland after being abandoned. From meticulous researches, the foremost expert on Britain's woodland history, Oliver Rackham (1986), calculates that at the time of the Domesday Book, 1086, about 30 per cent of the county, mostly in the south, was wooded; thus a good deal of land was open.

The Anglo-Saxons were well organised, delineating major and minor administrative boundaries. For example, and based upon strategic and military importance, the town of Hertford was created in 913 A.D. Communities were well developed, most of the woods supplying the needs of these were distinctively defined and were probably so managed that they already fell into one or more of the main woodland stand types now recognised. (*See* Chapter 7.) Of the major stand types, Sessile Oak occurs on sandy and lighter loam soils, Pedunculate Oak dominates heavy clays, Field Maple with Ash is most frequent on the Boulder Clay of the north east and oak with Hornbeam covers large parts of the south and south east. Beechwoods of the Chalk escarpment were to be a much later addition to the landscape.

Many of the still extant banks of wood edges, usually with associated ditches, date from Saxon divisions of land into parishes, estates and tenures. These early managed woods, and those of mediaeval times, were frequently margined by banks, often topped with a hedge to inhibit stock. Formed from soil thrown up from ditches outside the woods, it was the ditches not the banks that marked legal boundaries. Centuries of ditch maintenance, with removed silt being thrown up onto the bank, often gives ancient woodbanks a characteristic profile, steeper on the ditch side, with a broad top sloping gently into the wood. More recent woodbanks are generally narrow and steep-sided. Post-19th century woods, such as those created or re-defined by the Enclosures (*see* Chapter 11), or plantations are usually devoid of banks and hedges. Ancient woodbanks are large and difficult features to erase from the landscape and in many places may remain although the woods they formerly bounded have long gone. Over the centuries, and particularly as management has lapsed, many woodbanks have become colonised by trees, shrubs and herbs from the woodlands. In places, where woods have been cleared and replanted, say with conifers, the banks may retain enough relict flora to enable a good interpretation to be made of the former habitat. Contours of banks and ditches frequently become indistinct with age and lack of management but can sometimes be traced through vestiges of ancient layered hedge, lines of mature or pollarded trees and particular characteristics of ground flora. Saxons and, later, their Norman conquerors established legislation to control the use of and give protection to the diminishing woodlands. New forms of intensive woodland management were developed. Coppices, protected against grazing stock, and pasture-woods became major woodland types which, in many parts of the county, were already isolated amongst arable fields, pastures and meadows.

Throughout the 13th and early 14th centuries population growth was such that great pressures were put on woodlands by the demands of production. Further woodland clearances led to a situation, as Rackham (1986) emphasises, 'reducing the woods to something like their present extent by 1350'. Bubonic plague, known also as the 'black death', which swept through the countryside in 1349 and reduced the population by as much as a third, temporarily halted this onslaught. There seems, however, to have been little reversion to woodland, except perhaps in a few marginal areas on very poor soils, and it is considered that most of Hertfordshire's primary woods, that is those derived from the wildwood, were already well defined. Secondary woods, that is those without continuity with the wildwood but which may have developed naturally on previously unwooded land, may be of any age from prehistoric to recent. It may now be very difficult, sometimes impossible, to separate primary sites from very ancient secondary woods, although more recent secondary woods are often dominated by oaks, birches, Ash and Common Hawthorn, species which readily invade open ground. Ground flora and invertebrate fauna are usually less diverse in these secondary woods.

A tradition started by many of the Norman landowners, and extended throughout the next few centuries, was the establishment of parks. Some may have been created to include existing woods or pasture-woods, but most, it seems, were formed from new plantings. All enclosed wild or semi-wild, sometimes introduced, animals for either the 'pleasures' of hunting or, importantly, a ready source of meat. Contemporary records show that amongst the animals that stocked the early parks were Brown Hare, Roe and Red Deer, Wild Boar and Wild Cattle, all of which were native species. Normans introduced the Fallow Deer into Britain and for centuries after these with Red Deer were most frequent as park animals, although rarely running together because it was thought that Red Deer stags would kill or maim the Fallow bucks during the rutting season. Later deer keepers found this to be a misconception and allowed both species to run together. In the early 17th century, Elk were kept at Theobolds Park near Cheshunt.

Deer Parks were of considerable variety and size. Ranging from a few to several hundred hectares in extent, most contained large tracts of woodland or pasture-wood. Scattered pollarded trees in grassland became a common feature of many parks and often timber trees were grown. Larger parks supported other land uses within their bounds, including arable cultivation, sheep and cattle grazing. Of importance were park boundaries which, in view of the nature of the emparked animals, were expensive to build and maintain. Ditches were a feature of many early parks, with steep banks outside them topped by strong fences of cleft oak stakes – the park pale. Some had strong, thick hedges and, later, high, brick-walled boundaries appeared. Most mediaeval and earlier parks were functional in the local community and were often enclosed with oval or rectangular outlines.

Over ninety parks are known for Hertfordshire, one to every seven square miles of land, most of which were in existence before the 14th century. Although now disparked and long since put to other land uses, the sites of many of these can be still traced through place names and surviving topographical features, for example, Stagenhoe Park near Preston, Cassiobury Park near Watford, Moor Park at Rickmansworth and Woodhall Park near Watton-at-Stone. The 18th-century fashion amongst wealthy landowners for landscaped parks gave a new lease of life to many mediaeval and Tudor parks as well as encouraging the establishment of new ones. Such Capability Brown and Humphrey Repton parks were more picturesque than functional and often involved considerable landscape transformations. James Edmund Harting (1881), in a paper, read before The Hertfordshire Natural History Society, noted ten existing deer parks in the county, most of which were well-stocked with sizable herds of Fallow Deer, while a few held Red Deer. With the exception of Knebworth Park, all have been effectively disparked, and even at Knebworth the modern wire fence only partially follows old park boundaries. Harting showed that deer parks were declining from late-mediaeval times a trend that increased in the 16th and 17th centuries, to provide more farmland or, perhaps, woodland. Little information is available on the wild flowers of these parks but, from examination of places like Knebworth Park, it is assumed that, depending on soils and treecover, they would have supported a combination of woodland, open heath or grassland species. One interesting survivor, most frequently recorded from old parks and often on limes, is the woody, evergreen parasite Mistletoe *Viscum album* (2–4).

From the time of the black death until the latter part of the 19th century, there was probably very little change in the extent of wood and pasture-wood in Hertfordshire. Because of their importance, both social and economic, to local and wider communities, as a major renewable resource, these areas would have remained relatively stable, although most were intensively managed. Many provided their owners with a good income for little expense. The general pattern of management remained more or less the same for centuries, although, to suit demands or make quicker profits, some deviations were likely, such as longer or shorter coppice cycles or earlier removal of standards. Rackham (1986) has blown open the myth about shortages of timber for the building of warships from the 16th century onwards. He says that the contemporary British Navy was 'short of funds, not of trees' and that civilian dockyards had no difficulty in obtaining timber at 'market prices'. Also, with the rise in merchant shipping, cheap timber was imported and, from the 18th century onwards, there was a fall in the use of, by then, more expensive home-produced timber. So, for some centuries, woods remained relatively stable features of a countryside increasingly patterned by interlinking trackways, lanes, fields, hedges and growing settlements. As shown above, the south of Hertfordshire was traditionally more wooded, the Chalk escarpment quite open and other parts were variable in woodland cover, although few places were without at least some small tracts of woodland, so important for the provision of everyday materials. With their historical links and continued management, these 18th century woods would have retained a rich wildlife. Within the span of three human generations, however, many were to disappear or to be radically altered and degraded, and their wildlife consequently greatly impoverished.

In the latter part of the 18th century timber prices rose, and many landowners, as always keen to consolidate their assets, concentrated on the cultivation of standards, especially oaks, at the expense of under-wood and coppice. But the expected value of these trees was not realised, for their maturity, in the middle of the 19th century, coincided with the coming of the railways and the 'cheaper than coppice or timber' distribution of coal, bricks and other building materials to the countryside. An agricultural boom (to some extent facilitated by government subsidies) coming as it did between 1840 and 1880 – when timber prices were at their lowest – inevitably led to some destruction of woods to provide more farmland. An agricultural slump followed, and with it, neglect of pasture-woods and commons, leading, by natural succession, to the development of scrub and secondary woodland. At Rothamsted near Harpenden, a small plot of land, now known as the Broadbalk Wilderness, on which wheat had been grown from 1843 to 1882, was deliberately allowed to 'run wild' for experimental purposes. Woodland rapidly established itself, with, now, some fine trees of Pedunculate Oak, Ash, Field Maple and Hazel. Its ground flora, however, over a century later, lacks most of the plants typical of ancient woods and is dominated by Ivy, Dog's Mercury, Herb Bennett and Wild

Arum or Cuckoo-pint. Often such an impoverished ground flora is a useful indication to more recent secondary woodland.

Economic and social changes have always brought new techniques and fashions to the countryside. During the second half of the 19th century many landowners began to establish whole new woods or replant parts of existing ones with alien conifers and hardwoods. Sycamore, hybrid limes, Horse Chestnut *Aesculus hippocastanum* (5–6), elms and rhododendrons were widley used and, on the Chalk, many of the beech plantations date from this time. The *underwood*, the ground flora and fauna, so typical of previous woods, was greatly reduced in these 19th century successors.

A saviour of many ancient woods and copses, which remains important today, was an increased interest in field sports. In spite of the activities of gamekeepers, slaughtering many birds of prey and other 'vermin' and fortifying their coverts against general access, and the heavy toll taken by vast numbers of Pheasants of woodland invertebrates, notably butterflies such as the fritillaries, game rearing helped in the retention of much of the wooded countryside; in many places the woods were used solely to support game.

Over the years coppicing cycles at many sites had been growing steadily longer; towards the end of the 19th century the practice was rapidly declining and by the end of the 1940s this once widespread technique had to all intents ceased completely. Unchecked, coppice stools grew up and produced their own closed canopies, making woods darker, damper and much impoverished in ground flora. Many declines and local extinctions in woodland fauna were direct results of the loss of regularly opened-up, sunlit coppices. Common Dormouse, Nightingale, Purple Emperor and Silver-washed Fritillary are a few of the now uncommon species, but Pearl-bordered, Small Pearl-bordered and High Brown Fritillaries have completely gone, probably for ever. In fact, of the thirty-seven species of butterflies recorded from Hertfordshire's woodlands, thirty-five rely upon suitably managed shrubs and ground flora for breeding.

There has, in recent years and mainly at the instigation of conservation bodies, been some return of small-scale coppicing. The effects on ground flora are quite impressive, giving a glimpse of what woods in the past were like, but it is unlikely that much of an increase in fauna will occur unless the practice is more widely adopted. Also, notably for butterflies, *wider* conservation is needed, to create and maintain those aspects of the 'traditional countryside' – mosaics of woods with sunny rides and glades, flowery lanes and meadows – that were formerly Hertfordshire. Even if some of this could be achieved it would probably still be necessary to reintroduce some of the lost species, such as butterflies, that are unable to cross the hostile expanses of arable and urban lands.

Two World Wars brought great demands for timber; many woods were badly or clear- felled – certainly few were properly maintained – as manpower, by necessity, was directed elsewhere. The intervening years of depression saw significant changes in land tenure and there were many examples of clearances to provide much needed immediate capital for landowners. Cessation of grazing regimes during this period allowed natural succession to proceed. Considerable areas of several of the county's extensive commons were invaded by shrubs and trees; these places, such as Chipperfield Common, parts of Berkhamsted Common and the Ashridge Estate, although of a well-wooded appearance, lack many elements shown in the ground flora of more ancient woods. Similarly, parts of the Chalk downland were abandoned, scrub started to spread on these but was, to some extent, kept in check by rabbits until the 1950s, when outbreaks of myxomatosis virtually eliminated the county's rabbits. Closed scrub and secondary woodland rapidly developed.

After the Second World War, a number of ancient woods were completely or partially destroyed as farmland expanded and towns spread. New conifer plantations, ranging from small amenity blocks to the extensive plantings seen in the Broxbourne and Bramfield Woods area, were added to the landscape, all too frequently within ancient woods. It is estimated that between 40 and 60 per cent of the ancient woodland present in Hertfordshire before 1940, was destroyed or very seriously degraded, by the mid-1980s; today, only 7 per cent of the county remains wooded, and of this 7 per cent only 2 per cent (and this very fragmented) is ancient broad-leaved woodland.

Figure 6.3 *Many of the once extensive and open commons of southern Hertfordshire are now overgrown (Commonwood Common, near Sarratt)*

7

Ancient Woodlands in Hertfordshire

Appendices
1.1, 1.2, 1.3
As indicated in the previous chapter, the character of our extant ancient woodlands, that is, those present before the 16th century, has changed over the centuries. However, with a little searching, one can find several sites that retain some historical features and here and there it is possible to get some feel of what the wildwood was like. Patient fieldwork and the use of maps, old and new may reveal wood banks and hedges, old pasture-woods, coppices, enclosures, management compartments and archaeological remains, all of which can help to piece together the story of our woods. There is much to be learned from concentrated studies of woods, singly or in groups.

The range of flora and fauna of our ancient woods results from combinations of climate, underlying soils, water regimes and lengthy interference by man. Each wood has its individual character. Some adjoining sites are only subtly different, with perhaps just slight variations in the age or density of trees; others vary considerably because of changes in soil, local climate, drainage or differing historical management. The last has been particularly important in Hertfordshire, producing enduring semi-natural features that allow the majority of woods to be categorised according to a complex classification developed by Dr G. F. Peterken of the Nature Conservancy Council. The Peterken system relies on studies of past management and ecological succession, postulating that when one species is felled, another may take over and that, in time, the first species may return or another species come in to the community. It classifies woods according to their *stand-types* – reasonably uniform areas of certain significant species of trees and shrubs, present in coppices or as ancient trees and pollards in pasture-woodlands. Over forty stand-types have been identified in Britain, which can be grouped into twelve basic stand groups. In Hertfordshire, nineteen stand-types have been recognised, falling into three major and five lesser groupings. (*See* Table 7.1 and Figure 7.1.) A good many woods, especially the larger ones, are composed of several stand-types reflecting soil differences and historical management.

Within ancient woods there are a number of wild flowers, including grasses that, because of their reliance on particular soil, micro-climate and long-standing management factors, are unable or very slow to cross alien habitats and colonise more recent sites; such species can be used as indicators of ancient woodlands. It is not surprising, bearing in mind the more recent history and present state of the county's woods, that several of these species are now rare or declining. It should be no surprise, of course, to learn that the really reliable indicators do not include the more familiar woodland flowers such as Bluebell, Dog's Mercury, Common Dog-violet, Early Dog-violet, Bugle, Yellow Archangel, Goldilocks Buttercup, Primrose and Barren Strawberry; these may be found in other

TABLE 7.1 *Stand groups found in Hertfordshire's ancient woodlands (major groups shown on Figure 7.1 are marked thus *)*

Peterken Group number	Stand group
1	Ash/Wych Elm woods
*2	Ash/Maple woods
3	Hazel/Ash woods
6	Birch/Oak woods
7	Alder woods
*8	Beech woods
*9	Hornbeam woods
10	Suckering Elm woods

habitats frequently derived from woods, or have the ability to move readily into secondary woods from adjacent hedges or lanes. In conjunction with other species, as shown in Table 7.2, these can, however, be of some use as indicators. Table 7.2 lists a selection of indicator plants found in the three major stand groups of Hertfordshire. It should be noted that these refer to very broad categories. Some species may be very restricted to a particular stand-type within a group or limited by certain conditions, for example very localised soil regimes; others may be found

Figure 7.1 *Map showing the major woodland types of Hertfordshire (after Hinton, 1978)*

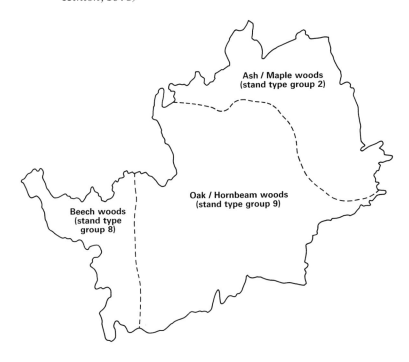

TABLE 7.2 *A selection of wild flowers used as ancient woodland indicators in the three major Hertfordshire stand groups*

	Ash/Maple	Oak/Hornbeam	Beech
Reliable indicators – more or less confined to ancient woods	Wood Anemone Oxlip Giant Bellflower Early-purple Orchid Herb Paris Greater Butterfly Orchid Thin-spiked Woodsedge Wood Small-reed	Violet Helleborine Wood-sorrel Yellow Pimpernel Ramsoms Opposite-leaved Golden Saxifrage Toothwort Great Wood-rush Hairy Wood-rush Pale Sedge Wood Melick	Sweet Woodruff Wood-sorrel Narrow-lipped Helleborine Yellow Bird's-nest Bird's-nest Orchid Fly Orchid Common Wintergreen Wood Melick Wood Barley
Strongly associated with ancient woods, but also frequently found in other habitats	Bugle Goldilocks Nettle-leaved Bellflower Primrose Stinking Iris Creeping-Jenny Greater Burnet-saxifrage Common Spotted-orchid Pendulous Sedge Wood Sedge Giant Fescue Bearded Couch	Bugle Goldilocks Slender St John's-wort Imperforate St John's-wort Moschatel Creeping-Jenny Pignut Foxglove Wood Spurge Short-fruited Willowherb Yellow Archangel Common Cow-wheat Three-nerved Sandwort Greater Stitchwort Wood Sage Wood Speedwell Heath Wood-rush Wood Sedge Grey Sedge Giant Fescue Wood Millet Wood Meadow-grass	Wood Spurge Goldilocks Slender St. John's-wort Giant Fescue
Frequently found in ancient woods, but readily colonises secondary woods	Wild Angelica Enchanter's Nightshade Bluebell Dog's Mercury Common Dog-violet Early Dog-violet Marsh Thistle Common Figwort Hairy St John's-wort Common Twayblade Remote Sedge Hairy Brome	Broad-leaved Helleborine Enchanter's Nightshade Bluebell Dog's Mercury Common Dog-violet Great Willowherb Marsh Thistle Common Figwort Barren Strawberry Heath Groundsel Water-pepper Remote Sedge Pendulous Sedge Hairy Brome	White Helleborine Spurge-laurel Bluebell Dog's Mercury Common Dog-violet Early Dog-violet Wood Sanicle Wall Lettuce Barren Strawberry Hairy Brome

in a wide range of woods. Ancient woodland can thus be reasonably accurately identified from examination of its stand-type and the occurrence of indicator plants. The presence of at least one reliable indicator provides positive evidence of antiquity, although without corroboration from historical documents this cannot be regarded as conclusive. Much of the information regarding the location and determination of stand-types that follows, relies heavily upon data collected for the *Survey of Ancient Woodlands in Hertfordshire* (Hinton, 1978). Further detailed research, especially into some of the less frequent stand-types, may necessitate revisions to some of the original findings.

7.1 Ash/Maple Woods

In north-east Hertfordshire, on the heavy soils of the Boulder Clay, a wet variant of Ash/Maple predominates. This may also be found in a few places on the London Clay and Clay-with-Flints. On drier soils a dry Ash/Maple variant occurs, together with the occasional example of pure Maple wood. Most stands are characterised by the presence of coppice, with Hazel and Ash as well as Field Maple. Standard and self-sown Field Maples are not uncommon, standards of Pedunculate Oak may be frequent and even Ash can occasionally reach standard proportions. In pure Maple woods, Ash is absent as coppice but might be self-sown, and wet Ash/Maple stands generally contain a good deal of Hazel.

Ash has always been a valued tree, especially for the great strength and elasticity of its coppice poles, which have been variously used for tool and axe handles, ladders, spears, bows, rakes and cogwheels and in the building of carts and coaches. It is often the last of our woodland trees to come into leaf; the ancient rhyme – 'Ash before Oak, we're in for a splash, Oak before Ash, we're in for a soak' – may not invariably prove accurate but it does sum up what's happened in many of our recent late springs! The Ash tree has been associated with many magical qualities; to the Norsemen, it was the 'Tree of Life', with crown in heaven and roots in hell. Potions from various parts of the tree were prescribed for ailments ranging from sore throats to plague, perhaps with some foundation, for its bark does contain small quantites of quinine.

Field Maple was probably mainly used as source of fodder for stock, although its timber, turning and carving well, was valued for luxury items such as fine inlays, bowls, spoons, musical instruments and furniture.

Hazel seldom grows to timber size, although if it is left uncut it is capable of forming a small tree with a distinct trunk. From prehistoric times traditional hazel coppices provided important local resources; cut poles are easily split amd when fresh are very pliable, and so they were fashioned into hurdles to fence stock, wattles for the wattle-and-daub walls of houses, thatching spars and fishing rods; Hazel waste burns well and was therefore used to fuel many country ovens; and it is the only native species to bear large edible nuts and so, before the days of imported chestnuts and walnuts and the introduction of the voracious Grey Squirrel these were highly prized and carefully harvested.

As will be seen in the checklist of characteristic flora (*see* Appendix 1.1), all Ash/Maple woods have particular shrubs associated with them; wetter

Figure 7.2 *Woodland wild flowers – Bluebell, Honeysuckle and Dog's Mercury*

Figure 7.3 *Ash/Maple woods characterise Boulder Clay soils of north-east Hertfordshire (Pondbottom Wood, near Nuthampstead)*

variants have significant Blackthorn, Honeysuckle and Midland Hawthorn, drier areas usually have higher frequencies of Holly, Spindle and, in south-west Hertfordshire, Whitebeam. Most of the county's Ash/Maple woods have now reached the stage of over-mature coppice and with over-shading, often coupled with declining ground water resulting from drainage of adjacent arable lands, are losing much of their formerly lush and varied ground flora, but reasonable examples can still be seen at Northey Wood near Anstey and Friars Wood near Sandon and at Great Hormead Park, where some recent coppicing has been carried out.

In general, lack of coppicing over recent decades has resulted in more than just a reduction in ground flora. Many sites are now so dark that virtually nothing survives. Even in more open places, probably because of changes in the nature of the soil from accumulated leaf litter, dead twigs and fallen branches, and possibly also from drifted agricultural chemicals and effects of acid rain, plant communities are changing as species characterisitc of nutrient-rich soils move in, such as Stinging Nettle, Ground Ivy, Dog's Mercury, False Oat-grass, Cow Parsley and Hogweed. The majority of woodland flowers bloom in early spring, to make full use of available sunlight before the leaves of trees and shrubs open fully but often even the tangled branches cast so much shade that declines are inevitable. Once not uncommon species such as Herb Paris and Greater Butterfly-orchid have declined drastically and, perhaps, face local ex-

Plate 2 (*Top*) Herb Paris *Paris quadrifolia*; (*Bottom*) Greater Butterfly Orchid *Platanthera chlorantha*

Plate 3 (*Top*) Foxglove *Digitalis purpurea*; (*Bottom*) Fly Orchid *Ophrys insectifera*

tinction from these effects. Nevertheless, some woods still contain a good variety of wild flowers whose diversity is enhanced, particularly in damper areas, by species associated with open glades and rides, ditches and pond margins. It is probably the poorly drained soils that have survived most unscathed in these woods, some being so damp that they support, in rides and waterlogged ruts, a number of marsh species. (*See* Chapter 10.1.)

7.2 Oak/Hornbeam Woods

Between north-eastern Hertfordshire, dominated by Ash/Maple woods, and the Beech woods of the south-west lies an extensive area where the main ancient woodland stand-types are Hornbeam coppice with oak standards. Hornbeam was valued as coppice, as it provided good firewood said to 'burn like a candle' – its name may be connected with the old folk spelling 'lanthorn' (for lantern), though a more probable derivation is the toughness or 'horniness' of the wood, which was once favoured for manufacturing tool handles and mill cogs. Very scarce or absent in northern Britain, Hornbeam is considered to be native only in the Home Counties.

Within Hertfordshire two oak/Hornbeam stand-types are recognised, on a variety of soil types. In these, Hornbeam is present as coppice or self-sown trees, sometimes in almost pure stands. The associated oaks may be either Pedunculate Oak, the predominant species, or Sessile Oak, most frequent and usually dominant on the shallower, more acid soils of the south east. In the latter area stands can be found with the Sessile/Pedunculate Oak hybrid. For centuries oaks were in great demand, their strong resilient timbers being especially valuable for roofing and major supports in buildings, for wooden-hulled ships, railway sleepers, wine barrels, lock gates, furniture, vehicle chassis and flooring. Oak bark was an essential ingredient in the tanning process; coppicing or pollarding of oaks may have been practised to provide raw materials for charcoal burning; in many woods and wooded commons swine were turned out in autumn to fatten up on fallen acorns, and herbalists made use of at least three parts of the tree, bark and leaves in remedies against 'spitting blood, profuse menses, bleeding piles, diarrhoea and dysentery' and acorns to relieve colic. In addition to having all these practical uses in the distant past, certain oak groves or ancient trees formed secret or sacred meeting places; oaks are also, of course, often associated with historical events or legends.

As noted above, Pedunculate Oak/Hornbeam woods are quite frequent and many of the county's, and probably the world's, finest bluebell woods are on the soils of the clays and gravels. Good examples, at least in parts, are Birchanger Wood near Bishop's Stortford, Wain and Hitch Woods near Preston, Monks, Whomerley and Astonbury Woods at Stevenage, the Knebworth Woods complex, Bramfield Park Wood, Harmergreen Wood near Welwyn Garden City, Plashes Wood near Standon, Balls Wood at Hertford Heath, Northaw Great Wood, Whippendell and Bricket Woods near Watford. At a good many sites, Pedunculate Oak is present, mostly as standards over Hornbeam coppice, although mixed coppice is not infrequent, with Field Maple, Hazel and Ash, plus a number of other species. Birches and Honeysuckle will be found but in less abundance than in Sessile Oak/Hornbeam stands. Reflecting past and, rarely, contemporary pasture-woodland or park grazing, are stands of pollarded Hornbeam. Examples can be seen at Knebworth Park, by Harmergreen Wood and in Northaw Great Wood. The best examples of Sessile Oak/Hornbeam are found in Hoddesdon Park and Wormley Woods, parts of the Broxbourne Woods complex, both now owned by The Woodland Trust.

Soil and water variations, even within a few metres, will significantly affect ground flora, and considerable differences may be found. On well-drained acid soils, usually indicated by the presence of Hazel and birches, ground flora is often at its poorest, with perhaps little more than dominant Bracken and brambles after a few early flowers such as Wood Anemone and Bluebell, although the latter may be in great hazy sheets. Wetter, neutral-to-slightly-basic soils, where Field Maple and Ash may also be present, have a considerably richer ground flora, with many species common to other stand-types, especially such near-ubiquitous species as Dog's Mercury, Bluebell, Enchanter's Nightshade, Lords-and-Ladies and Wood False-brome. Despite this diversity, the list of reliable ancient woodland indicators is relatively short. (*See* Table 7.2.) On soils of increased acidity, such as those developed on London Clay, Reading Beds and Pebble Gravels, the character of oak/Hornbeam woods changes quite markedly. Ground flora, particularly in rides and clearings, becomes very 'heathy' in nature, in fact many sites represent natural regenerants from abandoned pasture-woods and heaths, some to be later brought into woodland management regimes. A good proportion of the wild flowers found there are, as will be shown in Appendix 1.2, more typical of heath and acid grasslands, especially in rides and clearings. (*See* Chapter 9, sections 5–7.) Damper rides and rutted tracks add further diversity, with species of cudweed, rushes and occasionally bog plants. (*See* Chapter 9.8.)

7.3 Beechwoods

On the soils of the Chalk and, probably, the Clay-with-Flints, natural climax woodland would have contained relatively high proportions of beech but most, if not all, of Hertfordshire's extant beechwoods are the results of quite recent plantations, especially during the 19th century. Although beech generally grows better on thin, acid, silty clays of Tertiary origin, it is best represented in the west of the county on Clay-with-Flints and the thin calcareous soils along the edge of the Chalk escarpment. A late developer in the British flora, beech, which does not coppice well, was valued throughout history as a source of timber for the manufacture of furniture, particularly in the Chilterns. It was second only to oak in value, for when sawn, it yielded timber of great strength. Many of the woods and plantations of the Ashridge and Tring area, created to supply chair makers or bodgers, have outlived the craftsmen. Apparently unpalatable to grazing animals, beech could be grown in pasture-woods and on commons, such as those near Ashridge and Berkhamsted. Beech branches provide excellent firewood and some of the

Figure 7.4 *Most beechwoods are relatively recent plantings (near Markyate)*

ancient pollarded trees that survive, for example at Frithsden near Berkhamsted, may have fuelled local fires for centuries. Queen Victoria is reputed to have demanded 'coals' (charcoal) from Burnham Beeches in Buckinghamshire.

Botanically, closely related to oaks and chestnuts, Beech is one of our most distinctive trees, its usually much branched crown overtopping a tall straight trunk with smooth, greyish bark. Long-pointed, slender buds produce oval, softly silkily hairy leaves which give a bright green freshness to the woods of April and early May. Later these become shiny and darker green above, casting the dark gloom so typical of the dense summer plantations. Flowers, which open with the leaves, develop into shiny, brown, triangular nuts, called mast, contained within four-lobed involucres, prickly on the outside, smooth inside and ripe in October. Very high production of mast usually follows a hot summer in the previous year. Early October brings the growing season to an end and the trees begin to 'shut-down' for winter. As they withdraw valuable nutrients from leaves, for storage in trunks and roots, so colour changes occur. Beech is fabled for its autumn hues, the subtle pale yellows of October gradually give way to fiery reds, then orange and brown as leaves fall in November. It is thought that Beech leaf litter, and possibly also that of Hornbeam may significantly acidify some soils but on the Chalk such effects would be largely masked by the inherent calcareous component of soils.

Five ancient beechwood stand-types have been recognised in Hertfordshire, mainly as high forest, plantation or developed from former pasture-woodland regimes. The last are often on acid soils and have a ground flora with many heathland and acid grassland elements. (*See* Chapter 9, sections 5–7.) Beech stands growing in association with oaks or Ash, often as coppice, may depending on soil-type, be more open, supporting a diverse ground flora with many affinities to those of Ash/Maple and oak/Hornbeam woods (listed in Appendices 1.1 and 1.2). Pure stands of Beech often cast such dense shade that little can survive beneath it. On Clay-with-Flints, deeper *plateaux* soils produce beechwoods of a more open character, with a richer ground flora also having similarities to those of the woods already described. Where oaks are reasonably frequent, Wood Sorrel is quite characteristic. On the Chalk there are many, sometimes large, plantations of Beech although very few sites remain that possess a reasonably natural ground flora reflecting the antiquity of the once extensive Chiltern Beech forest. Those that do survive are the beech *hangers* on steep slopes, such as Grove and Stubbings Woods near Tring and small sites in the vicinity of Great Offley. On dry, poor soils, dense Beech stands are typified by, often rather spindly, trees with shallow spreading roots. Little light or rain water penetrates the sombre canopy, nutrients are at a premium and, as noted above, ground flora is species-poor. However, in places, a few very special well-adapted wild flowers may be found, some of which are county rarities. These include Yellow Bird's-nest, Bird's-nest Orchid, Fly Orchid, White Helleborine, Green-flowered Helleborine, Sweet Woodruff, Common Wintergreen and Coral-wort. In the part of Hertfordshire between Lilley and Breachwood Green, Wild Cherry is fairly frequent, and with Hornbeam and Beech forms an intermediate stand-type. In glades and at margins of beechwoods on the Chalk many calcareous scrub and grassland wild flowers will be found.

Over recent decades there has been a noticeable increase in the alien Sycamore invading many Beech plantations, even at well established sites. This increase has been particularly marked where original trees have been felled, especially by the hurricane-force winds of 15 and 16 October 1987 and in January and February 1990. Ash too is increasing in many places and it remains to be seen what the final outcome will be, for there is also ample natural regeneration of beech.

7.4 Birch/Oak Woods

A wood that has oaks, whether they be Sessile or Pedunculate Oak or both, according to the now widely used Peterken classification of stand-types, is not necessarily an ancient semi-natural oak wood, even though the oaks may be its most obvious feature. The important question to be resolved concerns the nature of the original woodland structure. Were oaks, whether as coppice, high forest or in pasture-woodland, part of the ancient wood? Oaks can be very invasive and, in the not too distant past, may also have been planted into woods composed of other stand-types. True oakwoods, especially where coppicing was carried-out, are most often found on sands and gravels, where soils are too dry, too acid or lack the nutrients for the development of Alder, Ash, Beech, elms, Hornbeam or Field Maple. On such soils, both Silver Birch and Downy Birch are integral parts of the woodland community. Certainly in the original succession to wildwood, birches played their part and would have been ready colonisers of areas laid bare by fallen trees. Felling and coppicing of oaks would aid their rapid spread, at times allowing them to become part of management regimes, hence birch/oak woods. Birch trees are short-lived, seldom exceeding a century, and even young specimens are prone to attacks from mortiferous fungi. However birch, also known as 'lady of the woods', probably supplied some raw materials for fuel, small tools, cotton reels, tanning, insulation, besoms and the infamous birch-rod, once much used for corporal punishment and now advocated by sex manuals for stimulation, if required!

In Hertfordshire, where soils are somewhat more varied, two birch/oak stand-types can be determined, often in close proximity and at times intergrading. Care must be taken to identify the oak species in these, for Sessile, Pedunculate or their hybrid may be present. Any reference to birch/oak woods in Hinton (1978) should be treated with care. Most of the ancient examples in the county have a heathy ground flora, containing many species listed above, and are often associated with former pasture-woods and commons, for example those on Berkhamsted Common. Stand-types containing Sessile Oak with birches, especially Silver Birch are known as Lowland birch/Sessile Oak woods and they may also contain some Pedunculate Oak. Good examples can be seen in parts of Sherrardspark, Broxbourne, Oxhey and Whippendell Woods. Here Holly, Cherry and Rowan are usually present with, on slightly less acidic and wetter soils, Hazel, and occasionally Wild Service Tree and other shrubs.

Woods of this type on more acid soils have an impoverished ground flora, bracken and brambles usually dominating, but amongst the other species to be found may be Wood Anemone, Wood Sorrel, Wood Sage, Betony, Common Cow-wheat, Greater Stitchwort, Common Dog-violet, Great and Hairy Wood-rush, Honeysuckle, Yorkshire Fog, Creeping Soft-grass, Wood Millet, Wavy and Tufted Hair-grass.

Lowland Birch/Pedunculate Oak woods, where Sessile Oak is entirely absent, have been identified in a few places in south and east Hertfordshire. Here, on highly acid soils, ground flora is extremely poor and most frequently dominated by Bracken. In slightly less acid or damper patches there is a little increase in diversity, with some Hazel coppice containing, in addition to those species noted in the preceding paragraph, Bugle, Marsh Thistle, Yellow Archangel, Herb Bennet, Ivy, Yellow Pimpernel, Barren Strawberry, Primrose and Wood Sedge.

7.5 Hazel/Ash Woodlands

This group encompasses those stands with Ash as standards and, invariably, Hazel as dominant coppice. Birches, Midland Hawthorn, Honeysuckle and coppiced or standard oaks are associated components. Field Maple, Hornbeam, Beech and elms are absent. Although scarce, Hazel/Ash stands have been identified within woods on a variety of soils, with examples in parts of Earls Wood near Barkway, Brick Kiln Wood near Brookmans Park, Lees Wood and Waterdell Spring to the west of Watford and Hill Wood near Great Gaddesden. Ground flora is more or less the same as that of the neighbouring major stand-types.

7.6 Ash/Wych Elm Woods

Wych Elm *Ulmus glabra* (2–3) occurs as coppice or as standards, the spreading crowns of the tallest sometimes reaching up more than 40 metres, the bark smooth in young trees but becoming rugged as they mature. Unlike several of the other elms, it does not produce suckers. Young twigs are hairy, becoming smooth and grey in their third year. Well before leaves appear, many small unstalked flowers with con-spicuous reddish stamens are produced, which mature into pale green, flat, discoid, curiously notched fruits with seeds at their centres. Leaves are broad to elliptical, rough above, hairy beneath, with one longer side that often obscures the short stalk. Elms produce tough wood that is very resistant to rotting in both wet and dry conditions. It was used for drains, water pipes, water pumps, buckets and coffins. The attractive, resilient-to-splitting timber formed the seats of many cottage chairs with beech legs and ash backs. Although Wych Elms appeared to be less susceptible to Dutch Elm disease (*see below*), many eventually suc-cumbed and few mature trees remain.

Where Wych Elm occurs with Ash, but without Beech, Hornbeam or other elms, this stand-type is designated. Hazel, Pedunculate Oak, Elder. Midland Hawthorn and sallows are common associates. In Hertfordshire examples are to be found on damper soils in the Welwyn Garden City area, mostly as small components of larger woods such as Harmergreen and Sherrardspark Woods. Ground flora has the same characteristics as the adjacent major woods.

7.7 Invasive Elm Woods

In the past, elms *Ulmus* spp., of two or more species which reproduce mainly by suckering, were a very significant feature of the countryside, especially in hedges. Unfortunately, virtually all these majestic trees have now gone, devastated by Dutch Elm disease – a fungal infection, spread from tree to tree by elm bark beetles, which kills by blocking the vascular system that transports nutrients and water throughout the tree. Particularly virulent in the decades after the Second World War, this disease and the aftermath of clearing dead and infected trees has completely changed the character of much of the county. Elms continue to sucker into hedgerows and woods, as they have done throughout history, but they seldom produce trees as continuing outbreaks of the disease strike them down. In the past, elms suckering into areas of cleared wood or failed coppice may have been managed to produce trees, or more likely, coppice to provide winter fodder for cattle. Invasive elm woods are frequent throughout Hertfordshire, usually as small com-partments at woodland edges. In some places only gaunt dead trees remain and in others abundant fresh suckers are found but in many the elms are being ousted as other trees and shrubs invade.

Two main species of suckering elms have been recognised for Hertfordshire, although elm study has been rather neglected by botanists, perhaps because of the confusing taxonomy that includes numerous localised races, clones and hybrids. Apparently most widespread in the county is English Elm *Ulmus procera* (2–3). Its stout, hairy twigs have small, oval-shaped leaves that feel rough on their upper surfaces and are hairy beneath. As with all elms, it prefers damp, nutrient-rich soils. Less common and more restricted to northern and eastern parts of the county, Smooth Elm. *U. minor* (2–3) has longer, slenderer twigs with smaller, smooth leaves with shiny upper surfaces. Herbal remedies using elm were many. Bruised leaves were said to heal infected wounds, cure scurvy, help mend broken bones and cleanse skin. Scum from roots boiled in water was a valued 'cure for baldness'.

Invasive elm wood ground flora reflects that of the stand-types invaded although these are often obscured, especially where there are dying trees. More light penetrates the open canopies and soils are noticeably richer, perhaps as a result of accumulations of nutrients, such as phosphates, from dead, fallen and decaying trees. Dog's Mercury does well and many sites become colonised by wild flowers typical of such enhanced soils. From adjacent hedges, field borders and road verges come opportunists such as Stinging Nettle, Cow Parsley, Hogweed, Rough Chervil, Goosegrass, Elder, Herb Robert, Herb Bennet, Ground Ivy, Rough Meadow Grass and Barren Brome.

7.8 Alder Woods

Woodlands of Alder *Alnus glutinosa* (2–3) are scarce in Hertfordshire, but there are good examples at Oughtonhead Common and in the upper valley of the Purwell near Hitchin. These typify the stand-type, being found in valleys, adjacent to rivers and spring lines where soils are more or less permanently waterlogged and flushed with mineral nutrients. Alder readily colonises, but was also often planted and coppiced. Timber was used for broom-heads and other turnery. Coppiced poles, being water-resistant, were ideal for the strengthening of river banks. Bark, utilised in the tanning industry, was probably once locally obtained from around Hitchin, where a tannery flourished until relatively recently. Black gunpowder came from alder charcoal; stripped wood and roots produced dyes. Perhaps, the 18th century 'extensive hedges' and coppices, that grew along the River Gade where Hemel Hempstead now stands, helped supply such raw materials. Stripped roots were a remedy for fevers, decoctions were prepared that 'purges and vomits them vigorously, and carries off the disease'.

Ground flora of alderwoods is frequently composed of a mixture of some of the species of the wetter parts of woodlands, described above (Chapter 7, sections 1 and 2) and elements of marsh and riverside flora. (*See* Chapter 10.) Most contain some Ash, Pedunculate Oak, Grey Willow, Field Maple, Wych Elm and other trees, with Marsh Marigold, Angelica, Yellow Iris, Hemlock, Buckler- and Lady Ferns, Tufted

Hair-grass, rushes and sedges not infrequently present. Dry ground plants are rare or absent, although conspicuous tussocks of long-lived sedges, notably Greater Tussock-sedge *Carex paniculata* (5–6) may provide suitable small habitats, upon which these and even small trees may colonise. Away from the really marshy areas, Stinging Nettle often dominates in its true habitat. Small Teasel *Dipsacus pilosus* (8) is known from one of the Hitchin alderwoods and a few other damp, calcareous woods, mainly in the east of the county. Generally smaller than its more widespread close relative Common Teasel, Small Teasel is only prickly on stems.

Figure 7.5 *This ancient layered Hornbeam has outlived the wood it once protected (Priors Wood near Kimpton)*

8

Recent Woods and Plantations

In our countryside there has been a long tradition of creating new woods, although the techniques and tree species utilised have changed markedly in more recent times. As noted in Chapters 6 and 7, most of Hertfordshire's ancient semi-natural woodlands developed their structure through management to provide resources for local and national economic requirements. In the very distant past, felled areas were left to regenerate naturally. Later, selective management or planting with seeds or saplings predominated, local requirements determining the ultimate species mix and thus stand-types. Recent plantations have a very low level of 'naturalness', that is, biological similarity to wildwood, although some, for example those containing native hardwood trees, have potential, in time, to attain semi-natural status. Tree-planting has been carried out over the centuries and gradations occur that are difficult, perhaps impossible, to resolve. Some conifer plantations planted over former ancient woodland have failed, on account of inadequate soil conditions or poor management, and have developed a high diversity of flora and fauna, indeed there are a number of relatively recent conifer plantations that are of considerably greater interest to the naturalist than many secondary woodlands planted on virgin sites, sometimes centuries ago.

Woodland changes have been an integral part of the developing landscapes of Hertfordshire, their nature being very much dictated by contemporary requirements and management capabilites, although changing fashions have also made their mark. Initially, changes would have been barely detectable, with, perhaps, the sowing of a few acorns to create a grove of oaks to be cosseted for timber or a future supply of acorns for pigs, or with some coppices being allowed to regenerate into woods. As timber demands grew, techniques for clear felling and replanting or selective felling and regeneration were employed, and these would bring more evident landscape changes. The early 'new woods' and plantations usually contain closely spaced, even-aged trees, often of just one or two species. Consequently, in comparison with ancient woods, associated wildlife was less diverse. Many of these were sited on lands, for example heaths, commons and marshes, that were unsuitable for crops or good grazing. Here, woodland ground flora would be normally quite sparse and some evidence of former habitats often remained in rides and along margins.

As early as 1503, it was noted that the forests of England had been 'utterly destroyed'. It is widely written that the Royal Navy expressed considerable concern over the abilities of our forests to supply the right kind of timber for the construction of 'men of war', although as Rackham (1986) has shown, it is more likely that this was related to a lack of national funding of the navy than lack of trees. However, these protestations did lead to the 16th century establishment of some woods, notably with oaks, where trees were planted close together to ensure the production of tall, straight trunks. The writings of John Evelyn and his 17th century contemporaries stimulated great changes, most of the relatively modern plantations of hardwoods, and later conifers, owe much to the publication of such works as Evelyn's *Sylva: or a Discourse of Forest Trees* published in 1664. Some plantations were purely aesthetic to enhance the appeal of landscaped parks and estates, using not only native trees but also some of the newly introduced foreign species collected by intrepid travelling botanists of the period. Included, although seldom used in any quantities were limes *Tilia* spp., Horse Chestnut *Aesculus hippocastanum*, Sweet Chestnut *Castanea sativa*, Walnut *Juglans regia*, poplars *Populus* spp., alien oaks, many conifers, Norway Maple *Acer platanoides* and its close relative Sycamore *A. pseudoplatanus*. The last, although now well naturalised like many of these introductions, is seldom found in ancient woods. Thought to be the *sycamorus* or fig-mulberry in the Bible, which Zaccheus climbed to watch Christ ride into Jerusalem, Sycamore is native to mountainous areas from southern and central Europe to the Caucasus. Because of the religious connotations, people wanted the tree close to their houses. Today it is a well-distributed and common species, indicating establishment in recently cleared woods or invasion of poorly managed sites.

During the last three hundred years or so, a great many plantations were established for economic purposes; the 18th century saw the development of Beech plantations, especially along the Chalk escarpment (*See* Chapter 7.3); larch and Scots pine were particularly favoured during Victorian times and throughout most of this century, there has been a great and often damaging expansion in the planting of alien conifers. As noted above, some clues to the dating of secondary woods can be found in the trees themselves – the species used and, often, the presence of a single-age class planted in discernible rows. Periods of selective felling, like some forms of replanting or regeneration, however, may obscure this, and sites developed by natural succession from, say, former pasture-wood or scrub encroachment may be difficult to distinguish. Invariably ground flora will be relatively low in diversity, but the nature of any site will be dependent upon history, geology, hydrology, proximity to potential seed sources and the types of trees planted. Plantations of hardwood species and in some cases conifers, established on ancient woodland sites may occasionally retain much of the former characteristic flora and fauna. However, generally speaking, most secondary woods and plantations have considerably poorer ground flora and lack most, if not all, indicator plants.

Ivy is particularly characteristic of newer sites. Its glossy, dark, evergreen leaves on woody runners spread rapidly, sometimes to carpet the ground and, if allowed, clamber by tiny clinging roots up trunks. Coppicing and the grazing of pasture-woods inhibited Ivy and, today, it is still rather sparingly found in ancient woods. All sorts of other plants may invade 'new' woods and over long periods the ground flora is likely to undergo many changes. Where there have been soil disturbances, species such as thistles, nettles, willowherbs and many others will

47

become temporarily established. In heathy places, considerable areas can be dominated by Bracken. This fern has long, creeping, underground rhizomes and tall rough stems (*petioles*) with spreading pinnate leaves or fronds, which bear spore-producing organs (*sori*). Bracken spreads rapidly and can be very persistent.

Domination by one or a few species is a common feature. On acid soils, as well as Bracken, clumps of the hairy, broad-leaved and towering, pink-purple, occasionally white, tubular-flowered Foxglove *Digitalis purpurea* (6–9) may be found. At times, some of the plantations on the Chalk about Hexton glow pink from the massed five-petalled blooms of Herb Robert *Geranium robertianum* (5–9) or later russet, as the triangular, deeply-cut, aromatic leaves age. On neutral soils, common umbellifers such as Cow Parsley, Rough Chervil and Hogweed quickly invade from hedgerows and road verges. On damper soils, other taller umbellifers are not infrequent, the highly poisonous Hemlock *Conium maculatum* (6–7), with distinctive purple-spotted stems, and the massive Giant Hogweed *Heracleum mantegazzianum* (6–7), an alien from south-west Asia, the juices of which, in conjunction with sunlight, can cause serious burns to skin (*photodermatitis*).

In time, especially as tree canopy develops and closes in, many temporary species such as these will fade from the community and a more typical woodland ground flora develops. Sites adjacent to older woods or hedges are more likely to acquire typical woodland wild flowers than the isolated examples. Bluebell and Dog's Mercury may move in quite rapidly. Other, more demanding, species, especially the indicators of ancient woodland, may take centuries, or perhaps will never enter the community, because of lack of continuity with the wildwood and subtle ecological inadequacies.

After the depredations of World War 1, The Forestry Commission was set up in 1919, to coordinate and increase home supplies of timber. From that date, many, and frequently extensive, conifer plantations became a feature of our landscape, not only for their timber, but in some areas with open landscapes as wind breaks and shelter belts. Conifers, especially alien species, grow quickly on poor soils and larger plantations are particularly evident in southern Hertfordshire – for example at Broxbourne and Bramfield Woods. There are many places where parts of or entire ancient woods were clear-felled and replaced with the sepulchral gloom of conifers. Fortunately the rate of clearance and replacement with wholly alien conifers has reduced in the latter part of this century.

In the early stages of development of a conifer plantation, there may be a rich and varied flora, a mixture of what was there before plus adventive weeds that capitalise upon the disturbance of planting. This is usually short-lived, for as the conifers grow up their evergreen-leaved branches come together to form a closed, all-year-round, canopy. Much solar radiation is relfected and, in most cases, so little penetrates that hardly any ground flora can survive. In addition, larches excepted, because they are evergreen, conifers dispose of more water from the soil through both transpiration and evaporation. Their tough leaves or *needles*, are continuously shed, fall to the ground but lack of light and, often, shortage of water mean that decay is slow. Leaf and other litter builds up and the soil and humus, frequently already acidic, become increaingly acidified. Few of our indigenous wild flowers can withstand such conditions and a great many conifer plantations have a less diverse wildlife than some of the world's great deserts. A few species, such as Bluebell, Foxglove and Bracken have a fair degree of tolerance and may persist in some areas and of course, because there are many fungi that do not require sunlight, even the densest of plantations is not without some botanical interest.

Conifers or softwood trees have, in comparison with the broadleaved trees or hardwoods, a simple structure and growth pattern. Identification is not always easy, because the species vary so little and close examination of leaves, from the second year's growth onwards, and of flowers, fruits and overall shape is necessary. All conifers have scaly buds and narrow leaves, and, with the exception of larch leaves, these are evergreen and individually and erratically shed. Most species produce resins that impart a fragrance to needles, bark and timber. Regular branching from a straight trunk creates a geometrical symmetry of shape. Botanists classify conifers as *gymnosperms* or *naked-seeded* plants. Other flowering plants, classified as *angiosperms*, have female flowers, where the eggs, or *ovules*, develop after fertilisation into seeds that are protected by specialised structures, called *carpels*. Ovules of conifers are borne upon exposed scales of immature cones, the female flowers. Male flowers, separate from female flowers but usually on the same tree, are catkin-like. They produce vast quantities of wind-dispersed pollen, only a small proportion of which ever reaches female flowers. Once fertilised, the female cones develop and become tightly shut to protect the seeds within. Once the seeds ripen, the cones open in response to dry weather and the small winged seeds drift away. Although most conifers flower in spring, their cones may not ripen until the following autumn, next spring or, in a few species, some eighteen months later.

Apart from Yew and Juniper, neither of which is a major timber producer, the only native conifer used in plantations is Scots Pine *Pinus sylvestris* (5–6). Today it is far less frequently grown than in Victorian times for, amongst the scores of alien conifers brought back to Britain from many parts of the world and subjected to years of trial growing, a few have been found to be well suited to our climate and more useful timber producers. Other imports, commercially less useful but aesthetically attractive, became favoured for ornamental planting and landscaping. Probably because of their obviously relatively recent and alien origin, both commercial and decorative conifers have to some extent been ignored by students of the county's flora and consequently little distribution data exists.

Possibly the most widely planted conifer is a variety of Black Pine, known as Corsican Pine *Pinus nigra* spp. *laricio* (5–6). Native to the island of Corsica, this is a close relative of Scots Pine, with larger cones and much longer needles. Corsican Pine grows rapidly in our climate and, like Scots Pine, is the source of timber used as 'red deal' for joints, rafters, box-making, paper pulp, wallboard and, when weather-proofed, telegraph poles, railway sleepers and fences. Another commonly planted species is larch which is resinous, producing excellent fences, posts, gates, planks and poles. Differing from other popular conifers in being deciduous larch is found as two species in Hertfordshire, (plus a hybrid between them which, possessing variable parental features, is not easy to identify), European Larch *Larix decidua* (3–4) and Japanese Larch, *L. kaempferi* (3–4). European Larch, which is native to the Alps and central European mountains, has straw-coloured twigs and pale green needles; Japanese Larch which was introduced into Britain from the mountains of Japan has russet-brown twigs and bluish-green needles, each with two noticeable white bands on the underside; both species have small, attractive female flowers, sometimes referred to as larch roses.

Pyramidal in outline, the spruces are readily identified by their needles, borne singly in two rows along twigs and arising from small peg-like structures. If the needles are deliberately pulled, the pegs come away, but in natural leaf-fall the pegs remain. Norway Spruce *Picea abies* (5–6), the true 'Christmas Tree', is arguably our most familiar conifer, for, apart from its cultivation, and premature cutting or uprooting as a seasonal decoration, it is one of the world's leading timber producers. Native to much of northern and central Europe, and mountains further south, Norway Spruce was probably first introduced into Britain during the 16th century. Its soft, mid-green needles are blunt-pointed and the long, cylindrical cones always hang downwards. Rather similar in appearance, but apparently less frequently planted in Hertfordshire, is Sitka Spruce *P. sitchensis*. This has short cones with distinctively crinkly-edged scales and bluish-green needles that are roughly pointed – a feature that renders the species most unsuitable for indoor decoration, but many are sold in the guise of 'Christmas Trees', much to the chagrin of those who have to pot them, carry them indoors and remove the inevitable piles of prickly fallen needles during the festive season! Sitka Spruce is named after a small town in Alaska and its native range extends right down the western seaboard of North America, but strains from the mid-part of this range grow best in Britain. Spruce timber provides much of the 'whitewood' for internal building work and joinery, furniture and packing cases and, when treated, fencing and poles.

Amongst the few other species planted in Hertfordshire in small quantities may be Douglas Fir *Pseudotsuga menziesii* and Western Red Cedar *Thuja plicata*, both native to western North America, Western Hemlock *Tsuga heterophylla*, from North America and Asia, and Silver Fir *Abies alba*, from the mountains of Europe.

9

Grasslands

Any plant community, natural or artificial, dominated by grasses is a grassland, although, as will be shown, a great many other wild flowers are often abundantly associated with such habitats. In Hertfordshire there are no natural grasslands and all sites have been created and are maintained by human interference, such as the introduction of grazing stock or cutting regimes. In our climate, with no great herds of herbivorous mammals and without such human interference, all grasslands would, through natural succession of invasive shrubs and trees, revert to woodland. In earlier chapters the clearance of the wildwood has been described. This was done to provide areas for pastoral and arable farming. Some of the county's extant grasslands may, at least in parts, date back to prehistoric times, with a more or less unbroken continuity of management that prevented the return of shrubs and trees. From early beginnings of small glade-like clearings in the wildwood, grasslands extended as the populations of humans and their grazing stocks increased. Grasses, and other wild flowers with adaptations to survive in the more open areas and tolerant of grazing, trampling and cutting, moved in. It is possible, even in very early times, that some sites were deliberately planted or certain species particularly encouraged. Over centuries, distinctive grassland communities evolved or were created. The nature of each of these communities closely relates to soils and long-term management. It is probable that many of our better extant grasslands have had a chequered history; some may have been in and out of cultivation, or even undergone periods of woodland cover. In most cases, the remaining sites of great botanical interest have almost certainly had a long history of sympathetic management.

Appendices 1.4, 1.5, 1.6, 1.7, 1.8

Throughout Hertfordshire, grazing of some form survived as a major land use until at least the late 19th century. Before the days of mechanisation and, latterly, the use of chemicals, a range of traditional grasslands flourished, from the short, flower-rich and scented turf of Chalk downlands in the north and west, through the lush meadows and pastures of neutral soils, to the dry acid heaths of the south. The need to increase food production through arable cultivation, occasioned the loss of many grasslands during the First World War. But even in the 1930s Hertfordshire still had 41 per cent of its landscape under permanent or rough grazing (Stamp, 1941). During the Second World War it was necessary to plough up further grassland for the same reason, but since then the destruction has continued more or less unabated, although the need is not always so clear. These losses have been further exacerbated by the conversions of most of the surviving grasslands to rather sterile habitats through 'improvement' with chemical herbicides and fertilisers or by the ploughing up of ancient turf and reseeding to create leys with a few very productive, sometimes alien, grass species and little else. Other losses have been incurred through urban and industrial expansion, mineral and water extraction, afforestation, recreation and the withdrawal of traditional land uses facilitating scrub and secondary woodland encroachment. The scale of loss has been so great that the Hertfordshire Grassland Survey, carried out between 1985 and 1987, records only 12 per cent of the landscape under permanent grass, of which a mere 1.7 per cent is of semi-natural quality (Hertfordshire County Council, 1988). There remain few places where anything like traditional meadows, Chalk downs or grassy heaths survive. The destruction continues. Only a handful of sites, fortunately including some important areas, have protection as Sites of Special Scientific Interest, designated by the Nature Conservancy Council, or Hertfordshire and Middlesex Wildlife Trust nature reserves. A few others are 'protected' by virtue of agreement between landowners and the Hertfordshire County Council as 'Heritage Sites', although the terms of these agreements are rather tenuous and rely heavily upon the goodwill and sensitivity of individuals concerned.

Hertfordshire has twelve, or more, differing soil types, ranging from highly calcareous derivations from Chalk and Chalky Boulder Clay to acidic sands and gravels. Relationships between these soils, drainage and grassland management, past and present, has resulted in a quite wide variety of grassland types. Individual types are, generally, recognised and classified by the presence of one or two dominant species of grasses (occasionally a herb species is used) although many other grasses and herbs may be present. In some areas of varying soils, water availability and management, several different, but usually closely related, grassland types may be found within a single site. Based upon soil chemistry and water relations, the grasslands of Hertfordshire, to be described below, are placed into four rather broad categories, thus:

Calcareous
Neutral
Wet (calcareous, neutral and acid)
Acid

9.1 Calcareous Grasslands

There is archaeological and ecological evidence to show that at least a few of Hertfordshire's remaining calcareous grasslands are of great antiquity. Some, perhaps, were in existence 4000 years ago. Calcareous grasslands are found where Chalk or very chalky Boulder Clay outcrop, notably along the escarpment from Tring to Royston, although there are a few outlying sites elsewhere. (*See* Figure 9.1.) As has been shown, much of the early wildwood clearance was for the provision of arable cultivation plots. Original soils would have been very fertile, with rich humus and minerals resulting from the former tree cover. Cultivation and erosion reduced soil fertility, particularly rapidly on Chalk, and some areas were abandoned to return to woodland; others increasingly became used for pasture. The introduction of grazing stock, especially close-cropping sheep, prevented a return of shrubs and trees. Grazing

Figure 9.1   *Chalk downland at Church Hill, Therfield Heath, with Bee
Orchid, Sweet Briar and Small Scabious*

and trampling over a very long time span created a highly stressful habitat where only certain, often specialised, wild flowers were able to colonise and survive, a habitat we now know as downland. Chalk downland plants need to be able to withstand grazing pressures as well as the rigours imposed by the shallow, poor Chalk soils. The full extent of Neolithic and early Bronze Age forest clearances is uncertain, but it is probable that considerable tracts of the Chalk were open and quite heavily grazed. Clearances and increased grazing continued and it seems that, by Roman times, virtually all the Chalk escarpment supported short-cropped, flower-rich downland, much of which was to remain into the last century.

In all probability, at least some of the extant downland of the county has had a varied history. It is not always possible to be absolutely certain that all areas are as ancient as once thought, for many Chalk plants will readily colonise areas where soils have been disturbed, for example abandoned arable fields. There are, however, a number of species which, if found together in some numbers, are reasonably good indicators of downland that has been undisturbed for at least 150 years or so. These include Clustered Bellflower, Field Fleawort, Bastard Toadflax, Squinancywort, Rock-rose, Dropwort and Horseshoe Vetch.

Chalk downland flora is so specialised and markedly different from that of the preceding wildwood that it is interesting to reflect on its origins. Various theories have been postulated, but the most widely accepted suggests that some open Chalk habitats remained through late-glacial and early post-glacial times; within or at the margins of the wildwood throughout south-east England there were unstable river gorges and sea cliffs and some areas may have been kept more or less open by native herbivores. When Man opened up the landscape, the Chalk plants moved in, much as they will still do today. But this is a pioneering flora and, unless natural succession is controlled, will be superseded by scrub and woodland. Sheep and, probably, goat grazing was the control. It was a combination of the close grazing, so typical of sheep, and the physical nature of the Chalk and its soils that dictated the richness and distribution of downland flora, typically composed of low-growing fine-leaved grasses and many herbs. In 'ancient' downland turf it may not be unusual to find forty or more grasses and wild flowers within an area a metre square.

A large proportion of British wild flowers are lime-lovers or calcicoles; chalk outcrops, therefore, determine the presence of many plants. A soft, porous rock, chalk readily absorbs water, is well aerated and warms up quickly. But its composition is 90 per cent or more calcium carbonate; other nutrients which plants might require are in short supply, notably phosphates and nitrates. Because of this paucity, and particularly with grazing pressures, individual plants cannot grow large. There is, it is true, reduced competition for space, which allows many different species to enter the community, but individual plants are very much in competition for nutrients and light and there are a number of species, such as Kidney Vetch, that will only thrive in really open places, such as disturbed track margins or animal scrapes. Soils formed on the top of virgin Chalk, called rendzinas, are often no more than 30cm or so thick, black with humus and immature, formed as they are on steep slopes where material is continuously moving downward. A characteristic of most downland slope rendzinas is that they have a slightly convex profile, being somewhat deeper about mid-slope before accumulating at slope bottoms. As products of decay are not readily washed down into the Chalk and abundant calcium carbonate inhibits decomposition, the black humus results. In fact, soil reaction would be acid were it not for the proximity and neutralising action of the Chalk. As will be shown, most plants root through the rendzina into the Chalk below. It is possible on the tops of some hills when upward-percolating ground water levels are low, for a relatively acid soil to develop, especially if a thin cap of gravel or loess is present. In such situations, acid-loving or calcifuge plants may thrive to form Chalk heath. The last local example, on Lilley Hoo between Hitchin and Luton, with extensive Heather, Gorse and other interesting species, was ploughed up in 1944 as part of the War Agricultural Committee's directive to bring more land into, what was at the time termed, temporary cultivation. As at the many other sites that were ignominiously destroyed in this way, the former use, sheep grazing, was never reinstated.

Water supply can be a serious problem for downland wild flowers, particularly in the height of hot, dry summers. Although Chalk is capable of retaining copious amounts of water – a cubic foot may hold two gallons without appearing wet – it is an extremely porous rock, extensively bedded and full of cracks and fissures, notably through the crushing and thrusting effects of the Ice Ages. Rainwater may readily drain downwards and sideways. Soil material filling interstices in the Chalk is exploited by plant roots. Carbon dioxide released through root respiration combines with ground water to produce carbonic acids, which, with other acids leached from the humus rich rendzinas, dissolve away Chalk. This further opens crevices, increasing drainage and accelerating erosion. In dry weather much water is lost through evaporation at the soil surface. Also each plant in the community removes moisture from the soil to carry out vital functions of growth and reproduction. Water taken from soil by roots is translocated via stems and relocated to various parts of the plant. The driving force behind these processes is called *transpiration* and occurs mainly in the leaves. Here, minute openings, known as *stomata*, in the, usually, lower leaf surfaces allow water and carbon dioxide to escape and oxygen, essential for photosynthesis, to enter. The amount of water used by plants can, to some extent, be regulated, as special *guard cells* surrounding the stomata control the size of opening, but there are limits, and with insufficient ground water wilting and death may follow.

The very nature of downland communities, which in their heyday would have supported thousands of sheep in carefully tended flocks, is a product of the adaptations made by the majority of species to withstand the severe physical conditions of their habitats. For example, most species are *hemicryptophytes*, that is, their budding organs are within or close to the surface of the soil; stimulated by, and/or to resist grazing, many develop low-growing rosettes of leaves or lateral growth; this reduces evaporation from the soil so creating a relatively humid

Plate 4 (*Top*) Chalk downland flora with Upright Brome *Bromus erectus*, Horseshoe Vetch *Hippocrepis comosa* and Common Milkwort *Polygala vulgaris*; (*Bottom*) Pasque Flower *Pulsatilla vulgaris*

Plate 5 (*Top*) Bee Orchid *Ophrys apifera*; (*Bottom*) Common Spotted Orchid *Dactylorhiza fuchsii*

microclimate just above ground level which lowers transpiration losses; some species, such as Fairy Flax, Milkwort, Wild Thyme and Rock-rose, have small, often narrow, leaves with only a minimal area over which water may be lost; other species, such as Autumn Gentian and several orchids, have thick cuticles to their leaves to reduce water loss; still others, for instance Pasque Flower, Hoary Plantain, Hairy Violet, Field Fleawort, Hoary Ragwort and Common Restharrow, retain moisture through having hairy stems and leaves and several of the narrow-leaved grasses roll up their leaves in dry weather, trapping inside moist air and protecting stomata from dessicating breezes.

A good proportion of the Chalk flora overwinters with leaf rosettes that allow an early start to food production and growth in the following year, thereby facilitating flowering, fruiting and die-back before the advent of the hottest and driest part of the year. The majority of orchids do this. Many early-blooming flowers have evolved yellow colouring because this attracts pollinating insects. Later in the year there is a predominance of mauves and blues; this is probably something to do with how pollinating insects perceive ultra-violet light reflected from petals, even at night. Annuals, with their soft succulent stems and shallow roots, are scarce; heavy grazing selects against them in favour of perennials, many of which possess tough, wiry, unpalatable stems and deep roots – careful excavation and studies of the rooting of species such as Burnet Saxifrage, Small Scabious, Salad Burnet, Perforate St John's-wort, Clustered Bellflower and vetches have revealed that roots may penetrate to considerable depths, five metres or more, into joints and fissures in the Chalk, thence spreading out into cracks and pores, exploiting water reserves. A number of species, including Bulbous Buttercup, Common Restharrow and orchids have food and water storage organs, *tubers*, which help to resist drought.

Some leguminous plants – vetches, trefoils, restharrow, etc. – help overcome the paucity of soil nutrients by forming association, or *symbiosis*, with another type of organism. They attract bacteria to their roots and enclose them with plant tissue to form small root nodules; in return for this shelter and the supply of some of the plants' carbohydrates, the bacteria synthesise atmospheric nitrogen into nitrates which are then available to the plants for the essential production of proteins and nucleic acids. Many orchids have evolved similar root associations with microscopic fungi, called *mycorrhizae*, which aid the assimilation of nutrients and the germination of seeds. The undisturbed nature of the Chalk soils provides conditions for development of certain mycorrhizae that conjoin with orchid seeds and effect germination, a process which may take several years. Mycorrhizae provide the developing plants with certain essential nutrients which are otherwise absent or in short supply and, in return are given shelter – another example of symbiosis, like that outlined above, which is far more complex than described here. Common and Knapweed Broomrapes have solved nutrient scarcity by becoming parasitic upon other plants; completely lacking chlorophyll they cannot synthesise sugar, but their roots extract nutrients readymade by penetrating those of the host plant. Yellow Rattle, Red Bartsia and the eyebrights do have chlorophyll but they are often partially parasitic.

Variation in aspect of downland slopes produces marked differences in the flora. North-facing slopes receive less solar radiation, the sun's rays slanting across them; consequently these slopes have damper, cooler conditions, noticeably limiting the distribution and productivity of many of the specialised downland wild flowers. Stemless Thistle, for example, may sometimes be found on north-facing slopes, but it is much more frequent and produces more abundant flowers and fruit on southerly facing slopes. These, on the other hand, hotter and drier from their longer periods of direct sunlight, support a greater diversity with several species more typical of southern and continental climates reaching the northern and western limit of their range in Britain. (Some of these species have only been able to extend their range because of the physical characteristics of the Chalk and the development of downland habitat.) Squinancywort, Quaking-grass, Horseshoe Vetch, Knapweed, Broomrape, Bee and Pyramidal Orchids belong typically to warm, dry, southern continental climates; Burnt-tip Orchid, Pasque Flower and Field Fleawort are much more frequent in continental grasslands with hotter summers and colder winters, and Bastard Toadflax is essentially a species of warm, damp, southern oceanic climates. Botanists, like entomologists, have long known that south to south-west facing slopes of the downland are the best hunting ground for many specialised and rare species.

Evidence suggests that for centuries vast sheep flocks constantly tended by shepherds ranged the escarpment from Tring to Royston. It is difficult, now, to imagine the immensity of these open, virtually treeless, rolling downs, with their carpets of short-cropped turf, abundantly streaked white from well-worn sheep paths and ancient trackways. Here and there patterns of small arable fields and settlements, ancient burial mounds, such as round barrows, and myriads of anthills, the nests of Yellow Meadow Ants would have broken up the smooth contours of the landscape. Rabbits, first introduced by the Normans and kept in warrens as a readily available source of food and fur, but long since escaped to colonise the downs in great numbers, helped to keep turf short and scrub at bay, and created extensive scrapes, so important for less competitive wild flowers.

It appears that, at least by late mediaeval times, considerable stretches of the flatter chalklands were under arable cultivation; shepherding then became a very organised part of rural life, with daily and seasonal routines adapted to other farming activities. Sheep flocks, composed mainly of a large, hardy and agile breed, horned in both sexes, known as the Western, Old Wiltshire or Old Hampshire, were managed for most economic production of meat and wool. In a time without mechanisation or chemical fertilisers these animals would crop the downs by day and when they were folded at night they would manure the arable land. In certain seasons, when stubble- or arable-cropping or weed-control of fallow was required, flocks would be penned there by day, and then moved onto the downs by night. The long, narrow parishes, of pre-Norman origin, that straddle the Chalk escarpment, especially in northern Hertfordshire, probably owe much to these methods of husbandry.

59

From the 16th and 17th centuries increasing inroads were made into the county's downland. New crops and improved dunging techniques were introduced onto the newly broken lands. Sometimes, perhaps as a result of soil infertility, cultivation was rather temporary, and land was returned to grass, but the 'seeds of destruction' were sown, for much of the native flora could not withstand even small scale disturbances. Fortunately, lack of mechanisation and inadequate development of fertilisers helped higher and steeper places to escape the initial onslaught and retain permanent sheep- and rabbit-grazed swards. The regular presence of breeding populations of Great Bustard near Royston up to the 17th century is good evidence for extensive tracts of downland. It was last recorded there in 1808 (Sage, 1964).

Further losses to arable occurred to meet needs of the Napoleonic Wars, 1790 to 1815, when many farmers also no doubt capitalised on inflated grain prices. As so often happens, grain prices tumbled after the wars and cultivation declined, but as before, much downland was virtually irreversibly damaged. Some places did revert to grazing but failed to acquire many of the typical wild flowers, particularly as soil disturbance favoured development of coarser, tufty grasses. Some of these features can still be seen today, for example on some of the lower slopes of Therfield Heath. The agricultural depression was short-lived and a great boom in farming followed, lasting until the final decades of the 19th century; with it came the inevitable expansion of arable cultivation. Downland declined and there were not inconsiderable losses resulting from reorganisation of land under the Enclosure Acts. Contemporary records show that sheep farming remained important, albeit on a smaller scale until the beginning of this century. A casualty of the poor weather – low temperatures and high rainfall – of the 1870s, agriculture once again slumped and remained depressed more or less continuously until the outbreak of the Second World War. Considerable areas of arable were deliberately re-planted as or allowed to revert to grassland but, as before, never fully regained a characteristic downland flora. Into the 20th century there were notable declines in sheep farming and, although rabbits helped restrict overgrowth from scrub, significant changes were starting. Dony (1967) notes the spread of the coarse, tussocky Upright Brome following withdrawal of sheep in the 1920s and 30s.

It is estimated that, in the early 1940s some 250 hectares of 'good' Chalk downland existed in Hertfordshire. During the next four and a half decades more than half of this was to be destroyed and most of the remainder seriously degraded. Improved mechanisation, demands for increased food production in wartime, introductions of fertilisers and herbicides and changes in agricultural economics all contributed to this destruction. With such an emphasis on arable cultivation, sheep farming rapidly declined and virtually all the downland that remained lost the grazing patterns of, perhaps, three millennia. Coarse grasses and scrub started to spread, although rabbits helped keep significant areas open. Then, from 1954 onwards, the devastating myxomatosis virus spread rapidly, in consecutive waves, throughout the countryside, at times all but eliminating rabbit populations. Most, if not all Hertfordshire's extant Chalk downlands were seriously affected by lack of grazing. Large areas were taken over by Upright Brome or, ecologically, more serious, scrub invasion. The short, springy, scented, flower-rich turf, so much a feature of the traditional downs, became largely history, as did a number of the formerly characteristic wild flowers.

In more recent years there have been attempts at several downland sites to prevent and reverse this natural succession. It may take a long time, or even be impossible, to recreate the full character of that ancient turf, especially if traditional sheep grazing is not employed. Nevertheless, a good proportion of true downland wild flowers survive, even though many are now county rarities, creating some of our most important wildlife conservation sites. Major locations include Tring Park, Aldbury Nowers, Sheethanger Common and Roughdown Common near Boxmoor, a few sites near Hexton and Pirton, Weston Hills near Baldock, Coombe Bottom near Kelshall and Therfield Heath. There are some smaller areas along the escarpment and on other Chalk exposures, mainly associated with pits, road verges or railway cuttings and embankments.

Within the great variety of chalkland wild flowers, there is a long flowering season which generally spans from late March well into October. Even in the depths of winter it is not unusual to find a few species making a brave show, even on the bleakest of slopes. Throughout much of the late spring and early summer, the better quality downs become a delightful patchwork of colours, best sampled on a warm, sunny day when multitudes of insects, so dependent upon the blooms, are active. At times, as in the great drought of 1976, the full harshness of the downland habitat is revealed, with much of the flora withering and dying from the acute shortage of water; without their vital food-plants, insect populations crash and some species, for example several specialised butterflies, can be threatened with local extinction. Similarly in long cool summers, plants that are at the extremes of their ranges may not be able to function and reproduce efficiently. The fundamentally hazardous nature of the climate, together with the continuing reduction, both in quality and extent of the county's downlands, (as described above), and their isolation and overgrowth, has significant effects upon the flora, especially the already rare and highly specialised species. The rarest of these (which are detailed in Appendix 1.5), include several orchids whose specialisations constitute the essence of their tenuous survival on the downs.

The very mention of the word 'orchid' stirs the imagination of most people – despite its derivation (relating to the shape of the plant's underground tubers) from the Latin and Greek words for testicle. 'Orchid-watching' is becoming increasingly popular, and to many of its devotees, and those with more scientific motives, the Chalk downs are favourite hunting grounds. About a dozen species may still be found in Hertfordshire, of which half are more or less entirely limited to the Chalk. As noted above, seeds of most orchids will only germinate after forming an association with a free-living soil fungus or *mycorrhiza*, which itself can only exist in certain, usually undisturbed, soil conditions. The existence of the warm, dry Chalk soils, particularly on south-facing slopes enabled some of the southern continental orchids to extend their ranges northward, and when the downs were well-grazed the open turf allowed the, largely poorly competitive, orchids to flourish. But, as we have seen, traditional sheep-grazing has disappeared and a number of orchids once known in the county have become extinct; several still extant species are very scarce, some under threat of local extinction. Other factors may affect the remaining populations, some of which consist of fewer than ten plants; these include soil disturbance, chemical changes from accrued litter, artificially applied chemicals or even acid rain, changes in soil moisture content which is likely to affect soil micro-organisms, and overgrowth and shading from more vigorous plants.

9.2 Chalk Scrub

References have been made to *scrub*, a term which has been variously defined but in general relates to a vegetational succession from a habitat dominated by herbs to one dominated by shrubs and small trees. It is thus possible to have a range of stages from a few low bushes in open grassland to tall, closed scrub with trees that may be difficult to separate from secondary woodland. Unless in some way hindered, all our grasslands would naturally follow this succession. Interference, through cutting, or grazing by stock or rabbits, can halt, and may even reverse, natural succession and, as already hinted, individual sites may show varying stages of scrub encroachment. By the very nature of soils, scrub invading the downlands will be largely dominated by calcicolous shrubs and trees. Quite extensive areas of Hertfordshire's downs, past and present, have been overtaken and their botanical richness degraded or destroyed by uncontrolled spread of scrub. However, there are a few places where its development is still in the early stages or is being controlled. Here, natural diversity may in fact be enhanced, combining facets of the downs with more sheltered, yet still open, areas amongst the bushes, the scrub itself and the developing secondary woodland components. Examples of this can be seen in parts of Aldbury Nowers, about Hexton, Weston Hills near Baldock, Ashwell Quarries Nature Reserve and Therfield Heath.

Some classic studies on natural succession were carried out at Rothamsted near Harpenden, where in 1882 a corner of an arable field known as Broad Balk, was fenced off and left. Over a century later, that half of the plot which remained untouched is a copse of mature trees. This and other studies have shown that the nature of scrub encroachment can be quite variable, even haphazard, and dependent upon a variety of factors, including availability of seed sources, numbers and viability of fruits and seeds, predation, nature of germination sites, types and levels of grazing or cutting regimes and the competitive abilities of the shrub species concerned. In general, the pattern of succession from open downland, through scrub, to woodland, in Hertfordshire, as elsewhere, passes through a number of reasonably discrete stages, known in ecological terms as *seres*. On the Chalk, initial seral stages see the short-turfed downland giving way to tall, often tussocky, grasses, with Upright Brome, Cock's-foot and False Oat-grass much in evidence; later, tall herbs and shrubs, and, usually later still, trees invade. Deeper soils, in coombes and at scarp slopes, are often scrub-colonised earlier, more evenly and faster than the steeper slopes, and from these there is a gradual spread outwards. Deeper soils will facilitate a more rapid development of trees, and several species may become established. Research on ancient downland sites suggests that climax secondary woodland will be dominated by Beech after a significant, and often prolonged, Ash-dominated sere (Smith 1980). As noted above, local variations may be many and complex. There are, for example, a number of locations where other species, notably the alien Sycamore, are now well established in old scrub or secondary Chalk woodland, and there have been invasions into Beech plantations. It remains to be seen if further seral changes will take place or whether such species will eventually dominate to form a new stand-type.

The finer details of scrub-development on the downs of Hertfordshire have received scant attention, although it seems that several patterns of establishment and community structure are present and there is scope for further research into these. As in other areas of the Chilterns, the most frequently encountered scrub community today is that dominated by Common Hawthorn – a fact undoubtedly related to the widespread use of the plant in hedges – and in a good many locations, particularly where scrub cover has been long-established, virtually pure stands of Hawthorn occur – it is a pioneer coloniser of deeper, damper soils that spreads readily and rapidly. In similar situations, Blackthorn may also form dense stands, not infrequently in conjunction with Hawthorn. Dogwood, which can colonise quickly by suckering, often forms patches of relatively pure stands, particularly on shallow-soiled, drier slopes.

Less competitive downland wild flowers will decline and most disappear as domination by tall herbs and grasses and seral scrub-succession progresses, although one may often be surprised by finding the odd survivor in quite unlikely overgrown and dark situations. Amongst the taller species typically found in more open glades and scrub margins will be Upright Brome, Red Fescue, False Oat-grass, Cock's-foot, False Brome, Agrimony, Wild Basil, Wild Carrot, Wild Parsnip, Rock-rose, Perforated St John's-wort, Marjoram, Ploughman's Spikenard, Common Valerian, Hogweed, ragworts and thistles. Twayblade and Common Spotted-orchid may sometimes be found in deep shade of quite mature scrub, and the Pyramidal Orchid, a pioneer in its own right is sometimes a feature of scrub margins. Apart from Common Hawthorn, Blackthorn and Dogwood, many other shrubs are likely to be found in early seral stages. Elder, which may also form fairly pure stands, is very characteristic of soil disturbance by rabbits, badgers or even long-abandoned cultivation lynchets. Small bushes of Wayfaring Tree and, in the south-west, Whitebeam add their distinctive colours and variety to the scene, as do the occasional saplings of Ash, Field Maple, Sycamore, Beech and birches.

Often associated with Dogwood is Wild Privet, a creeping to leggy semi-evergreen which should not be confused with the occasional escape or garden throwout of Garden Privet *Ligustrum ovalifolium* (7), a native of Japan with broader, more rounded leaves. Buckthorn *Rhamnus catharticus* (5–6) is found only on the Chalk and highly calcareous Boulder Clay and can form small, sometimes tall, stands amongst other shrubs. Its bark and especially the black shiny berries are strongly cathartic. One ancient herbal recommends 'of the fresh berries, twenty may be taken for a rough purge, but a very good one' – hence its often used alternative vernacular name 'Purging Buckthorn'.

In developing scrub, scrambling and climbing plants are often frequent, with brambles and masses of Wild Clematis much in evidence. Untidily attractive, low-trailing clumps or arching briars of five rose species may be found across the full range of Hertfordshire's Chalk scrub, their blooms adding great beauty in June and July, especially in early seral stages. Thick, large-thorned, often dead stems, found in later seral stages or even secondary woodland, can sometimes be used as a clue to earlier ecological history of sites. Most frequent and widespread is Dog Rose *Rosa canina*, the wilding rose of England, our national flower and a symbol of unrequited love. Slightly less widespread, notably amongst scrub in northern Hertfordshire, the lower-growing Field Rose *R. arvensis* is much more restricted to early seral stages. Named from its sweet-smelling, stickily glandular leaves, Sweet Briar *R. rubiginosa* is scarce, with recent reports only from Therfield Heath, near Great Offley, Little Wymondley, Hexton, Bayfordbury, near Easneye and Berkhamsted Common. Downy Rose *R. tomentosa* is rare and may be extinct from the Chalk; it was known from near Tring, Beechwood and Great Offley, but the only recent sightings have been from Hertford, the Broxbourne Woods and near Nuthampstead. Even rarer is *R. micrantha*, which has been found at Broxbourne Woods and Beechengrove Wood near Chorleywood in the past few years, but there is no indication of its survival in Chalk scrub in the Aldbury Nowers to Hudnall Common region where records were made in the 1960s.

Various other shrubs may occur, including such exotic, alien, garden escapes as Butterfly Bush *Buddleia davidii*, Laburnum *Laburnum anagyroides*, Walnut *Juglans regia*, Apple *Malus domestica*, Snowberry *Symphoricarpos rivularis* and *Cotoneaster* spp.

In closed mature scrub, a number of secondary woodland elements will usually be evident. Many shrubs become senescent, and as they die back trees move in, particularly Ash, Beech and Sycamore. In places birches, Field Maple, Hazel and, in the south-west, Whitebeam may be in evidence. Scrambling and climbing plants, especially brambles and Wild Clematis, trail over bushes and up into the developing canopy, helping further to shade out an already impoverished ground flora. As with many secondary woods, ground flora may be dominated by Ivy, with scattered patches of brambles, clumps of tall grasses and some pioneering woodland wild flowers. Little, if anything, remains of the downland flora except on more open margins and banks. At some sites, for example parts of Aldbury Nowers, in the Hexton area, near Great Offley and Therfield Heath, it is possible to detect relicts of scrub within quite mature secondary woodland or plantations on the Chalk.

Two shrubs worth looking out for are Yew and Box, neither of which has been well researched in Hertfordshire. It is uncertain whether either of these once formed important stands as they were known to do on other parts of the Chalk in southern England.

Yew *Taxus baccata* (3–4), a long-lived conifer often reaching tree proportions, is well known and typical in many country churchyards. The only British tree to have retained its Celtic name – *iw*, records indicate it to be fairly well distributed on calcareous soils throughout the county, not abundant but often in woods. It is one of the few species able to tolerate and flourish beneath the dense shade of the Beech, itself casting such a dense shade that virtually nothing survives beneath it. It is possible that Yews were once cosseted, their durable, strong and elastic timber producing bow staves for hunters and archers. Once the longbow was outmoded by firearms natural Yew resources were not renewed or may even have been selectively removed because their poisonous foliage was hazardous to grazing stock.

Although possibly under-recorded, Box *Buxus sempervirens* (4–5), which may occur as a planted hedge or ornamental shrub, is rather scarce, with scattered locations across most calcareous soils of Hertfordshire. Dony (1967) considered this evergreen shrub to be almost certainly native on the downs, and elsewhere. It is commemorated in several place-names. for example the deserted mediaeval village of Boxe near Stevenage, where Box wood, Boxfield and Boxbury Farms still stand. Box Hall is in nearby Benington parish and in the south-west there is Boxwell House near Berkhamsted, and Boxmoor and Boxted near Hemel Hempstead. Interestingly many of these locations are on Chalk, and Box survives at or close to many of them, although the origins of the various trees are uncertain and planting, possibly relatively recent, cannot be ruled out. In the 18th and 19th centuries, Box timber was much sought after for its heavy, close-grained timber used for the manufacture of wood-engraving blocks. Before the advent of the cheaper photo-engraving techniques developed in the 1890s, Box wood was such a valuable timber that, on the London market, some trees were traded a piece at a time. About 1748 the Duke of Bridgewater planted Box on the hills near Tring, possibly beneath Beech, for it develops well in shelter and shade on Chalk. There is a strong possibility that these were replacements for older, commercially harvested, possibly native stock. Box wood was also important for other local uses, including small wheels, cogs, pins and screws, and it seems probable that it was widely grown to supply the manufacture of these. Like wood-engraving, these were outmoded and replaced by developing Victorian technologies. As demands for Box wood decreased, incentives to replant declined, any remaining trees were sought out to supply the dying trades, and rabbit and sheep grazing, ploughing or new silvicultural practices probably removed the last traces. Several of the recent records of Box come from woods or mature scrub; some may be recent plantings associated with game cover but a number are suggestive of native sites, for example on Oddy Hill near Tring, at The Meg at Hexton, in Lilley Park Wood, by the side of the old Great North Road south of Baldock and near Barkway, all of which are on Chalk. Detailed further investigations might help resolve the history of Box in Hertfordshire and show that at least some of the steepest downs of south-west Hertfordshire were once naturally clothed with thick, almost impenetrable stands of this heat- and drought-resistant shrub, as they are at the Chequers Nature Reserve, not too far away in Buckinghamshire.

9.3 Neutral Grasslands – Meadows and Pastures

The bulk of Hertfordshire's extant grasslands lie on soils which are, in general, intermediate between alkaline and acidic, that is neutral. As such, these neutral grasslands are well distributed within a broad swathe across the county although because of agricultural expansion there is a greater concentration in the southern portion. An overview of their general development outlined above shows that they are semi-natural habitats, colonised, at least initially, by wild plants and maintained by grazing or cutting. Actual plant communities may, and often do, vary within a particular grassland, and especially from site to site, according to the local nature of soil, water and management. On the drier soils of the Clay-with-Flints and gravels, most grasslands are rather acid and heathy, but patches of a more neutral character are to be found, notably in damper places. In the north and east, there are increasing tendencies towards calcareous grasslands on the deeper, less decalcified deposits of Boulder Clay. Richer floras are usually found on the more calcareous soils. There have, in fact, been a dozen or more distinct plant communities identified within the very broad categorisation of neutral grasslands. Often intergradations of neutral and calcareous, neutral and acid, wet and dry communities occur, even within individual sites.

Grasslands managed by grazing are pastures, those cut for hay are meadows. Throughout history, at least from Anglo-Saxon times until the 19th century, both meadows and pastures were vital to the efficiency of the largely 'animal-powered' countryside. For centuries, all parishes would have operated an economical system of arable, meadow and pasture lands. First oxen, and later horses, worked the arable and, together with cattle and sheep, were put out onto pasture to graze. Meadows provided hay, cut in summer and stored, to feed livestock in winter when pasture grasses were not growing. In many parts of the county, the delightful pattern of flowery meadows would have been enhanced, particularly from Tudor times, by meandering, well managed, stock-proof hedges. Hay meadows were frequently sited on more productive soils, often close to water, where the grass would grow quick and lush to produce bigger, better and more hay crops. Some of these grasslands may have been in and out of cultivation over the generations. However, before the relatively recent advent of specialised seed mixes and fertilisers, it was well known that it took a long time to establish a really good productive pasture or meadow. It is reasonable to assume that most remained inviolate, permanent assets to rural communities. As with downland, it was this permanence that enabled the great diversity of wild flowers with adaptations to withstand grazing or periodic cutting to colonise. Even long ago meadows and pastures received some fertilisation, even if it was just the manure from grazing stock or carted out from stock pens. The effect of these fertilisers however, was very short-term; only small quantities of additives were involved with little or no real

Figure 9.2 *Unimproved meadow at Hunsdon Mead with Stone Parsley* ▶
    (seeding), Creeping Thistle and Timothy

consequences to the abundant wild flowers. In reality, it was the *lack* of nutrients, coupled with cropping, that stimulated the development of a rich flora.

Some of the most permanent grasslands, including downs and heaths, were commons and greens. Most of these developed as places where specified people (but not the populace at large) while not actually owning the land held certain rights, usually to graze a limited amount of stock. For the majority of commons, these rights were apportioned to (or appropriated by) Lords of the Manor, the Church or wealthy landowners. Today, none are owned in common, although some, such as those under control of local authorities, come close to this. Few commons or greens are now traditionally grazed; some, at least in part, may provide hay crops; a number have reverted to scrub or woodland. Many have become amenity features or been put to recreational uses, with little or none of the former wild flower diversity surviving. Some of the better neutral grassland examples may be seen, in part, at Moor Green near Ardeley, around Weston recreation ground, at Ickleford Lower Common, at Meesden Green, at Roe Green at Sandon and at Norton Common at Letchworth.

From the 16th century, the practices employed in creating new grasslands using specially prepared seed mixes were increasingly refined, but these did not really begin to affect the stability of permanent grasslands until the agricultural changes of the 18th century. The expansion of arable cultivation and the introduction of crop-rotation systems saw some loss of permanent grasslands to arable. Increasingly short-term grasslands or leys were seeded to help rest and resuscitate overworked, largely unfertilised arable lands, as well as to provide pasture and hay. The traditional flowery meadows were beginning to decline. Further marked losses resulted from the far-ranging effects of the Parliamentary Enclosure Acts of the 18th and early 19th centuries. Layouts of many parishes were completely changed as the land was shared out between the larger original tenancies. Straight-margined, new roads and fields were hedged by miles of *quickset* – Common Hawthorn. Gradually many old grasslands were ploughed or replaced with leys.

From the late 19th century, mechanisation and efficiency of agriculture increased, firstly with steam-operated machines and then, in this century, with petrol and diesel propulsion. As working animals declined from the countryside, the now unwanted meadows and pastures were put to other uses, mainly arable cultivation; the more powerful machines were able to tackle steeper slopes and heavier soils; more efficient drainage-methods were introduced and chemical fertilisers developed. All of these developments sounded the deathknell for vast areas of permanent grassland. Great losses occurred in the drive to produce home-grown foods to meet the needs of the First and Second World Wars. The Land Use Survey (Stamp, 1941) shows that between these wars there were about 25 000 hectares of semi-natural neutral grasslands in Hertfordshire. The Hertfordshire Grazing Lands Survey, completed in 1985, revealed only 1000 or so hectares remain. Some of this area was ploughed during the last war, much more went as landowners cashed in on the inflated grain prices of the next two decades.

Many sites, from the point of view of their interesting wild flowers, have been degraded or destroyed through 'improvement' – the application of chemical herbicides and fertilisers. The latter, particularly where large amounts are applied, have much the same effects as herbicides in reducing plant communities to just a handful of grass species and persistent weeds. This destruction continues. Even some of the better sites are being deleteriously affected by inappropriate management, for example cutting instead of grazing, or grazing by horses instead of cattle, which often results in excessive trampling and the spread of unpalatable ragwort, thistles and nettles. Meadows full of bright yellow buttercups or drifts of daisies frequently reveal unsympathetic management, for, as will be shown below, the indications are that most of the other potential wild flower community has probably been suppressed through excessive applications of fertilisers or herbicides or by selective or over-grazing by stock.

The little neutral grassland of any quality that survives in the county, is now all too rare and relegated to relatively small, scattered parcels. Sites are most frequently found on commons and greens. Occasional patches may occur around sports and recreation grounds, golf courses and road verges. Little remains in traditional agricultural use. Where management is restricted some good examples survive between the graves in certain churchyards, testaments to what has been lost from the surrounding countryside. In addition to the sites noted above, good examples of neutral grassland can still be seen at Moor Green near

Figure 9.3 *Almost a thing of the past, an unimproved flowery pasture (near Sandon)*

Ardeley, and at Reed, Sandon, Clothall, Weston, Ickleford, Letchworth Golf Course, Benington, Langley and Hunsdon.

Most of Hertfordshire's neutral grasslands have, as co-dominant species, Rye-grass and Crested Dog's-tail, although, as pointed out, physical and management characteristics can produce marked variations. Really old, well managed areas will support a wide range of grasses and herbs. All too often intensive managment reduces this range, and, particularly where chemicals are used, there is often little more than dominant Rye-grass with White Clover, Creeping Buttercup and a few other species. Lack of management encourages expansion of such competitive grasses as False Oat-grass, Cock's-foot and Yorkshire Fog and tall stands of Hogweed, Cow Parsley, Stinging Nettle, thistles, ragworts and docks. These develop quite rapidly at the expense of finer-leaved grasses and meadow flowers. Retaining the considerable interest of a flowery meadow, so much part of everyday life in our past countryside, is not easy. It requires skill, and, long-term commitment on the part of owners and managers, and is not cheap. If the rate of attrition continues, many of the remaining sites, including a number mentioned here, will be lost before we enter the 21st century.

9.4 Wet Grasslands

Wet grasslands are to be found in situations where groundwater levels are close to, but not permanently at, the surface and in places where the sward is affected by seasonal flooding. Such sites can be very wet at times, particularly during winter and spring, and yet relatively dry for the rest of the year. In Hertfordshire, wet grasslands were once extensive features of alluvial soils in river valleys and ill-drained heavy clays but, as will be shown, very little of any quality remains, especially on the clays. The wild flower communities of such habitats can be extremely lush and diverse, with variations within and between sites dependent upon the nature of underlying soils, water chemistry, duration of flooding, small- and large-scale topography, the effects of adjacent areas and cutting or grazing. Often there are mixtures of species, with some characteristic of marshes, river or pond margins, others more typical of drier grasslands and a number more or less limited to wet grassland. Such variations may readily be identified at some sites and can usually be related to such factors as localised spring sources or seepage lines, natural or even man-made hollows or hummocks, changing geology, trampling by stock, grazing and cutting patterns.

Some of the county's wet grasslands have been created by the drainage of former marshes, for example in the major river valleys of the Lea and Stort, and on parts of the Boulder Clay where drainage was so impeded by the heavy clay soils that peat formation was occurring. As with other unimproved grasslands, great losses have been incurred in the last century or so through drainage, general water-abstraction reducing the overall groundwater availability and levels, cultivation, urban and industrial development, mineral extraction, changes in traditional management, applications of chemicals and neglect. Today, only about 470 hectares of quality or reasonably good wet grassland remain in

Hertfordshire, mostly as small, scattered sites. Fortunately a number of these are afforded a degree of protection through designations as nature reserves or Sites of Special Scientific Interest. Most of the county's main river valleys contains at least one important site, for example, near Sarratt in the valley of the River Chess; close to the River Gade at Croxley Common Moor; by the River Ver at Redbournbury; along the River Lea at Rye Meads, Kings Meads at Hertford and east of Wheathampstead; near Tewin on the River Mimram; Waterford on the River Beane; near Braughing and Standon Lordship in the Rib Valley; along the River Stort at Hunsdon and Bishops Stortford; near Hitchin on the Rivers Hiz and Purwell; and close to the headwaters of the River Ivel near Baldock.

Throughout the county most of these alluvial sites, irrespective of the adjacent geology, tend to have neutral to slightly alkaline soils because many headwaters derive a good proportion of their water from Chalk aquifers. The wet grasslands that developed on heavy clay soils have fared badly and few sites remain. The best, some even retaining areas with active peat development on calcareous soils, may be seen at Rushy Meadow near Tring, Oughtonhead Common west of Hitchin, Norton Common in Letchworth, around Weston and Clothall, near Sandon, Ardeley, Barkway and Nuthampstead. The alkaline soils with supplies of calcareous water favour lime-loving species, and where peat develops on waterlogged soils there is a marked *fen* element to the flora. (*See* Chapter 10.1.) On poorer wetter and acidic soils, mainly in southern Hertfordshire, wet acid grassland and heath were once a not insignificant habitat, but this has been virtually obliterated by scrub-overgrowth, afforestation, mineral extraction and developments. Small vestiges survive at Croxley Common Moor, Bricketwood Common, in the Northaw area, near Knebworth, at Hertford Heath and at Patmore Heath an outlier to the north-west of Bishops Stortford. (The specialised floras of wet acid grasslands and heath will be described below, section 9.8.)

Most wet grasslands will contain a variety of wild flowers, many of which occur also, and often more commonly, in drier grasslands, especially neutral and calcareous types, but facets of more acidic grasslands may also be found. Research (Hertfordshire County Council, 1988) has indicated that most wet grassland communities in the county fall into three main categories, all of which relate closely to a Perennial Rye-grass/Crested Dog's-tail community, noted in the last chapter. On regularly inundated alluvial soils the dominant grasses will include Creeping Bent and Marsh Foxtail, with abundant Tall Fescue, Timothy, Creeping Buttercup, rushes and, in more permanently wet places, Floating Sweet-grass. Where heavier clay soils are permanently damp, probably waterlogged in winter and usually grazed, Yorkshire Fog, Creeping Bent and tussocks of Soft Rush predominate in a relatively species-poor community. Management can have a great influence upon these plant communities; when interference is low a rather tussocky sward develops dominated by Yorkshire Fog and Tufted Hair-grass; regular cutting or grazing will retard coarser species and stimulate the spread of such fine-leaved grasses as Red Fescue, Smooth Meadow-grass and Sweet Vernal-grass. Spring sources and seepage lines add considerable variety to the flora, allowing colonisation by some of the more specialised, and

71

sometimes rarer, sedges, rushes and water-loving, mineral-demanding herbs. Rushes are characteristic of permanently damp soils amd may form tussocky swards, the dominant species varying according to soil/water regimes. Hard and Soft Rushes are nearly ubiquitous but Compact and Jointed Rushes prefer less calcareous conditions. Meadow and Creeping Buttercups may often clothe the meadows in golden profusion, but their close relative Marsh Marigold or Kingcup is largely restricted to the permanently wet, mineral-flushed seepage lines and stream margins.

9.5 Acid Grasslands and Heaths

As in other parts of southern England, Hertfordshire's acid grasslands and heaths are semi-natural and, like the other grasslands and downs, they are largely products of human interference. The legacy of the last glaciation was a churned-up landscape, with most soils, at least initially, rich in nutrients. Ameliorating climate, as shown in preceding chapters, favoured the development and spread of wildwood. Even on many well drained sand and gravel soils, nutrients washed downwards by rainfall would be taken up by the spreading, deep-rooting systems of trees and returned to the soil again at leaf fall or decay. Humus- and mineral-rich, probably quite deep, brown forest-earth soils were almost universal throughout forested, prehistoric Hertfordshire.

The early forest clearances, accelerated by the arrival of Neolithic farmers some 6000 years ago, were apparently carried out where soils were drier. Here, removal of trees by axe or fire was easier, and rewarded the settlers with rich, fertile soils for cultivation and grazing. However, in many places cultivation was short-lived, especially where the underlying deposits were composed of sands and gravels or on parts of the Clay-with-Flints. Depleted of tree-cover, inherently well drained or deficient in mineral nutrients, these deposits were rapidly further impoverished by rainfall, humus and minerals, particularly bases, were leached away, acidifying the soils. Shallow-rooted crops and pasture grasses could neither reach sufficient nutrients nor replace them quickly enough; productivity declined and it is probable that areas were abandoned as settlers sought new areas to clear and cultivate. In many places these new clearings, the developing heaths, acid grasslands and pasture woodlands, remained suitable for rough grazing by domesticated stock, especially sheep. With increasing human populations, wildwood clearances on the lighter soils progressed and, with grazing, 'heathy' areas expanded across much of southern Hertfordshire. Where sites were totally abandoned, secondary woodland in time, developed with birches followed by oaks. Increased soil acidity and mineral deficiency, however, limited ground flora colonisation.

Patterns of development of the county's heathy areas are complex and relate to factors such as natural acidity of underlying deposits, rainfall, goundwater levels, the availability of acid-loving or calcifuge plants to colonise, the proximity of underlying Chalk or calcareous waters and the management regimes of many centuries. Deposits such as Reading Beds, Pebble Gravels and parts of the Clay-with-Flints produce acid soils. Removal of tree cover can result in almost totally leached soils on which true heathland rapidly establishes itself. This plant community is dominated by heather, with a few other plants able to tolerate the extreme conditions. Burnt or grazed regularly, these heaths would have lasted indefinitely. Where the natural acidity of soils is modified by the presence of underlying Chalk or the percolation of base-rich groundwaters there are marked changes in vegetation. This is particularly noticeable in grazed areas and, even within a few metres, transitions can be detected from acid to neutral grassland.

It seems probable that considerable tracts of southern and western Hertfordshire on acid soils were opened up in prehistoric times and utilised for many centuries as open or pasture-wood grazings. In the most acid places, removal of trees and subsequent leaching have led to the formation of podzolised soils. These, named from the Russian words *pod* – under and *zol* – ash characterise true heathland and have a distinctive structure. Below a shallow, dark-coloured, peaty surface layer, where because of high acidity little decomposition of litter occurs, the soil has been heavily leached. It is highly acidic, and'ash-like' in appearance, and may be devoid of virtually all mineral content except the silica of the sand grains. Beneath this is a red-stained layer formed from iron minerals and alkaline compounds washed down from above. Under certain conditions, usually waterlogging, these may form a hard, impervious layer known as an *iron-pan*. Podzols and other acidic soils tend not to support a great diversity of plant life, but plants that do colonise them are generally specialised to survive such harsh conditions.

As the heaths and acid grasslands of Hertfordshire developed the spread of some species into the county was no doubt facilitated by the existence of the extensive heaths of southern England which first offered the possibility of colonisation to plants originally of cliffs, screes and tracksides. Other species were probably already present as part of the wildwood ground flora. Evidence suggests that with grazing a rather short open turf was initially established in most areas, with few trees or other shrubs. A few grasses dominated, such as Common Bent, Heath Grass, Wavy Hair-grass and Sheep's Fescue, with a limited associated flora including Heath and Lady's Bedstraws, Tormentil, Harebell, Sheep's Sorrel, Heath Speedwell, Heath Woodrush and Pill Sedge. Floral diversity in the most acid places, with perhaps only four or five species per square metre, was very low in comparison to the often twenty or more species per square metre found on Chalk downland.

Regular grazing maintained these acid grasslands, probably over many centuries. Where it was withdrawn or reduced heathers soon moved in, with Gorse and Bracken especially on the podzolised soils, to create heathlands. Growth of heathers actually stimulates podzolisation, rendering soils largely unsuitable for the growth of most other species, hence their dominance over extensive tracts of country. Both in prehistoric and later times, it is probable that the spread of heathers and Gorse was not discouraged in some places, for both, if managed correctly, could provide useful local resources, for example as winter fodder for stock and as fuel.

Unmanaged by cutting, burning or grazing, both heaths and acid grasslands in the county will, in time, revert to secondary woodland with heathy ground floras. It is most likely that some sites became woodland only to be re-cleared and the cycle repeated. Little detailed research has been carried out into the history of such areas in Hertfordshire, although it is evident that not inconsiderable tracts remained relatively stable and open for a very long time, for example as manorial waste, commons or sheep walks. There were certainly some very large heaths and heathy pasture woods around Cheshunt, Northaw, North Mimms, Hoddesdon, Bricket Wood and above Berkhamsted. Not less than 5000 hectares, considered at the time to be too barren for cultivation, escaped official enclosure and survived as commons, although they have now lost their open-ness and much of the heathy flora as cessation of grazing has led to the expansion of gorse thickets, bracken spread, scrub development with brambles, invasion by aspen and birches and, in many places, degeneration into secondary woodland. This can be seen with the spread of birches and oaks on the acid soils about Ashridge, Berkhamsted and Bricketwood Common and with the development of oaks on the slightly richer soils at Kings Langley, Chipperfield, Nomansland and Gustardwood Commons. Rabbit declines from the 1950s onwards played a great part in accelerating these changes, although many sites had been lost decades before the introduction of myxomatosis. The scale of heathland loss in Hertfordshire is enormous. Some 83 per cent of the commons supported a reasonably good heathland habitat in 1940; by 1984 this had fallen to just 2 per cent, an appalling loss of 96 per cent. Today, no more than 30 hectares survive. The planting of conifer woods and development of recreation areas such as cricket pitches and golf courses have caused further losses and virtually all the formerly extensive Codicote Heath was destroyed for gravel extraction. Only small, often isolated, fragments remain, as pale reminders of what were once one of the county's most significant landscape features. Here and there, some footpath margins and mown rough of golf courses can provide glimpses of the former heathland flora. Better examples, although very small in comparison with what has been lost, where Heather is still reasonably frequent, remain at Colney Heath, Bricket Wood, Nomansland Common (the best site), Gustardwood Common and Patmore Heath, an outpost on the gravels of east Hertfordshire.

Less than 1000 hectares of good acid grassland survive in the county, of which most is in relatively small parcels on some of the commons. Even these, despite their escaping enclosure and agricultural improvement, are under threat of further reduction as grazing and cutting regimes lapse. Some of the better examples of acid grassland are also to be found at those sites noted in the last paragraph. Variations in soils can be quite marked, even within a few metres. These will be reflected immediately by changes in flora and it is still possible to find within a small area a range of both dry and wet heaths and acid grasslands, as well as gradations towards more neutral habitats. Elements of grassland flora will be found in most, if not all, of the county's surviving heaths and some acid grasslands will have traces of Heather or other heath species. (*See* section 9.6.)

As we have seen, there are sites where the underlying geology modifies soils to produce conditions intermediate between acid and neutral. At Harpenden Common acid grassland gives way to more neutral grassland on the upper slopes, where Chalk is closer to the surface. Similarly, at Gustardwood Common small tracts of Heather are seen in close proximity to neutral grassland and the famous, though much declined, juniper bushes. Groundwater, whether still or flowing, can have profound local effects. Colney Heath, still one of the most important heaths despite grazing declines, is quite peaty in parts because of the proximity of the River Colne, and sections of Croxley Common Moor near Croxley Green are neutralised by the adjacent calcareous waters of the River Gade. Patmore Heath near Little Hadham, the county's finest dry acid grassland and heath on the highly acidic sands of the Reading Beds, has underlying patches of Boulder Clay. These bring the water-table close to the surface, creating ponds and marshy areas. Here also, Chalk is at or close to the surface in places, adding further variety to this important site.

9.6 Wild Flowers of Dry Heaths

By definition, true lowland heaths must have one or more of the heaths or heathers as their dominant plant(s). These woody, low-growing shrubs, with tough stems, evergreen leaves and rather globular blooms, only really flourish in open situations upon acidic soils. In Hertfordshire the characteristic species, today, is Heather or Ling *Calluna vulgaris* (7–9), easily recognised by opposite rows of linear leaves and leafy spikes of pale purple flowers. It is occasionally found in small quantities along rides and in open, heathy woods across the southern half of the county. This distribution (Figure 9.4.) gives a fair indication of the extent of former heathland and emphasises the conservation importance of the few small relicts of true heath that remain, none of which supports an extensive colony of Heather. It is possible that other, closely related, heathers or heaths were present in some quantities in the past, although no detailed records are available. Bell Heather *Erica cinerea* (5–9), with red-purple, bell-like flowers and dark green linear leaves whorled in threes, was certainly not common in the 19th century and is thought by many to have been extinct before 1950, the last record being from Bricket Wood in 1939; a small colony, however, was noted at Colney Heath in 1988 a discovery that shows the value of detailed examination of even well visited sites and that our county still has some botanical surprises to offer. Similarly Cross-leaved Heath *Erica tetralix* (6–10), with compact, globular, pink flowers and four-whorled leaves, recorded at Colney Heath in 1913 and Bricket Wood in 1939, was considered extinct until in the 1970s a few plants were discovered at Patmore Heath, where it is still to be found. Plants of Cornish Heath *Erica vagans* (7–9), a rare native of the coastal heaths of Cornwall found to be well established at Bencroft Wood and also noted from Patmore Heath, have undoubtedly been introduced.

Like so many other legumes or 'pea flowers', the shrubby, woody-stemmed and yellow-petalled gorses and Broom survive well on

Plate 6 (*Top*) Great Pignut *Bunium bulbocastanum*; (*Bottom*) Zigzag Clover *Trifolium medium*

Plate 7   (*Top*) Green-winged Orchid *Orchis morio*; (*Bottom*) Snake's-head
or Fritillary *Fritillaria meleagris*

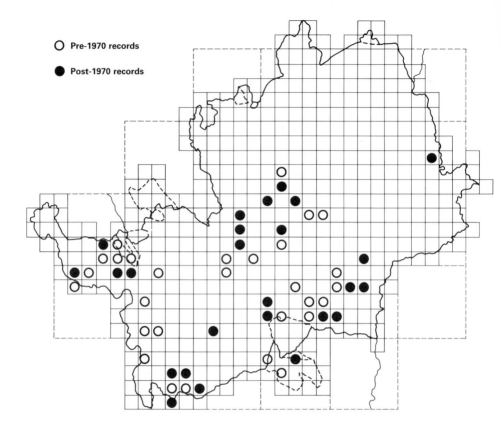

Figure 9.4 *Distribution map of Heather* Calluna vulgaris *in Hertfordshire*

nutrient-poor soils. As already noted, Gorse *Ulex europaeus* (1–12) readily encroaches onto unmanaged heathland. It has a wide distribution across the southern part of Hertfordshire and is occasionally found in the north of the county. Also known as Furze or Whin, Gorse may well have been encouraged to spread in some areas as young growth, cut early in the year and bruised, provided useful feed for cattle, the woody stems were good for cottage fires, a small bush made an excellent brush for sweeping chimneys and the growing plants, being leguminous helped to improve barren land. Unchecked, Gorse soon grows into an impenetrable mass of tangled branches, bristling with sharp spines, that overshades and destroys most other heathland plants and, in time, facilitates degeneration into secondary woodland. Few people, however, can fail to be attracted by the sight of the massed golden blooms with their almond scent. (They can be seen in any season, hence the oft-quoted line 'when Gorse is out, kissing's in'.) Even the great Linnaeus, on a visit to an English heath, was reputed to have been so moved by the beauty of its Gorse that he fell to his knees and gave thanks to God.

Very low-growing or prostrate, with shorter, thinner spines and smaller, paler yellow flowers, Dwarf Gorse *Ulex minor* (7–11) has always been very rare and is now known only from Nomansland Common and near Colney Heath. Often tall, straggly, shrubby and spineless, Broom *Cytisus scoparius* (4–6) is a strict calcifuge named from the former practice of using branches to sweep floors. Often associated with Gorse, Broom is less frequent and its distribution in southern Hertfordshire relates particularly to the more acid soils. Patches of Gorse or Broom are worthy of close examination for, beneath them, it is just possible occasionally to discover the very rare, pale brown, purple-tinged Greater Broomrape *Orobanche rapum-genitsae* (6–7). For at least thirty years this parasite has been known to exist in a single locality only in central Hertfordshire, but it may await refinding in some of its 19th century haunts about Hertford, Hatfield and Colney Heath.

Two further yellow-flowered legumes sometimes found on both heaths and acid grasslands are the low-growing shrubby Dyer's Greenweed *Genista tinctoria* (7–8) and Petty Whin *G. anglica* (4–6). The former is known from about a dozen localities including Croxley Common Moor, Claypits Meadow, Hertford Heath, Cole Green and near Langley. Close to the last of these stands the ancient Dye's Farm; the name of which must surely be linked with the old use of this deciduous spineless plant in the production of a green dye known as Kendal green. Slenderer and delicately spiny, Petty Whin is limited to about eight, fairly widely dispersed, small colonies, from Croxley Common Moor to Hertford Heath, on Nomansland Common and near Knebworth.

Of the grasses, the most typical, and often abundant, species on heaths and acid grasslands is Common Bent-grass *Agrostis capillaris* (6–8). It is sometimes called 'Brown Top' from the massed open *panicles*, with small green to purple flowers, giving the impression of a brown haze as they sway in summer breezes. The slim-leaved Red Fescue *Festuca rubra* (5–7) is common and widespread, whilst Sheep's-fescue *F. ovina* (5–7), although not uncommon, is more restricted to dry, shallow-soiled, open places. Their close relative, Fine-leaved Sheep's-fescue *F. tenuifolia* (5–6), with conspicuous *auricles* and *unawned lemmas*, is rare and restricted to just a few sandy sites, mainly between Knebworth and Hertford Heath. Squirreltail fescue *Vulpia bromoides* (5–7), a slender species with slightly nodding one-sided panicles, occurs quite frequently in central and southern Hertfordshire, often in spreading patches. Heath Grass *Danthonia decumbens* (7), attractive and low growing with dumpy elliptical spikelets, was once quite widespread in the south of the county. Oxhey Woods, Claypits Meadow, Bencroft Wood, Hertford Heath and Patmore Heath are the only locations for recent reports, emphasising the scale of heathland decline. There can be few plants which match the delicate annual beauty of our two rather scarce 'hair-grasses'. Silvery Hair-grass *Aira caryophyllea* (5–7), known from about a dozen sites, including open heathy woods as well as heaths, is slightly the more frequent and distinguished by its grey-green leaves with slightly rough sheaths and open panicles. Slenderer, with green leaves, smooth sheaths and compact, spike-like panicles, Early Hair-grass *A. praecox* (4–6) occupies similar habitats but is more restricted to sandy soils. A number of other grasses may be found, especially species more typically associated with acid grasslands, such as Sweet Vernal-grass, Creeping Soft-grass and Wavy Hair-grass. (*See* Appendix 1.8.)

Figure 9.5 *Heathland wild flowers at Hertford Heath, with Foxglove, Bramble, Heather and Bracken*

Turning to flowers, one particularly characteristic species, of the more open heaths as well as acid grasslands and occasionally arable fields and neutral grasslands, is Sheep's Sorrel *Rumex acetosella* (5–8); related to the docks, variable but usually low-growing, Sheep's Sorrel may be identified by the acid-tasting, arrow-shaped leaves. Also low down, amongst other heath vegetation, the small white, star-like, clustered flowers of Heath-Bedstraw *Galium saxatile* (6–8) will be eaily found; when not in flower, Heath-bedstraw can be separated from Lady's Bedstraw, which is also quite common on heaths, by its broader, elliptical, prickly-edged and pointed leaves, arranged in whorls of four to six around stems. Also fairly frequent is the creeping, sometimes patch-forming, Tormentil *Potentilla erecta* (5–9). This is not strictly confined to heaths and is known from several acid grasslands, heathy wood margins and a few wet sites on the Boulder Clay, although records indicate significant declines in the county over the past thirty years. Related to compound-leaved, five yellow-petalled cinquefoils, Tormentil has four petals and, usually, three leaflets plus two leaf-like *stipules*; its vernacular name derives from its use to treat toothache, but herbalists also valued the plant as efficacious against contagious diseases such as 'the pox and measels', and particularly astringent preparations of the roots were used to relieve both internal and external disorders; it was also used for tanning hides. Throughout much of central and south-eastern Hertfordshire, Tormentil has been found to hybridise with the ubiquitous Creeping Cinquefoil *P. reptans* (6–9), which has five petals and leaflets. This hybrid, *P. × mixta*, more closely resembles *reptans* but may have three to five leaflets and four or five petals; it may be easily mistaken for the very rare Creeping Tormentil *P. anglica* (6–9), which with four or five leaflets and solitary four or five petalled flowers, has been found on heathy sites at Oxhey Woods, near Cheshunt and close to Hoddesdon in recent years.

Because of the impoverished nature of soils, heathland plant communities generally contain few, but specialised, wild flowers. Included amongst these are some common and widespread species with obvious abilities to adapt to exacting habitat conditions, such as Yarrow, Common Bird's-foot-trefoil, Harebell, Ribwort Plantain, Cat's-ear. Mouse-ear Hawkweed, Autumn Hawkbit and Field Wood-rush. As with all the county's declining habitats, heaths too have their botanical gems representing the last tenuous links with the past. For example, the exquisite powder-blue-petalled and pale-yellowish-spurred Heath Dog-violet *Viola canina* (4–6) is now found in small numbers only near Knebworth, at Brookmans Park and at Patmore Heath. Very rare, Heath Milkwort *Polygala serpyllifolia* (5–8) is similar to Common Milkwort, which may also occur on heaths, but has opposite lower leaves that are larger than the upper and darker blue or pink flowers; its distribution is restricted to a few plants at Claypits Meadow and Panshanger Park and on heathy rides in Knebworth Park. Also very local, on the more acid, open areas, at Colney Heath, near Hoddesdon, Mardley Heath, Codicote Heath and Patmore Heath, is the prostrate, leguminous annual, Bird's-foot *Ornithopus perpusillus* (5–8). Large Thyme, a county rarity even in its more normal downland habitat, is known from a few heathy sites,

81

including Patmore Heath, where it can be found growing upon anthills. Heath Wood-rush *Luzula multiflora* (4–6) may occasionally be found together with the more frequent Field Wood-rush *L. campestris* (3–6).

9.7 Wild Flowers of Acid Grasslands

From surveys carried out in the early 1980s (Hertfordshire County Council, 1985), it is apparent as mentioned earlier, that under 1000 hectares of good or reasonable-quality acid grassland survive in Hertfordshire. The great loss can be attributed to many of the same factors that have reduced other grassland types although overgrowth has been relatively more important, particularly on common lands. Losses continue through development, ploughing and applications of fertilisers and herbicides. Poor management is especially noticeable in many places, as horses, often overstocked, replace the traditional cattle and sheep – extensive stands of ragwort and thistles are good evidence of this. Soil and water regimes vary and, in addition to the species listed in Appendix 1.8, it is not unusual to find wild flowers representative of more neutral habitats close to the acid grassland associates, together with a few heathland species. In general, because of poor soil-fertility, acid grasslands have a considerably lower floral diversity than our other semi-natural grasslands, with just a few species having dominant or extensive populations.

Figure 9.6 *Despite secondary woodland encroachment, conifer plantations and other developments, a few commons retain tracts of acidic grassland (Chorleywood Common)*

9.8 Wild Flowers of Damp Acid Grassland and Wet Heaths

Where highly acidic soils are permanently wet, seasonally waterlogged or damp for much of the year, but not overgrown with scrub, plant communities associated with 'wet' heath may occur, one of the scarcest habitat types remaining in Hertfordshire. Such sites may result from natural impediments to drainage, such as underlying clay deposits or seepage lines, or be related to man-made depressions, for example ancient ponds or sand pits. Areas of slightly less soil acidity, but where there are still relatively high moisture levels constitute damp acid grasslands; these support relatively distinctive plant communities and exist, usually as small patches within drier areas. Less than 50 hectares of damp acid grassland and just a few tiny fragments of wet heath remain in contemporary Hertfordshire. Considerable tracts of damp acid grassland probably existed before overgrowth and major reductions in groundwater levels began to diminish its extent. Wet heath, however, seems always to have been scarce, and one of its typical indicator plants, Cross-leaved Heath *Erica tetralix* (6–10) was known to the pioneer 19th century botanists only as a great rarity from sites near Northaw, south of Tring and on Berkhamsted Common. More recently this species was found at Colney Heath, a single specimen between 1913 and 1927, Bricket Wood in 1939 and Patmore Heath in the 1970s. Diligent searching of these areas, for the compact heads of pink, globular flowers topping grey downy stems with leaves in whorls of four, may lead to the rediscovery of this botanical treasure. Other distinctive wet heath plants, including certain sedges, rushes, grasses, heather and mosses of the genus *Sphagnum* can still be found at the few extant sites. The plant communities of damp acid grassland, although distinctive, with specialised and often rare species, including some of wet heath, also contain elements of the dry heath and acid grassland floras. The premier sites can be found at Croxley Common Moor, Hertford Heath, Patmore Heath and near Knebworth, most of which also hold relicts of wet heath.

In some permanently damp places, because of the naturally high acidity decomposition of organic materials is very slow and a peaty sub-soil has developed. Peat formation may be accelerated if heather and carpeting *Sphagnum* spp. are present, leading to further acidification and bog-like conditions. Of the four species of rush most frequently encountered in wet or damp acidic conditions, Hard Rush *Juncus inflexus* (6–8) and Soft Rush *J. effusus* (6–8) are nearly ubiquitous. Jointed Rush *J. articulatus* (6–9) and Compact Rush *J. conglomeratus* (5–7) are quite widespread but prefer at least slightly acidic conditions. More reliable as an indicator of acidic conditions is Sharp-flowered Rush *J. acutiflorus* (7–9); named from its acutely pointed sepals and seed capsules, this is infrequent, and found mainly on the London Clay and wet gravelly soils. Bulbous Rush *J. bulbosus* (6–9), a great rarity restricted to two or three sites in the extreme south of the county, has a variable appearance; in drier situations it is tufted and grass-like, but in wetter places, where it floats in the water, it is many branched. In the 19th century, Heath Rush *J. squarrosus* (6–7) was known from wet heaths at Northaw, Milward's Park near Hatfield and at Colney Heath, where it remained until about

1930; in the 1960s, a number of the densely tufted and curved-leaved plants with rigid flower stems were discovered at Patmore Heath, and, this population, now increased, today represents Heath Rush's sole county locality; it is also a tribute to the assiduous conservation carried out at this important nature reserve. Also found at Patmore Heath and, possibly, still a few other locations in the south of the county is the naturalised Slender Rush *J. tenuis* (6–9); first recorded for Britain in 1883, its range slowly expanded, to reach Hertfordshire about 1952.

Amongst the sedges which may be found at the wetter acidic sites are a number of fairly common species with distributions that encompass other damp habitats. These include Grey Sedge *Carex divulsa* (6–7); Hairy Sedge *C. hirta* (5–6); Common Sedge *C. nigra* (6–8); Spiked Sedge *C. spicata* (6–7) and Glaucous Sedge *C. flacca* (5–6). As might be expected with such scarce and specialised habitat types, several rare or very rare sedges occur with, unfortunately, small and declining populations. Two that have become much scarcer in the past thirty years or so are Oval Sedge *C. ovalis* (7–8) and the delicate Pill Sedge *C. pilulifera* (5–6). On the basis of recent records, each of these is now confined to about ten locations, including Oxhey Woods and Patmore Heath where they may be found together. One of the Yellow-sedge *C. demissa* (6), group of species, whose members can only be distinguished by close examination of the flowers and measurements of the ripe fruits, is restricted to Claypits Meadow, Patmore Heath and open rides in Knebworth Woods. Two of Hertfordshire's rarest plants, Green-ribbed Sedge *C. binervis* (6) and Star Sedge *C. echinata* (5–6), both appear to be limited to single locations. The former in rides at Knebworth Great Wood and the latter at Patmore Heath.

One of the best indicators of damp acid habitats is Brown Bent-grass *Agrostis canina* (6–7); its relative scarcity and scattered distribution across the southern portion of the county (*See* Figure 9.7) illustrates the overall paucity of these habitats, particularly as few of the locations shown are extant heath or grassland. Mat-grass *Narduus stricta* (6–8), so typical of the wet moors and mountains of Britain's uplands and a strict calcifuge, is restricted now to four sites on very acid, peaty and open soils; its low tufts of harsh, bristle-like leaves, which become whitish and persist long after death, are unpalatable to grazing animals and may form broad patches in otherwise heavily grazed areas; Mat-grass can be found easily at Hertford Heath and, especially, Patmore Heath, where it is locally dominant. Another species typical of the upland moors and fens, as well as wet heaths, is Purple Moor-grass *Molinea caerulea* (6–8); its tussocks of attractive tapering leaves and long, fine, green or purplish-shaded panicles are only found in a few Hertfordshire localities where conditions are wet and peaty, such as on wet heath at Patmore Heath and Hertford Heath, and more calcareous fen-like peat at Norton Common, Letchworth.

As with the more extensive wet heaths of southern Britain, the relict or marginal sites in Hertfordshire are generally floristically depauperate. As already noted, heather, and several other species more characteristic of dry heath and acid grassland may also be found in the damper areas.

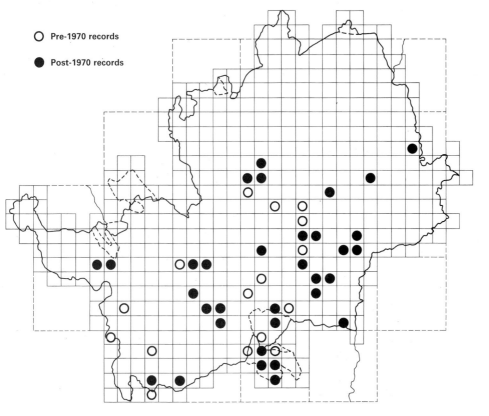

○ Pre-1970 records

● Post-1970 records

Figure 9.7 *Distribution map of Brown Bent-grass* Agrostis canina, *in Hertfordshire*

Some wild flowers representative of more basic habitats will invariably be present too, illustrating their tremendous range in ecological tolerance. Often one of the most abundant species on wet heath is Bog Stitchwort *Stellaria alsine* (5–6) and in damp acid grasslands, if grazing is not too heavy, its massed, small, star-like flowers can appear more dominant than the grasses supporting the creeping four-angled stems. Marsh Speedwell *Veronica scutellata* (6–8) generally prefers, but is not limited to, wet soils tending towards acidity, scarce, but fairly widely distributed in a dozen or so locations across the county, it may also be found by ponds and ditches; it is similar to the Pink and Blue Water-speedwells of the wetlands (*see* Chapter 10), but slenderer and rather pubescent, with yellowish-green leaves, sometimes purple-tinged, and distinctive alternate spikes of white or pale blue, often purple-lined, flowers.

A rarity, recorded in recent years only from Crouch Green, near Knebworth, and Claypits Meadow, is the partially parasitic Lousewort *Pedicularis sylvatica* (4–7); preparations from the spikes of tubular, two-lipped, pink flowers and toothed, deeply cut, pinnate leaves were once used to combat body lice. Heath Spotted-orchid *Dactylorhiza maculata* ssp. *ericetorum* (5–7) is unusual amongst our orchids in its preference for damp, peaty, heathland soils; consequently distribution is very limited and latest county records show that the strongest colony is at Bricketwood Common, with up to a hundred plants in good years; small colonies are at Claypits Meadow, where there are probably fewer than twenty plants, and at Burleigh Meadow near Knebworth, where a maximum of two plants were seen in the early 1980s. Apart from habitat preference, Heath Spotted-orchid may be distinguished from the similar Common Spotted-orchid by its more pointed leaves, usually with small circular spots, and by its pale pink flowers in which the central *labellum* lobe is smaller and shorter than the outer two.

In bare, wet places it is worth searching for the diminutive, straggly, tiny white-flowered Blinks *Montia fontana* (5–10). This has apparently always been rather rare but is easily overlooked. In 1983 it was found at Colney Heath following soil disturbance by a funfair. Also difficult to spot is Lesser Skullcap *Scutellaria minor* (7–10). It has been seen in recent years only along wet, heathy rides and stream-sides at Northaw Great Wood and there is hope that it awaits discovery at some of the former haunts elsewhere in south Hertfordshire. In the 19th century, feathery-headed Common Cotton-grass *Eriophorum angustifolium* (5–6), a native of bogs and acid fens, was known from several sites in the county; with the last sightings being made at Patmore Heath and near Ardeley in the 1970s, both well-botanised places, it seems certain that this attractive plant must now be regarded as lost from our flora. Narrow Buckler-fern *Dryopteris carthusiana* which is known mainly as a woodland plant, may, as at Patmore Heath, become a not insignificant part of the wet heath community. Here also can be found the hybrid *D. × deweri*, which is intermediate in character between its parent species Narrow Buckler-fern and the more widespread Broad Buckler-fern *D. dilatata*.

If unmanaged, damp acid grasslands and wet heath will inevitably suffer encroachment by Bracken, and scrub species such as Downy Birch, Aspen and oaks. Willows and sallows are also possible invaders, and among these may be two species that are restricted to heathy soils, rare, and of conservation interest, Eared Willow *Salix aurita* (4–5) and Creeping Willow *S. repens* (4–5). Eared Willow is closely related to Goat and Grey Willows, both of which are common and widespread, but is much smaller; it has widely angled twigs with ridges beneath the bark and wrinkled, rounded leaves subtended by large ear-like stipules; it is now apparently found only in the Broxbourne Woods. Creeping Willow, as its name suggests, is a creeping, often prostrate shrub, seldom exceeding a metre in height, with dark grey to yellowish-brown stems contrasting markedly with white, sometimes silky, leaves. Always rare, Creeping Willow now appears to be on the verge of local extinction, its total county population being probably less than half a dozen plants divided between Hawkshead Wood and Hertford Heath.

10
Wetlands

In an ecological context, wetlands encompass a range of habitats where the presence of permanent water, static or flowing, is the over-riding environmental factor. In Hertfordshire these habitats include springs, streams, rivers, marshes, ponds, lakes, reservoirs, flooded mineral workings, wells, sewage works and watercress beds. The particular nature, ecological diversity and quality of each wetland will be influenced by several environmental factors, some natural and others man-made, including local geology, topography, sources and abundance of water, water and habitat management, drainage, pollution and natural succession. There are, today, no wetlands left in the county which have not been affected in some way by human interference; in fact a great many sites were constructed or have been adapted to suit human needs.

Appendices 1.9, 1.10, 1.11 1.12, 1.13

In early post-glacial times, much of the thickly forested landscape was much wetter than can be readily appreciated in Hertfordshire today. Also, the legacies of the ice sheets and their tumultuous meltwaters left an assortment of debris creating extremely uneven landforms within which water-catchment areas would evolve. Geological evidence shows that the precursors of at least some of the county's present-day rivers were larger with, at some time, extensive margins of swampy ground. Further swampy ground formed across the landscape as water accumulated in lower parts of the hummocky terrain. By the time the first settlers arrived the main river courses and their major tributary streams had long been defined. However, throughout history, many changes were wrought upon the landscape, altering local topography, quality and, in places, even the courses of rivers, destroying swamps and creating new wetlands. Even after the clearances of wildwood, settlers on the wetter soils would have needed to accelerate and improve drainage to make way for their new meadows, pastures and homesteads, whilst on the drier lands the acquisition of water was of paramount concern. Thus, new ditches, streams, ponds, wells, and marshes came into being.

10.1 Marshes and Swamps

Some marshes develop naturally from static or slow moving waters; here, marginal swampy vegetation, especially reeds grows rapidly, and dead and decaying remains accumulate to form a substrate for further growth. Even today, places can be found where this type of natural succession is occurring, with swamp and marsh spreading outwards into the water bodies, perhaps in time to cover them completely. Many wetlands of this type represent transitional habitats between open water and dry land, for, as the slowly decaying remains of the swampy plants build up towards and above the natural water-line, conditions in the newly formed peat

87

change; species such as reeds decline and marsh plants are able to invade, forming a more diverse community. If there are no changes in the water supply, this community may last indefinitely so long as the vegetation is cut or grazed: without interference, natural succession will inevitably follow its full course to scrub and ultimately woodland.

Until the last century large areas of Hertfordshire remained as wet woodland or were used as seasonal grazing marshes. The natural water-line was considerably higher than it is today because groundwater abstraction was not happening on a large scale, and the human- and animal-powered agricultural machinery available was unable to cope with draining or cultivating very wet land.

But in the 19th century increasingly significant groundwater abstraction began to be necessary to supply the needs of expanding populations in the county and in London, and this soon had adverse effects, which still continue, on many habitats. Certainly substantial reductions of marshes and wet grasslands have been documented.

In the 18th century extensive tracts of marsh existed along the lower courses of the major rivers, especially in south-east Hertfordshire and on the impervious London Clay and Boulder Clay. The flora of these bogs and marshes was well known to the early botanists. They regularly gathered such species as, the now extinct, Sundew, Butterwort, Grass-of-Parnassus and Bog Pimpernel, from sites now completely lost or changed almost beyond recognition, through water abstraction, improved drainage, reclamation schemes, ploughing, urban and industrial development, chemical application and mineral extraction. Further losses have accrued with abandonment of grazing and neglect, allowing natural succession to progress. In places, plantations of water demanding shrubs and trees hastened succession, creating conditions in which few marsh plants are able to survive.

The relicts of marshes that survive today are some of Hertfordshire's most important sites for rare wild flowers. Scattered across the county, most of them are very small and, despite the fact that a good number are nature reserves or Sites of Special Scientific Interest, they are extremely vulnerable to radical changes, isolated as they are within largely inhospitable countryside. Developed in differing situations of geology, topography, water regimes and historical management, these sites illustrate well the wide range of wetlands that have so far been loosely referred to as swamps and marshes. A finer classification of these wetlands is based upon their inherent nature, their annual water-levels and the plant communities that develop on the available substrate.

Areas that are covered by water all the year, except perhaps in extremely dry years, are termed *swamps*. These are usually dominated by tall reeds or by sedges, sometimes called 'reed-marshes' or 'sedge-beds'. Good examples of reed-marshes can be seen around parts of the margins of Tring Reservoirs, at Tewinbury and Stanborough Reed-marsh near Welwyn Garden City; fairly extensive sedge-beds are found at Oughtonhead Common and Purwell Ninesprings near Hitchin. These swamps are characterised by their wet, peaty sub-soils, composed largely of the decaying remains of the reeds or sedges.

Marshes form on a mineral substrate, where summer water-levels are at or close to the surface of the ground. Many county sites fall into this category, although a number have, in part, some peat development. In the valley of the River Chess there are delightful examples between Chenies and Sarratt Bottom. South-east Hertfordshire has good sites near Rye Meads and along the Stort Valley, notably Sawbridgeworth Marsh. Several areas remain along the River Mimram east of Welwyn Garden City and along the River Hiz and its tributaries around Hitchin. Only small remnants can now be found on the Boulder Clay, some also with local peat development, a pale reminder of similar areas that were once extensive enough to be called 'moors'. The best of these are at Oughtonhead Common, Norton Common, around Sandon, Ardeley and near Barkway.

Where peat develops as a substrate and remains wet for most of the year, further differentiations of habitat can be made relating to the nature of groundwater and plant communities. Water arising from highly calcareous deposits, such as Chalk or Chalky Boulder Clay, will usually make an alkaline peat, on which a *fen*-type plant community develops. However under certain conditions, for example where water-levels are low, the surface of the peat, perhaps only very locally, may be neutral or even acid in reaction, and support some plants more typical of bogs or wet heaths alongside fen species. Fen vegetation can also be seen, in places, beside the upper courses of a number of rivers and streams arising from the Chalk, as well as in small parts of Boulder Clay marshes.

Figure 10.1 *Marshes fed with highly calcareous waters can support a great diversity of wild flowers (Oughtonhead Common, near Hitchin)*

At Croxley Common Moor the calcareous waters of the River Gade produce some marginal fen, whose flora contrasts interestingly with that of the acid peat beyond. On the southern outskirts of Stevenage is Ridlin's Mire Nature Reserve, where fen peat build-up is deep, dome-shaped and down-slope of a vigorous seepage line and known technically as a *rheotrophic hangmire*. This important site is unique in Hertfordshire with Great Horsetail *Equisetum telmateia* as a locally dominant plant.

Where waterlogged peat occurs on acid soils and groundwater is also acidic, decomposition rates can be almost negligible and *bog* develops. Past records of species such as Sundew and Butterwort, particularly in southern Hertfordshire, indicated the presence of bogs. This habitat has now gone, although a few sites closely approaching it occur in the Broxbourne Woods area, at Hertford Heath and Patmore Heath.

At many sites there will be seen gradations in habitats from marsh to wet, and even dry, grassland or woods. As with those other habitats, nature of soil, water and management will largely determine the presence of many wild flowers. Most sites will support at least some species tolerant of wider environmental conditions. There is, for example, a fine dividing line between wet grasslands and marshes, which may in some instances be difficult to detect, as at some Boulder Clay locations. Many neutral grassland species will be found in the base-rich sites, and more acidic places will contain elements of heathy vegetation, but generally most marshy areas can be tentatively identified from a distance by the presence of, often dark and tufted, stands of rushes and sedges.

As noted above, marshes are basically transitional semi-natural habitats and are usually maintained at this stage in natural succession by cutting or grazing. Therefore it is not unusual to find wild flowers that represent earlier or later stages of succession. Long- and short-term changes in water supply, through natural or artificial circumstances, can influence the plant communities of whole or parts of sites. With higher than average rainfall over a few years or because of a localised impediment to drainage, water-levels may rise to or above the surface, allowing swamp species such as Common Reed or Reed-grass to spread. Most evidence in the county today, points towards reductions in water-levels, causing the sapping of springs and seepage lines. Removal of adjacent woods, hedges and meadows, together with over-deepening of ditches, accelerates drainage and hastens the drying out of marshes, facilitating invasion by plants of drier habitats. Such changes, to varying degrees, are particularly evidenced by the grasses present. Except in a few really wet places, extensive populations of wet and neutral grassland species will commonly be found such as Tufted Hair-grass, Cock's-foot, Yorkshire Fog, Creeping Bent, Meadow Foxtail, Crested Dog's-tail, Red Fescue, Smooth Meadow-grass, Rye-grass, Timothy-grass and others.

Marshes supplied with calcareous waters, especially those of the Chalky Boulder Clay have an extremely rich and colourful array of wild flowers, somewhat reminiscent of the East Anglian fens. Amongst these will be species found in other habitats such as Meadow Buttercup, Creeping Jenny, Marsh Thistle, Tormentil, Tufted Vetch, Water Figwort, Brooklime, Water Mint, Angelica, Great Hairy Willowherb, Devil's-bit Scabious, Field Wood-rush, Twayblade and Common

Spotted-orchid. Like grassland flora, marsh flora tends to be rather volatile and in some years particular species may be much more in evidence than in others. In 1987 this was illustrated at a small marsh by the River Ivel just north of Baldock where, following the wet winter and spring, great drifts of Ragged Robin formed vivid pink patches amongst sheets of golden buttercups. Marsh-orchids have good and bad years; the colony at Norton Common has ranged from just two plants in 1977 – an all-time low after the previous year's great drought – to over a hundred in 1981.

Little more than 200 hectares of swamp and marsh remain in Hertfordshire, including about 20 hectares of traditionally grazed marsh, it is therefore not surprising that a good number of rarities will be cited in the checklist of characteristic wild flowers. (*See* Appendix 1.9.)

10.2 Carr

If natural succession in swamps and marshes is unchecked, colonisation by shrubs and trees will occur. In certain places, usually where swampy peat is present with neutral to calcareous water and good nutrient supplies, wet-adapted species will invade, to produce a specialised type of scrub known as *carr*. As evidenced by the shallower margins of some of the county's relatively recent excavated gravel pits, this colonisation can occur rapidly, particularly by some species of sallows and willows, which may establish a foothold even before the build-up of reed and sedge detritus has reached the permanent water-level. In some cases, carr development may begin amongst the tangle of reed and sedge roots as they raft out into open water. Accumulations of leaves and dead wood accelerate the build-up of detritus, helping to trap more silt and, together with the dead and decaying swamp plants, increase peat development. Once the permanent water line is reached or exceeded, some colonisation by marsh plants will occur; increased shade, litter development and the sapping of groundwater will, however, inevitably result in the decline of these, as wet woodland develops.

The word 'carr' is usually used qualified by the name of the dominant invading tree or shrub species, for example 'Alder carr' or 'willow carr'. There are a few sites illustrating both these throughout the county, especially along major river valleys, but sites illustrating a reasonably full succession from swamp through marsh and carr to wet woodland are scarce. One of the best, with reed-marsh, sedge-beds, Alder carr and swampy Alder woodland can be seen at the Purwell Ninesprings Nature Reserve near Hitchin, and there is fine swamp and willow carr formation around the sinkholes of the Water End Swallow Holes near Brookmans Park.

In the past, Alder, willows and sallows would have been planted in some swamps and river margins, and natural growth there encouraged to spread; the trees would then have been managed to provide valuable local resources. Alder provided water-resistant poles, broom-heads, bark for tanning leather, dyes and charcoal for making black gunpowder and willows and sallows materials for basket making. Willow and sallow planting and management were particularly widespread and the present distributions often reflects the former importance of these shrubs in rural life. Natural willow carr of relatively recent origin can be quite obvious around shallow gravel pit margins and in some reedbeds or ungrazed marshes. Older examples may have had their origins in planted and intensively managed *osier* or *withy beds*. Commercial osier and withy production was not quite as straightforward as might be expected; very careful control of water-levels was essential to produce stems of the right quality and some of the wetter sites would have been drained to allow planting on damp fertile soils and then periodically flooded via a complex of sluices and drains. Basket-making and associated crafts flourished in several areas. Around Hitchin, until the early part of this century, there were extensive osier beds, providing materials used in the manufacture of all kinds of baskets – to haul potatoes, transport fruit, hold laundry, secure poultry and for many domestic and agricultural purposes. Over-taken by new technologies, many osier beds were lost to agriculture and urban development, and some, through natural succession, have become damp woodland; careful examination can reveal traces of their swampy and osier-bed origins. In places, large, domed tussocks of, sometimes still living, Greater Tussock-sedge *Carex paniculata* may be of considerable antiquity and, because they form a drier substrate, may have small trees such as oaks growing on them. Multi-stemmed or ancient pollarded willows are possible evidence of centuries of management; because of their rapid growth, osiers and withies could be rotationally cropped every year or two to provide the long, straight, pliable shoots essential for the fabrication of baskets.

On the basis of extant distribution, it seems likely that Osier *Salix viminalis* (2–4) was the most frequently used species. Still quite common and widespread, Osier can develop into a small tree, with fissured, grey-brown bark. Its long flexible twigs, softly hairy at first, become smooth and yellow-brown, bearing long, narrow leaves, densely silver-haired beneath. Utilised in a few osier beds, Purple Willow *S.purpurea* (3–4) is now a scarce species limited to about ten locations; being low-growing, it cannot compete with overshading from more vigorous shrubs and trees. It has smooth, grey bark with hairless, yellowish or greyish flexible twigs, sometimes tinged red or purple, and bluish-green, oblong leaves, paler beneath, which turn black when dried. Of similar distribution, but scarcer, and perhaps once planted as an osier, is Almond Willow *S. triandra* (4–5), a handsome robust shrub or small tree with smooth, dark grey bark, which sheds in large flakes, dark green, serrated-edged leaves and large, bright yellow catkins.

In more recently developed carr, Goat and Grey Willows will figure prominently and the creamy-flowered, scarlet-berried Guelder Rose is often an early coloniser. As noted above, while ground conditions remain wet and relatively open, a good many swamp and marsh plants will survive to form a botanically diverse habitat. It is not unusual, for example, to list Common Reed, various sedges, Marsh Marigold, Water Mint, Water Figwort, Angelica, Marsh Bedstraw, Creeping Jenny and Twayblade alongside Alder, sallows, willows and some initial wet woodland colonisers.

10.3 Running Waters – Rivers and Streams

There is no real scientific distinction between rivers and streams, although in general terms the latter are usually narrower and shallower. Hertfordshire's streams derive from a combination of water sources. Most originate from ponds, normally spring-fed, or from flushes and springs arising from subterranean aquifers. Some flow is generated by the pressure from subterranean sources but the most powerful force is gravity. Slope of the land determines the directions of drainage and also influences flow rates. Networks of streams join and, as water-flow increases eventually form rivers. Throughout these courses, further water is added through natural or artifical drainange of adjacent lands. Continental deformation during the Alpine mountain-building episode of the Tertiary period (*see* Chapter 3) created the syncline that we now call the London Basin. This has its northern limb across Hertfordshire, and all of the underlying rocks of pre-Alpine age dip south-eastwards. Most of the subterranean and surface waters of the county drain down this dip-slope, the latter draining into the River Thames whilst subterranean sources help to form the main aquifer that has helped supply London's water for centuries. Erosion of the Chalk, by ice-sheets and meltwaters of the Pleistocene period, to create the escarpment of the county's northern and western margins also formed a major watershed. Waters arising, mainly from spring sources, along the steep scarp slopes drain northwards, via the Rivers Ouzel, Hiz, Ivel and Cam or Rhee, into the River Great Ouse system. Three catchment areas are identified within the county, the Great Ouse, the Lea and the Colne. (*See* Figure 10.2.) The Lea and the Colne both drain into the Thames, but form discrete catchment areas delineated, at times quite finely, by the plateau of high ground between Redbourn and Hatfield. The Rivers Bulbourne, Chess, Gade and Ver are part of the Colne catchment, whilst the Rivers Mimram, Beane, Rib, Quin, Ash and Stort supply that of the Lea.

The types and distributions of wild flowers found within and beside running waters are governed by a complex of physical parameters, but supply and quality of water are of prime importance. There are great differences in flow-rate, chemistry, availability of light and temperature between the clear cool waters bubbling along in a shallow Chalk stream and the deep, often turbid, usually warmer, slow-moving lower reaches of the Lea or Colne. Water arising from acid gravels places a distinctive character upon the flora of streams in south Hertfordshire, many of which are also shaded by woodland, which imposes futher limitations on the species present. Near their sources, streams and rivers are generally shallower, with faster rates of flow as their waters travel down from the higher lands. These deepen and slacken as the gradient decreases. There are, however, many factors that, subtly or significantly, alter local conditions, thereby limiting or facilitating colonisation by different, but sometimes closely related species of plants. Even a narrow, relatively straight, stream varies in depth and flow-rate across its width. On bends, considerably faster, deeper water takes the outside course. In good Chalk streams, long wavy strands of water crowfoot mark areas of more rapid flow and domed masses of starwort somewhat slacker places.

Figure 10.2 *The river systems of Hertfordshire (after Dony, 1967)*

Impoundments, such as weirs, waterfalls, locks, lakes, watercress beds, canalisation and artificial widening, will all affect flow-rates, as will the addition of water from adjoining channels. In both fast- and slow-moving waters, localised turbulence will occur in the wake of fallen trees, submerged tree roots, posts, bridge piers, other structures or debris. In natural situations, banks will be formed and eroded by the passage of water, especially where the flow is strong enough to transport abrasive materials, with currents always seeking the easiest route downstream. Slopes of banks, above and below the water, range from very gentle to steep, even vertical or undercut. The nature of plant communities, whether growing on submerged or waterside banks, will be influenced by these factors, as well as by the types of soil or sediment, water chemistry, flow-rates, periodic flooding and presence or absence of adjacent competing or shading vegetation.

Throughout much of Hertfordshire, streams and rivers have rather unstable gravel beds and take water that runs off from neighbouring lands underlain by impermeable geological deposits. In periods of high rainfall, mainly winter, this run-off moves quickly into the waterways, causing rapid spates. At other times, many streams, particularly the host of smaller ones, may be reduced to a mere trickle or even quite dry. Known as *bournes* or *winterbournes*, these are typical of the higher reaches of the networks supplying both the Lea and Colne. Amongst the abundant bournes of central and southern Hertfordshire are some quite spectacular examples where periodic flooding, coupled with the rasping of water-carried flints, has formed deeply incised channels into soft underlying rocks. One of the best examples can be seen near Wood End, where the road from Ardeley to Puckeridge crosses the narrow, steep-sided, tree-shaded defile of the Old Bourne. Such erratic, sometimes forceful, flow does not allow the development of aquatic vegetation. Similarly inhospitable are the *dolines*, *sinkholes* or *swallowholes* as they are usually called, which are to be found in southern Hertfordshire. These are characteristic of places where Chalk or London Clay streams meet extremely permeable deposits such as sands of the Reading Beds. In places, the flow may abruptly disappear underground, sometimes to reappear some distance away. In times of flood, waters may back up to create a temporary lake, before eventually draining away into the natural sink. Dolines near Brookman's Park, the Water End Swallowholes, with two streams draining from London Clay into more than fifteen, steep-sided sinkholes in the Reading Beds, are one of Hertfordshire's most important landscape features. Although swamp, marsh and carr may be found in the area, the sinkholes, which can be twenty metres or so across, are often devoid of plant cover because of the fluctuating water levels.

On Chalk, Clay-with-Flints and Boulder Clay, rivers and streams are more stable as rainfall is more readily absorbed by the underlying rocks and released over a longer period of time. There are fewer surface water courses in these areas, but water supply and constancy of flow are less erratic with only occasional spates or dramatic reductions in levels related to excessively high rainfall or prolonged drought. Their aquatic and marginal plant communities are more permanent and diverse. Examples include the upper reaches of the Lea and Colne catchments, the Rivers Cam or Rhee, Purwell, Oughton, Ivel and Thame. According to underlying geology, erosion and sedimentation, the nature of the substrate of stream and river beds changes along their course. Eroded debris and materials washed into the waterways will be transported, sorted and often redeposited as sandbars, gravel shoals or silt, all of which will influence plant colonisation.

An over-riding factor, which increasingly has most significant influences upon waterway flora and fauna, is human interference. As will be detailed below, this has been taking place since settlers first arrived in Hertfordshire.

10.4 Waterways in History

Ever since the first arrival of settlers in Hertfordshire, waterways have been blessings to exploit and curses to control. Although there has been little alteration to overall drainage patterns (*see* Figure 10.2), some major

Plate 8 (*Top*) Sulphur Clover *Trifolium ochroleucon*; (*Bottom*) Early
Marsh Orchid *Dactylorhiza incarnata* and Southern Marsh Orchid
D. praetermissa

Plate 9   (*Top*) Marsh Helleborine *Epipactis palustris*; (*Bottom*) Heather or
Ling *Calluna vulgaris*

97

changes have been made affecting the capacity, quality and configuration of a great many streams and rivers. These have, without question, degraded many physical and biological characterisitcs to such an extent that little of the original character remains. In prehistoric times, as described above, most rivers were considerably larger than today, and often margined by extensive swamp, marsh and wet woodland which imperceptibly phased into the great expanse of wildwood. It is only rarely that one can now find a spot which gives the feel of what centuries of drainage, canalisation, dredging, urban sprawl, agriculture and pollution have destroyed.

Archaeological evidence reveals that significant waves of human colonisation travelled up the major river valleys. Apart from, the somewhat less densely forested Chalk escarpment, these were the most open and easiest routes to follow if the wildwood was to be avoided. Bronze Age, and particularly Iron Age, features suggest reasonably widespread settlement along the major rivers and into their headwater regions. It is possible that many areas had been settled well before these times. These early peoples obviously obtained water and food from rivers and streams. In a still largely forested landscape, however, watercourses also provided important, perhaps the only, routes for communication, they were amongst the few definable landscape features and many were adopted as territorial boundaries, as social, administrative and military orders began to evolve. Locations of shallows and fords on the larger rivers, for example the Lea between Hertford and Ware, were to become strategically important places, and no doubt many local conflicts took place over their control.

As populations grew and settlements expanded, so the nature of river systems slowly but inexorably changed. Fish and waterfowl were taken for food, as were some of the aquatic and waterside plants. Other products of the riverside were gathered for thatching, fuel, basket-making, animal feed, building and so on. Waste, of all sorts, would probably have been dumped into the rivers, although in early times any deleterious effects were negligible. Later, however, the commonplace habit of indiscriminate dumping and the discharge of sewage and other effluents were to become extremely damaging, and this problem has yet to be satisfactorily resolved.

In time, there came the need to exercise controls over certain watercourses, to alleviate flooding of expanding settlements and fields or to drain swampy areas for further human expansion. These would have involved early attempts at bank stabilisation, canalisation, diversions of flow and new systems of ditches and streams.

Archaeological studies suggest that a good proportion of Hertfordshire was settled at all events by Roman times, for one of the main Roman invasions is known to have followed the courses of the Thames and the Lea into central parts of the county, and it is possible that some tributaries of the Lea and other major rivers were also used. The Romans probably advanced in shallow-draughted boats, for the Lea, at least as far up as Ware, was tidal and navigable; the Danes certainly rowed or sailed longboats up the Lea to Hertford, where they established a fort, presumably to control the important river crossing and form a base from which they could move out into the surrounding countryside. As noted above, a number of other settlements were created where major rivers were navigable or fordable; for instance, Ware probably derives its name from the Old English *wer* or *waer* (weir) with reference to obstructions in the flow of the Lea that facilitated relatively easy crossing. The practicality of crossing the Lea at Ware and the navigability downstream to London created considerable wealth to Norman and later occupiers of the area, who transported large quantities of corn and malt to the capital. There is also evidence to suggest that quite early a variety of goods and materials were imported into the county by rivers. Waterways would have been used, in suitable areas, for shipment of much of the stone to construct churches; it is recorded, for example, that stone for Kings Langley Church arrived from Oxfordshire by way of the Thames, Colne and Gade. Even some of the smaller rivers of the north and east may have been used before trackways and roads sufficiently opened up the wildwood.

By the Middle Ages much of Hertfordshire was producing grain, to supply the expanding population of London as well as the needs of its own inhabitants. Before shipment, much of the grain would have been ground into flour. To cope with increasing demands, and well aware of the unreliable nature of wind-driven mills, millers turned to water power. There had been water mills in our countryside from at least Norman times, but suddenly their importance increased and they sprang up on all the county's small rivers and streams. Where flow proved insufficient to power mills, streams were canalised, artificially linked, diverted or impounded to provide the necessary heads of water. In these places, features of the watercourses were changed. Deeper mill ponds reduced flow rates, whilst mill races accelerated flow downstream. Sometimes, quite complex hydraulic systems were constructed to ensure continuity of water supply or to prevent damage from seasonal flooding. No doubt, waste materials like chaff were conveniently dumped into streams. Because populations were still relatively small, this and other sources of pollution, including the inevitable raw sewage, probably caused only very local and limited damage to aquatic life – William Camden, in his *Hertfordshire* published in 1607, described the county as 'rich in cornfields, pastures, meadows, woods, groves and clear rivers', and on the back of an early 19th century portrait of a local countryman in the collections of North Hertfordshire Museums is an anonymous poem that provides an almost unique insight into the contemporary quality of the River Ivel and its environs near Baldock. It reads as follows:

Thos Currel of Norton

> I knew a man in Hertfordshire,
> And he lived at Norton town,
> An aged man of some renown,
> And his name was Thos. Currel.
> He often went to seek a Merrele*,
> If he did not find it soon,   *(continued overleaf)*

*Probably Common Morel *Morchella vulgaris*, an uncommon and prized edible fungus

> The next thing was a mushroom,
> Then ups his old legs,
> He looked for Lapwing's eggs,
> If he could not find them to his wish,
> He grope the river for Crawfish,
> As in the holes he chance to feel,
> Sometimes he happen on an eel,
> He search the river round about,
> Till he found the watercress is out.

This seemingly idyllic situation was however soon to change forever. By the 17th century malting of grain had become more widespread and many water mills had been abandoned (although traces of some remain, notably in the form of mill pools and weirs); mainly on the larger rivers of southern Hertfordshire, water mills were being converted to power new industries, the most notable in the 18th and 19th centuries being paper-making for which large quantities of water were needed and silk-throwing. River control and pollution increased as by-products of these. At the same time, towns were growing up around these and other industrially developing centres, such as Harpenden, Watford, Hatfield, Rickmansworth, St Albans and Hitchin, and these were discharging domestic and industrial effluent into their adjacent rivers. In 1834, the House of Commons was warned that the River Gade was no longer suitable as a source of water for London as 'it was infected by the deleterious substances used for paper mills'.

About a century before the railways radically altered the economy of Britain, landowners and businessmen of Hertfordshire were well aware of the needs of London and other developing cities and also they knew of lucrative profits to be made, particularly from the supply of grain and malt. Road transport was still horse-powered and largely inefficient for bulk carriage but the waterways, if developed, had much to offer. In particular it was noted that river traffic on the Lea, once a main link to London, had declined on account of negligent management and excessive silting of some stretches. With a realisation of the river's economic potential, the Lea Navigation Act was passed in 1739 and work soon started to link Hertford and Ware with the centre of London and the Thames by commercial craft. This altered and destroyed much of the character of the lower Lea. Dredging, new channels, locks, towpaths, artificial banks and, ultimately, the inevitable spread of urban and industrial developments drastically disturbed and changed much of the former wildlife. The Stort Navigation Act of 1766 similarly affected much of the River Stort from Bishops Stortford downstream to its confluence with the Lea Navigation near Hoddesdon. Barge traffic facilitated the spread of aquatic plants, as well as various weeds and aliens from seeds in cargoes or from soil used as ballast.

In west Hertfordshire, during the last decade of the 18th century, construction of the county's only true canal, the Grand Junction, or Grand Union, Canal, was to have profound effects upon much of the rivers Bulbourne, and Gade and the lower reaches of the Colne. Designed to link the Thames and London with canal systems of the Midlands, the course of the Grand Union Canal took over considerable stretches of these rivers and quickly brought in far reaching effects of the industrial revolution. From Rickmansworth up to Watford, Hemel Hempstead and beyond, the foundations of urban and industrial conurbations were laid only at the expense of the quality of many waterways and a decline in native flora and fauna.

Well before these canalisations, there were already other places where the course and nature of streams and rivers had been manipulated, notably in some of the many parks for which Hertfordshire was so renowned. Waters were realigned or impounded as 'lakes' by landowners or landscape gardeners to add aesthetic appeal to estates. Watercress beds were established, especially in the headwaters of Chalk streams. Here, the often spring fed, clear waters were broadened or channelled into shallow beds, about a third of a metre or so deep, for commercial cultivation and harvesting of watercress – little else was allowed to compete against the cress. Elsewhere, along river valleys waters had been used for centuries to irrigate water meadows; at certain times of the year, a dyke was opened to allow river water to flow into a network of subsidiary channels across the meadows; these overflowed, watering and enriching the grassland soils with silt, then via complementary channels returned water to the river downstream. Today, virtually all traces of water-meadow systems have been erased from the Hertfordshire landscape. In places on major rivers, winter floods were used and controlled by dyke systems to irrigate more extensive areas. Kings Meads at Hertford is the sole surviving flood-meadow system.

At the beginning of the 20th century, much of the county's drainage pattern had been formalised, especially in the extensive arable regions. New and increasingly refined techniques for land drainage were applied; new and existing ditches were opened up to accelerate run-off from fields; many water courses were straightened or deepened by dredging and excavated spoil was piled up on banks to help prevent flooding. These practices continue, their effects further degrading both aquatic and marginal habitats. With a decline in semi-natural wet grasslands, marshes and woodlands, rates at which rainfall runs off the land are increased, resulting in greater scouring of beds and banks, localised downstream flooding, silt accumulation and changes in the chemical composition of the water. The last, particularly since the Second World War, has been accentuated tremendously by vast amounts of dissolved agricultural chemicals which have caused massive environmental damage.

Many other factors have, over the years, combined to further degrade virtually all of Hertfordshire's once beautiful and naturally diverse waterways. Water abstraction for domestic and industrial consumption has reduced natural supplies and flow rates. A quite considerable decline in the natural sub-surface water levels has been documented, especially in the south-east where the demands of London are greatest. There are now many springs and streams seriously deprived of water. Even on the Chalk, most springs and streams, the major suppliers of rivers, exhibit marked reductions in flow as local pumping operations deplete underground sources. A not inconsiderable proportion of several rivers derives from water that has been used for domestic and industrial purposes. Raw or poorly treated sewage and other equally or more noxious effluents were, until comparatively recently, commonly disposed of into rivers, with little consideration to the lasting damage that was being wrought upon the environment; some of the upper reaches of the River Lea, for example, originate from the outfalls of Luton's sewage works and many people will still recall how untreated detergents used to create masses of foam over the weir below Wheathampstead. Happily this no longer occurs, but the waters are still largely unnatural, having been through the treatment systems.

Some of the more insidious forms of pollution so far identified have stopped, and there are indications that the rivers will, to a degree, recover some of their diversity. But how far this recovery will go and how long it will take, remains to be seen; moreover because change and pollution have been going on for so long, we shall probably never know the full extent of what has been lost, especially with regard to plant life. Unfortunately, most watercourses still receive considerable amounts of damaging pollutants in the form of agricultural chemical run-off, oil, dust and salt from roads. Sometimes effluent such as pig slurry 'escapes' from farms; storm water in urban and industrial areas may wash down all sorts of materials and, relatively recently identified, acid rain is no doubt having lasting effects, although these may be masked by the calcareous nature of the majority of water supplies. In some streams, the only visible life may be an ugly mass of the pollution-tolerant, filamentous algae *Cladophora* spp. and a few other species; collectively known as 'blanket weed', these thrive on certain dissolved organic compounds, such as agriculturally derived nitrates. Their metabolism can seriously reduce oxygen levels within the water, while their expansive growth reduces light levels, inhibiting other aquatic life.

The beds and banks of many watercourses are unnecessarily dredged and scoured by river maintenance teams, and despite increased knowledge of the far-reaching effects, some stretches of water and banks are still 'treated' with herbicides. Although some aquatic plants may return fairly rapidly because dredging makes the banks steeper and tends to inhibit much marginal vegetation and allow colonisation by drier-adapted more vigorous species, such as False Oat-grass, Great Hairy Willowherb, Stinging Nettle and shading scrub. Where artificial banks and other structures occur, riparian vegetation will be largely absent, although the fabric of older lock gates, bridges and walls is worth checking for plant life, which may include small ferns, mosses and liverworts as well as the occasional interesting wild flowers. Motor boats can damage banks and waterside flora with their wash, oil and spilt fuel can cause serious pollution problems. Allowed access to river and stream margins, grazing stock can virtually destroy all traces of marginal vegetation. In well fished places, anglers sometimes remove or trample extensive patches of bank vegetation to reach their quarry. The dumping of unwanted bait is an additional form of pollution. Untended, a stretch of water and its banks may soon become overgrown and sensitive species shaded out.

It is difficult to appreciate fully the magnitude of the destruction and neglect of Hertfordshire's waterways and the associated losses in wildlife. Today, the county's major rivers and canal (Lea, Ash, Rib, Beane,

Figure 10.3 *One of Hertfordshire's better stretches of waterway, the River Gade near Water End*

Mimram, Chess, Colne, Bulbourne, Gade and the Grand Union Canal), with a total length of some 240 km, have between them about 20km of reasonably good aquatic or marginal habitat left. There are no precise data available on the hundreds of miles of smaller streams that network throughout the Hertfordshire countryside but, together with spring sources, it is estimated that over 70 per cent are heavily degraded, often with very serious habitat damage. Water is essential to all life and such catastrophic figures must be taken as a salutary warning of much wider environmental implications. There are a few encouraging signs that the state of the county's waterways is being improved, but it will require a great deal more time, effort, co-operation and finance to resuscitate most.

The nature of a waterway changes along its course downstream, as gradient decreases, water capacity increases, flow slackens and chemical changes occur. The changes so influence the associated vegetation that three broad categories of sub-habitat can be used to subdivide marginal and aquatic floras namely,

1 headwater flora
2 middle-course flora
3 lower-course/canal flora.

Field studies will show many overlaps between these. In this text, reference will be mainly directed towards the more typical aquatic and riparian floras. As pointed out above, there have been very significant changes and losses in traditional Hertfordshire river habitat. Considerable stretches now support little aquatic flora and frequently bank vegetation is little different from many inferior road verges or waste areas.

10.5 Headwaters

Springs, small streams and field ditches, up to about three metres wide, complexly draining watersheds and higher ground form what can be collectively referred to as *headwaters*. Characteristically, these are fast flowing and shallow, with little deposition of silt over beds of sand or native rock. In places where watercress or other plants spread out from margins, flow can be reduced and silt will build up amongst stems and roots. In the vicinity of vigorous springs and along very shallow, rapidly flowing, streams, aquatic plants may be scarce or absent because of the lack of suitable substrate for attachment and an overall paucity of nutrients. Many narrow headwater streams are over-shaded by trees, shrubs and tall herbs and flora is therefore inhibited. Many others, which often form field-margin ditches, are over-deepened as part of local drainage operations, with consequent loss and reductions in flora. Nevertheless, there are a few good examples still to be found, notably the spring-fed, sparkling, clear Chalk streams on the River Oughton near Hitchin and on the River Mimram near Whitwell and Kimpton. Although these have ample evidence of degradation, from reduced flows, chemical pollution, overgrowth, dredging and neglect, there are still some fine stretches with waving masses of water crowfoot, submerged domes of starwort and attractive marginal plants. Streams on London Clay and Boulder Clay receive more silt washed out by rain; their beds are relatively more unstable and therefore less vegetated. As noted above, many of southern Hertfordshire's headwater systems, the bournes, are subject to summer drying and winter spates; under such harsh conditions, little aquatic life can develop or survive.

As will be seen in the checklist of characteristic wild flowers in Appendix 1.10, some care is necessary in identifying many water plants. Three species of water-crowfoot may be found, which require close examination of leaves to determine the exact species. Even more difficult are the starworts, of which four species have been identified in Hertfordshire. Leaves can be used to aid identification, although these may vary according to whether plants are submerged, emergent or aerial, and particularly with depth and current speed. Studies of ripe fruits produced from minute green flowers are the only certain means of determination. Waterweeds *sensu stricto*, are generally rather scarce in headwaters, although here and there slacker flow may allow a few to colonise. (*See* section 10.6.)

A common *emergent* plant (that is, one rooted in water with aerial leaves and flowers) along most streams is watercress. In shallow, un- or lightly shaded, stretches it may spread right across the flow, causing excessive amounts of silt to be deposited and shading out submerged plants. It is quite likely in many places that two similar species and their hybrid will be present. Most widespread is Green or Summer Watercress, with broad straight pods holding two rows of seeds; with green autumn leaves, this is the commonly cultivated species of modern cress beds. As the vernacular name suggests, One-rowed Watercress has a single row of seeds in narrow, often curved, pods; its autumn leaves are purplish-brown in colour. This species is not cultivated and it is found more frequently in less calcareous streams. The hybrid, Brown or Winter Watercress, was formerly widely cultivated and may still be found where both parents occur. In similar situations and often with watercress, the poisonous Fool's Watercress may also be abundant. There have been instances of unpleasant results to people who have gathered and eaten leaves of this umbellifer, thinking it to be watercress proper. Watercresses have hollow, angular stems with one to three pairs of leaflets and four-petalled flowers. Fool's Watercress, apart from its short-stalked umbels, has finely furrowed stems and three to six pairs of bright green, shiny leaflets.

Streamside vegetation, particularly where flushed with clear, base-rich waters, can be very lush and diverse. Flote-grasses, Hard and Soft Rushes may be interspersed with a colourful array of wild flowers, including many of those found in Boulder Clay marshes, such as Marsh Marigold, Water Mint, Brooklime, Angelica, Marsh Thistle, Ragged Robin, Water Figwort and Great Hairy Willowherb. Together with these may be species which are generally more closely allied to downstream river courses. Local variations in topography causing deepening, slackening of flow or increased sedimentation facilitate colonisation. Unless controlled, natural succession will lead to moisture-tolerant shrubs and trees invading banks. Ready colonisers include Purple and Common Osier, Goat Willow, Common Sallow, Alder, Guelder Rose, Woody Nightshade and Hop. Inevitably, their shading leads to reductions in many marginal and aquatic plants. Although some overhanging trees and shrubs are beneficial for the fauna, there are all too many streams now virtually fully over-shaded and, with loss of flora plus the other factors, are almost devoid of animal life.

In recent years, two tall and poisonous umbellifers have become frequent and unwelcome colonisers of many stream sides. These are Hemlock, distinguished by its smooth, purple-spotted stems, and the enormous, in every respect, Giant Hogweed. The latter, a native of the Caucasus, has become naturalised in northern Hertfordshire, spreading rapidly along some of the ditches and streams on the Boulder Clay. This unmistakable species, up to four metres tall with leaves a metre long and umbels half a metre across, is difficult to control. Its cut or crushed stems exude aromatic juices containing furocoumarins which, in contact with bare skin and exposure to sunlight, cause photodermatitis; severe and irritating blistering develops within twenty-four hours of contact, lasts for about a further twenty-four hours, and frequently leaves a permanent brown pigmentation on affected parts.

10.6 Middle-course Rivers

Draining down from higher land, headwaters converge to form wider, deeper waterways where flow rates tend to slacken with some resultant deposition of basal silt. Along the long profiles of rivers, such stretches, about four to eight metres wide, are defined as the *middle-courses* and they support identifiable plant communities, although local conditions can be quite variable; for example, shallows allow the down-stream spread of headwater species and in deeper places some lower-course species may occur. Deeper water inhibits water-crowfoot and starwort but, with more stable and silty beds, a greater variety of submerged and emergent aquatics such as pondweeds and waterweeds have potential to root. Where outside interference has been restricted and shelving banks remain, a marked increase in marginal wild flowers will be seen. Some of the better examples can be found in a few places along the River Lea between Hatfield and Hertford, by the River Colne between Colney Heath and Watford and along the lower reaches of the rivers Mimram, Beane, Rib and Ash.

With increased silt deposition in places of slack flow and gently shelving margins, swamp, fen and carr development can be seen, adding to the intrinsic natural diversity of riparian habitats. As with headwaters, considerable lengths of Hertfordshire's middle-course rivers have been severely degraded by pollution, dredging, canalisation, impoundment, over-shading and neglect. It is just possible, although most unlikely, that conservationists have overstated the losses in some of the aquatic plants, notably certain pondweeds and waterweeds. For these may lurk at depth, with no aerial parts, and the botanist would have to resort to line and grappling hook to seek specimens. Even then, identification would not be easy, for some pondweeds *Potamogeton* spp. have leaves that vary in shape with depth, and critical separation of the two introduced water-weeds *Elodea* spp. depends upon close studies of length, shape and colour of leaves. Of all the county's semi-natural habitats, rivers seem to be the least studied by naturalists in terms of both flora and fauna.

10.7 Lower-course Rivers and Canals

Millennia of erosion, wrought mainly by water, have formed the low-lying, flat lands through which the lower courses of the county's rivers flow, the Stort, Lower Lea and Lower Colne valleys. In early post-glacial times, torrents of meltwater armed with abundant abrasive flints removed vast amounts of the soft underlying rocks, largely creating the topography seen today. Extensive deposits of sands and gravels ac-cumulated across the valley floors from these torrents, and later, wide but somewhat slower-flowing river systems. Initiated by these events, natural drainage systems converged into the valleys. The low-lying topography reducing flow rates and creating wide, deep, sluggish channels. Prone to extensive silting, these lower courses frequently meandered across the landscape and, with periodic flooding, formed extensive swamps, marshes and wet woodland within the valleys.

Although their general drainage patterns remain much the same, changes, notably in the past two and a half centuries, have radically altered the landscape and the nature of these major, once fine, rivers. Little of what remains can be regarded as more than poor quality canal. Changes to the River Lea are perhaps best documented, but these typify what has happened in the Rivers Stort and Colne. From Hertford, where it is joined by the Rivers Mimram, Beane and Rib, the Lea formerly flowed as a sizeable and, as shown above, navigable, waterway. Three hundred years ago its qualities were extolled by Izaac Walton, famous angler and writer, whose *Compleat Angler*, first published in 1653 and still in print,

Figure 10.4 *The River Mimram at Poplars Green, with Monkey Flower and Brooklime*

107

is full of descriptions of the river – its trees, flowers, otters, some twenty-seven species of fish – and of the adjacent meadows. Most of this has now gone. The Lea Navigation or New River (virtually a canal), constructed in the 18th century, significantly affected the flow of the Lea. Although a few relict stretches remain depleted of water by these developments, much of the old course and its smaller tributaries have disappeared in the recent complexes of gravel workings. Flow was reduced by new locks, eventually resulting in heavy silting. Most banks were steep and artificial, unsuitable therefore for marginal flora. Subsequent extensive urban and industrial developments along the Lea Valley, together with the far reaching effects of new forms of agriculture, have brought irreversible changes and many aspects of pollution which continue to degrade the quality of the waters and their wildlife.

Much of the River Stort has been similarly affected, as has the River Colne below Watford, where it parallels and sometimes conjoins with the Grand Union Canal. The most recent survey of Hertfordshire's main rivers (Nature Conservancy Council, 1978), shows that the old River Lea, below Hertford, is still the county's best example. It is, however, quite heavily polluted, particularly by phosphates and nitrates mainly of agricultural origin, and seriously disturbed. Research shows that reasonably good numbers of aquatic species can still be found but marginal vegetation is poor, with many invasive weeds due to disturbance. The survey shows the Stort to be similar, but the New River less diverse in

Figure 10.5 *Canalisation, pollution and disturbance have severely reduced aquatic and marginal vegetation of lower-course rivers (River Stort Navigation at Eastwick Mead)*

aquatic plants and very poor in true riparian vegetation. Nitrate and phosphate levels were found to be very high in the River Colne, especially below Watford; consequently aquatic flora was very poor. Here also, generally much disturbed bank vegetation is dominated by weeds, tall rough grasses, nettles and scrub.

In west Hertfordshire, at least above Watford, stretches of the Grand Union Canal have been less affected by development. In places the canal follows the old river courses or receives less polluted waters from Chalk streams, such as the Bulbourne and Gade. Here more diverse flora and fauna can be found, to some extent showing what has been lost from other deep, slow-moving waterways. The overall aquatic flora of the Grand Union Canal is much like that of the old River Lea, with a similarly patchy distribution of more interesting stretches. Of particular interest is the branch, known as the Wendover Arm, adjacent to Tring Reservoirs. This receives little boat traffic and retains a relatively high natural diversity, with good submerged and emergent flora and, interesting, although artificial banks. Near Northchurch and the source of the River Bulbourne, canal and banks are more natural, supporting a good flora. Similarly, where the River Gade joins the the canal at Cassiobury Park in Watford, a reasonable abundance of aquatic plants can be found. Elsewhere, towpaths, artificial banks, overgrowth, development and agriculture have reduced riparian vegetation. There are continuing pressures on the canal's wildlife, notably pollution and bank damage from increasing pleasure craft. Waterside meadows are being drained and ploughed for arable cultivation, with consequently increased chemical run-off into the waterway.

Despite the great changes and losses in the flora of the county's lower-course rivers and canals, a quick glance at the checklist of typical species (*see* Appendix 1.12) will show that there is still a reasonable diversity to be seen, although a good proportion of species are somewhat restricted in their distributions. Current knowledge of the river flora is far from complete, particularly for submerged aquatics, and studies of material dredged from deeper waters by grappling hooks could provide much useful information. Together with the species more typical of sluggish water and swampy margins will be found many of the wild flowers noted for the middle-course rivers, as well as some more characteristic of the still waters of ponds and lakes. In a few fast flowing shallows, headwater species may be present such as crowfoot and starwort.

Within sluggish and still waters, communities of plants develop through their adaptations to occupy different ecological niches within the aquatic environment. With water to support them, submerged aquatics require little strengthening tissue, although they retain specialised tissues to give tensile strength against current flow and, in some cases, gas-filled cells to ensure buoyancy above the silty bed. Roots, if present are for anchorage only, and many species have fine, thin, dissected or ribbon-shaped leaves to provide increased surface areas for the exchange of nutrients and gases. Particularly in slow-moving and still water, these plants are very important, for they remove carbon dioxide and, through the process of photosynthesis, release the oxygen so vital for aquatic fauna. Flowers of many submerged aquatics are water-pollinated. Several aquatic plants have both submerged and floating leaves, for example some crowfoots, pondweeds and water-lilies. In these there are notable differences in the structure of the two leaf types enabling the plants to utilise facets of both aquatic and aerial environments. Some plants obtain nutrients through their roots, other just anchorage. Floating leaves are frequently rather leathery on the upper surfaces and waxy in appearance; this allows water to run off and not block the tiny pores, *stomata*, through which gaseous exchanges occur. Water-lilies also have tough floating leaves which, together with their extensive root systems, decompose slowly and can accelerate silting. All three species noted for Hertfordshire are declining.

Really still, even quite heavily polluted, waters usually hold small, but often abundant, floating aquatics. One or more of the duckweeds may at times form green carpets along or across waterways. These tiny, rather strange, stemless, *thallus*-like plants have no apparent leaves and the flowers, when present, are minute and without petals. Floating upon the surface during summer, they take in nutrients from water via tiny aquatic roots; food reserves are stored in the tissues and then, as winter approaches, the stomata are closed and the plants sink downwards to overwinter. Duckweeds reproduce almost exclusively by asexual budding, which under certain conditions can lead to rapid population growth covering stretches of water, reducing light and inhibiting submerged aquatics. Readily adhering to the bodies of waterfowl, duckweeds may easily be spread from place to place. Water Fern, a native of tropical America, may occasionally turn up unexpectedly, particularly in warm summers, having been thrown out of an aquarium and transported in the same way.

In a few of the least disturbed lower reaches, where gently shelving margins merge into banks or silt beds have accumulated, colonies of emergent aquatic plants can be found. These have their lower parts in water, the roots taking nutrients from the rich substrate, whilst the upper stems, leaves and flowers function in the same way as terrestrial plants. The roots and stems trap silt and on death, being rich in cellulose, decay slowly, causing the build-up of detritus. Unless this is washed away by seasonal flooding, swamp development will occur, followed by natural succession to marsh, carr and wet woodland. (*See* Chapter 10.2.) In places, vigorous species such as Common Reed and Greater and Lesser Pond-Sedges may form dense, sometimes almost mono-specific, marginal stands. Amongst the potentially variable and rich emergent and other marginal flora of these better stretches on the lower-courses will be many of the species noted for middle-course rivers, ponds and lakes.

10.8 Standing Waters – Ponds and Lakes

There is little resemblance in the contemporary terrain of Hertfordshire to that of prehistoric times. Then, even in the dense wildwood, land surfaces would have been very uneven from the passage of ice, meltwaters and relatively recently deposited debris. Groundwater levels were high, rivers and streams more vigorous and there would have been an abundance of natural standing waters, large and small, especially on the lower lying ground of clay soils. Colonisation by aquatic and marginal wild flowers followed, but, as is characteristic in stagnant waters, repeated cycles of plant growth and death were self-destructive; dead and decaying remains, in the absence of flushing currents, accumulated, eventually eliminating their habitats. This process of natural succession, which leads from open water through swamp and marsh to carr and, finally, woodland, is a continuing phenomenon. Unless these natural processes (termed the *hydrosere*), are in some way interfered with, the existence of any such body of water can be seen to be finite and, at least until historical times, the pattern of natural ponds and lakes was ever-changing. It appears that human intervention is the only reliable control over such changes.

Water is vital to all life and, as archaeological evidence has revealed, early human occupation and settlement of Hertfordshire was by way of the Chalk escarpment with its numerous spring sources and along the major river valleys. Initial spread of colonisation into the wildwood was probably directed along the courses of the minor rivers and their sub-sidiary streams. Further expansion led to the opening up of the wildwood, although the availability of easily accessible water would, no doubt, have been of prime importance in the selection of settlement sites. Natural springs, water-filled hollows, even small streams impounded by – then native – beavers, can all be visualised as providing ideal places for early occupation. If a water source failed or was overtaken by natural succession, the settlers probably abandoned the site and moved to a new location. Probably in late Neolithic and certainly before Roman times such nomadic options were declining as settlement densities increased across the landscape. Farmsteads, hamlets and villages were now more permanent and the establishment of territorial boundaries would begin to limit and polarise settlement patterns. Although many natural resources were abundantly available, some would have required careful harnessing to meet the demands of growing populations. So, in many places, evolved the care and control of water supplies. To maintain ponds, silt or overgrowth would be controlled, banks raised or cut back and, if necessary, local streams diverted to increase capacity. In suitable places new pools were dug or formed by damming streams. The latter type would become more widespread with the development of water-powered mills for grinding corn, although, because they have a detectable flow, mill pools have different characteristics from those of the stagnant waters of ponds, and their flora is more closely allied to that of deeper rivers.

It is not impossible that some of the water-filled hollows in the landscape today had their origins in prehistoric times. Certainly a few have associations penetrating the mists of time, retaining a certain 'naturalness', yet obviously, by virtue of their having survived so long, having at some stage undergone interference. Over centuries, ponds and other standing waters became significant additions to the Hertfordshire landscape, supporting distinctive plant and animal communities.

Ponds and lakes are generally differentiated according to their size but, as many authorities point out, there are no really clear distinctions, especially between 'large ponds' and 'small lakes'. As etymologists have

111

shown, although many natural and artificial depressions holding standing waters for most of the year were present in Anglo-Saxon times, contemporary writings referred to them all as *meres*. It was not until the Middle Ages that the word 'pond' came into general usage and this was derived from 'pound', meaning an enclosed or dammed body of water. 'Lake' has its origins in the Latin *lacum*, meaning a large sheet of water surrounded by land. For the purposes of general studies in natural history, a pond is a small body of stagnant water shallow enough to have a relatively even temperature throughout it, including the bottom. A lake is a larger body of still water, often too deep in its middle for rooted plants and, usually, with a marked difference between surface and bottom temperatures. This temperature variation or thermocline, created by warmer, less dense waters above lying over cooler, denser waters beneath, is an important feature of larger, deeper lakes in summer. Little evidence is available for Hertfordshire but it is probable that thermoclines are found only in a few flooded mineral workings with depths in excess of ten metres or so. Most so-called lakes in the county are really just large ponds.

Although historical associations are often difficult to trace, it is evident that a good proportion of ponds, largely dug by hand, were at the heart of many settlements from at least Roman times until the end of the 19th century. Across these centuries, more and more ponds were added to the landscape. They were an important part of life, to be cossetted in a countryside without the planned and piped water systems of today. Few, if any, served aesthetic purposes; rather, they played an integral part in the rural economy, providing 'filling stations' for stock and draught animals and, later, steam engines. On heavier soils, more suited to cattle-grazing, virtually every field had a pond. Sometimes a field-edge or corner pond might service two or more pastures. To the early part of this century, some rural communities still relied heavily upon their ponds for drinking and washing water. If the worst were to happen, water had to be drawn from ponds to extinguish serious fires. Some ponds might also have provided fish or wildfowl for the meal-table, marginal reeds for thatching or willows for basket-making. In dry seasons, water might be taken from ponds to irrigate the land. Cleared silt would have been useful as 'manure' and there are references to sticklebacks being collected and spread on land as fertiliser. Perhaps as much the centre of village life as church or 'pub', many ponds are steeped in historical fact and folklore; some were traditional places for the 'swimming' of witches, who were thought to be influenced by Satan or the 'ducking' of lunatics, petty offenders, drunks and scolds; many were places to gossip or muse and generations of country children would have found a major source of their entertainment in and around the village pond.

The majority of Hertfordshire's more recent ponds – certainly virtually all the extant examples – were man-made, mainly to supply water for human and stock needs. Many have some traces of banks, sometimes quite steep; some have shallower parts which were designed to allow easy access for stock to drink and for water carts or so that journeymen could cool the wheels of their wagons in summer and collect ice in winter to store in ice houses for use in summer. Ponds of this sort are frequently associated with trackways, footpaths or green lanes. Either by accident or design, other excavations in the ground have been or periodically become flooded; there is, for example, a long history of small pit digging, especially on common land, for sand and gravel to repair roads, for loess or brickearth to manufacture bricks and tiles, and for clay for pottery-making or the production of daub to apply between the wattles of old houses. Marl, a chalky clay, was dug and applied as fertiliser to acidic and dry soils. Marling, probably originating in Roman times, became particularly important in the 18th century agricultural boom, before the advent of commercially produced fertilisers. To save labour, pits in suitable areas were often excavated in the middle of fields to be marled; many of these were not infilled until the beginning of this century and a few remain as isolated ponds amongst arable crops.

Hertfordshire has many moated sites, particularly on the heavy, wet Boulder Clay soils of the north east. Early moats were usually four-sided, square, rectangular or irregular, and dug and flooded around a settlement for defensive purposes. Many date from the Middle Ages and, notably later ones, were formed as fashionable status symbols surrounding a wealthy landowner's house or garden. Sometimes the 'moat' was a single linear pond enhancing the frontage of a less wealthy abode. Larger and deeper moats, like some ponds, may also have been used for fishkeeping or, presumably when they did not constitute the local water supply, as convenient places to dispose of rubbish and sewage. It is still possible to find a few of these moated sites, now largely deserted and often heavily over-shaded within woods; usually they are of little botanical interest, although the well-known site at Rye House near Stanstead Abbotts retains a reasonable pond flora.

A number of ancient ponds may have other origins; possibly before Anglo-Saxon times some were created in woods in association with silviculture and charcoal-burning, others to provide heads of water to power machinery; there were too fish-pools to store living food. As mentioned above, by the Middle Ages, quite refined techniques in water-power were driving water-mills and complex series of fish-breeding and stock ponds were constructed, often near settlements to prevent poaching, holding different species and sizes of fish. In places, particularly in woods, decoy ponds were dug to attract wildfowl for food or 'sport'. On well-drained soils of sands, gravels and Chalk, water supplies were more of a problem and in many places ponds had to be specially constructed to catch and retain rainwater. Their construction would be the work of a specialist who first lined the excavated hollows with branches, and then sealed the bottom with puddled clay. Although little evidence survives, it is probable that the so-called *dew-ponds* on the Chalk hills were fashioned in this way. It is thought that the Romans knew how to make these ponds (also known as 'mist' or 'cloud-ponds'), but most date from the 19th century. Mainly supplied by rain, said to never dry out and to possess magical qualities, many were revered by country-folk, some even believing that God filled them and that they ought therefore to be called 'Dieu-ponds'.

Other water-filled hollows may once have been saw-pits or associated with industrial processes; some may have resulted from land subsidence or even from bomb craters from the Second World War. Important and not insignificant additions to the county's pondscape are the innumerable garden ponds. All the existing large ponds or lakes of Hertfordshire are artificial. With the exception of flooded mineral workings, reservoirs and sewage lagoons (detailed below), the majority were created as ornamental features in the landscape. Some of the finest, in terms of landscape design, were the work of great 18th century landscape gardeners such as Humphry Repton and Capability Brown. On many estates, such as Tewin Water and Brocket Park on the River Mimram, lakes were created by impounding streams and rivers with dams and weirs. Like mill-pools, these have some flow and their ecological characteristics have facets of both ponds and slow-moving rivers. Despite their glorious history these and virtually all the other ponds in the county have lost a vast proportion of their former wildlife interest.

Today it is perhaps not easy to appreciate the attitude of landowners, past and present, that once a pond has lost practical use in the countryside it is of little more than nuisance value, to be disregarded or used as a convenient dumping-ground and turned to crop production or other uses after draining or filling in. Despite growing awareness of the biological and historical importance of ponds in the landscape, however, degradation and loss continues at an alarming rate. Like so many semi-natural habitats, ponds are dynamic and must receive regular management to retain their intrinsic natural history interest; without management, natural degradation will destroy ponds; overhanging bushes and trees will inhibit light, create detritus build-up from shed twigs and leaves, leading to reductions in water plants and lowering of oxygen levels. Silting facilitates expansion of marginal vegetation and natural succession to carr and woodland. Although not unknown in the past, unnatural pollution has accelerated in this century to reduce water quality drastically; increasingly ponds have become dumping grounds for domestic and agricultural waste. Flushing WCs came to the countryside before sewer systems and it was not unknown for cesspits to overflow via ditches into ponds; the effects of these were, however, generally small in comparison to those of the last few decades. As will be shown below, hardly any ponds have escaped some pollution or degradation, even relatively recently created ones. It is evident that those lovingly and expensively landscaped lakes noted in the previous paragraph have suffered correspondingly.

Chemical herbicides, pesticides and fertilisers applied to the land find their way into ponds through wind-drifted sprays, run-off or groundwater seepage, sometimes years afterwards, and with devastating results. Waters with slimy algal scum indicate pollution by fertilisers; known as *eutrophication*, the effects of fertiliser pollution are as damaging to most aquatic life as those of pollution by herbicides and pesticides. Similarly, via drains and ditches, there is run-off into ponds from roads, consisting of acid rain, oil, rubber dust, winter-applied salt, and dissolved minerals and chemicals from roadstone and tar. Disgracefully too universal is the fly-tipping of all sorts of unwanted items into our ponds, from old tins, bottles, bicycles and bedsteads to heaps of 'soured' grain, unmarketable potatoes and 'empty' containers often containing traces (but, to the pond habitat, lethal quantities) of chemicals. Urban and industrial developments, car parks and road-widening schemes also threaten ponds – it takes only an hour or two, with modern machinery, to infill a pond. Some pond owners quite happily accept handsome payments from contractors wishing to dispose of a lorry load or two of unwanted topsoil or rubbish. It must be said that there are still many villages and landowners who are proud to care for their ponds; unfortunately, all too often, the caring goes too far, with manicured banks and excessive populations of semi-wild or domesticated ducks and alien fish. Ducks feed on aquatic and marginal plants and stir up silt, clouding the water, killing off vital micro-organisms and submerged aquatics, and their droppings pollute the water, (as do the uneaten remains of the copious amounts of bread and other food supplied by well meaning humans). Some species of introduced fish will destroy vegetation and fishing can lead to trampled margins and problems caused by the careless discarding of tackle and bait.

An awakening as to the overall plight of the countryside and its wildlife, has brought the poor state of ponds to the fore. The full extent of what has been lost will never be known, but the results of a survey carried out in 1986 (Hertfordshire County Council, 1987), give great cause for concern. The survey estimated that while some seven thousand ponds were to be found in Hertfordshire in 1882, by the 1980s this had fallen by almost 50 per cent to about 3600 – a loss of one pond every week and a half. Even more appalling findings show that of the over seven hundred ponds surveyed in detail over 80 per cent were in an extremely poor state. Just 3 per cent supported what could be identified as relatively reasonable plant and animal communities, and even these suffered some form of degradation, such as pollution, neglect

Figure 10.6 *Once, virtually every field had a pond; few of any quality for wildlife survive today (Burleigh Meadow, near Knebworth)*

Plate 10 (*Top*) Water Mint *Mentha aquatica*; (*Bottom*) Purple Loosestrife
Lythrum salicaria

116

Plate 11 (*Top*)Common Duckweed *Lemna minor* with Water Fern *Azolla filiculoides*; (*Bottom*) As larger bodies of standing water mature with reed bed and carr development, they become habitats for a wider range of wildlife such as this nesting Great Crested Grebe

117

or unsympathetic use or management. Assessment of data collected for these ponds took into account such factors as age or 'naturalness', management, habitat stability, biological interest and diversity and potential for future conservation. Not one of these ponds achieved top, or Class A, rating. Only twenty-two sites – the 3 per cent noted above – were rated Class B. These had good zones of marginal, emergent and submerged vegetation and a rich aquatic fauna but their interest was restricted by lack of some essential features. In most cases, given the right care and attention, their wildlife value could be enhanced, perhaps to become Grade A sites. Among the ponds in the Grade B category were those near Cokenach, Meesden Green, Lamsden Common, Balls Wood, Willow Corner at Bayford, Park Street (gravel pit) and Tykes Water Lake. About 18 per cent of ponds were identified as Class C, lacking some important elements of flora and fauna, and a further 30 per cent of Class D sites were suffering relatively severe reductions from overshading, neglect or pollution. The massive 48 per cent of Class E sites were seriously degraded by pollution, silting, heavy shading and natural succession – some had no water at all. As a large sample of ponds was surveyed it seems reasonable to assume these to be representative of the county as a whole. Even if there are a few top-class ponds yet to be identified, the survey reveals a most depressing situation for what should be a major wildlife, amenity, educational and aesthetic resource in the county. As the survey report stresses, the potential value of ancient ponds has been promoted for over twenty years but, unless some more positive action is taken quickly, further irretrievable losses will continue to escalate. The survey sets out clear guidelines as to the long-term commitments necessary if we are to improve and manage these important parts of our heritage.

In some respects, the tremendous loss in ponds has been balanced by the construction of freshwater reservoirs, such as those at Aldenham, Hilfield Park and Tring, and the extensive flooding of mineral workings, such as those of the Lea and Colne valleys. These have some features in common with ponds together with others more characteristic of deeper lakes. (*See* Chapter 10, sections 9 and 10.)

In the ideal pond or lake, five distinct plant habitats or zones will be found. First is the pond edge, where a lush variety of marginal species are able to root in water for all or most of the year. Next comes a deeper zone which rarely dries out; to a degree intergrading with the first zone, this is colonised mainly by emergent species, with roots in the bottom and aerial-flowering spikes pollinated by wind or insects. The third and deepest zone supports only submerged aquatics. The water surface, with floating aquatics such as duckweeds is the fourth zone, and the pond bottom, where plants rest or germinate, the fifth. As shown above, few of Hertfordshire's ponds exhibit all these zones. Water chemistry is an important factor affecting plant distribution and under the influence of calcareous rocks, soils and water supplies, most of the county's ponds are lime-rich and well-supplied with natural nutrients. They should therefore be rich in plant and animal life and, in ecological terms, regarded as *eutrophic*. This should not be confused with the term *eutrophied* which relates to *over*-enrichment by certain unnatural

Figure 10.7 *Picturesque Hertfordshire! Polluted, no marginal vegetation, all but lifeless and uncared for ponds are much too typical (Albury)*

chemicals, such as phosphates and nitrates, too often found polluting ponds and rivers. Such chemicals draining from farmland and all the other forms of pollution and degradation have combined to change the very nature of pondwater, reducing and eradicating many characteristic wild flowers. In just a few locations on acid soils, mainly in south Hertfordshire, are some small ponds where the waters tend to be acidic; these contain wild flowers more typical of the boggy pools of heath and moorland and these represent the final relics of the once plentiful similar habitats destroyed by water abstraction, urban development, forestry and agriculture.

Many of the wild flowers found in slow-moving rivers, canals, swamps, marshes and carr may also be met with in and around ponds. There are some specialised pond species, that would be unable to survive in moving waters, such as Water-violet, Water-milfoil, Hornwort and certain pondweeds. These produce buds or bud-like organs containing food reserves which become detached from the main plants and overwinter in bottom mud, rising again the following spring to form new plants. Some submerged aquatics produce aerial flowers for pollination; others are water-pollinated and many rely upon asexual reproduction. Fragmentation of even small pieces of Canadian Waterweed or Hornwort can soon produce new colonies, perhaps transported to new ponds by water birds. Such submerged species are most important in overall pond ecology. Roots, if present, serve only as anchorage. Absorption of dissolved nutrients and carbon dioxide from the water occurs over the entire, thin and often extensive, surface layers of the plant, stomata are absent. Oxygen from photosynthesis, diffuses into the water and benefits respiration of both plants and animals, as well as stimulating bacteria which decompose organic matter. Given well-oxygenated and not too acidic, water, decomposition of dead remains of flaccid aquatic plants will be virtually complete, allowing a cyclic build-up and decline of fertile nutrients. Even a small change to this cycle can upset the delicate ecological balance; for example, addition of a small amount of pollutant, such as nitrates, can cause excessive development of plants, perhaps in an already dominant species, which may reduce the light or lead to higher than normal oxygen levels thus affecting water chemistry and inhibiting decay and ultimately causing rapid accumulation of detritus. It is obvious that the ecological structure in most, if not all, of Hertfordshire's ponds has been more than slightly tipped out of balance. A great many of these have no hope of restoration and will in time only be outlines on old maps.

10.9 Reservoirs

Closely grouped and collectively known as Tring Reservoirs, Marsworth, Startops End, Tringford and Wilstone Reservoirs are some of the biologically richest areas of expansive standing waters in Hertfordshire. They have been a major attraction to generations of naturalists since their construction in the early 19th century to hold a head of water maintaining levels in the Grand Union Canal and its branches to Wendover and Aylesbury. Occupying former marsh and grassland below the Chiltern escarpment, the beds of the reservoirs are cut into Lower Chalk and in a few places some relicts of these species-rich habitats can still be found, for example Rushy Meadow by Wilstone Reservoir. Natural spring supplies give the reservoirs characteristics of shallow marl lakes, a rare habitat type on the English Chalk. Clear, nutrient-rich or eutrophic waters support an abundance of plant and animal life – which, over the years, is borne out by the long list of breeding, passage and wintering birds. Except in the deepest central parts, the waters are shallow enough to support well developed submerged aquatic floras with abundant Canadian Waterweed, Hornwort and Spiked Water-milfoil. Unfortunately few recent data are available but included in past records are Broad-leaved, Shining, Curled and Fennel-leaved Pondweeds, two species of Water-starwort with the common *stagnalis* and scarce *hamulata*, several Duckweeds and the scarce Fan-leaved Water-crowfoot *Ranunculus circinatus* (5–8).

Extensive lengths of banks along the reservoirs are artificial and steep-sided, and rather uninteresting botanically, but the shallow, shelving margins of the southern and eastern shores are quite natural in appearance, particularly at Marsworth and Wilstone. Here tall fen communities and carr development can be seen, dominated by Common Reed with frequent Reed Sweet-grass. Amongst the other emergent plants may be found Branched Bur-reed, Reed-grass, Great Reedmace, Lesser Reedmace, Mare's-tail, Water Dock, Water-plantain, Yellow Iris, Lesser Pond-sedge, Hard and Soft Rushes, Great Hairy Willowherb, Meadowsweet, Water Forget-me-not, Gypsywort, Nodding Bur-

Marigold, Celery-leaved Crowfoot, Brooklime, Orange Balsam, Alder, Common Osier and willows. At Startops End the rare Slender Rush *Juncus tenuis* (6–9) has been recorded, which has recent records from just one other site, Patmore Heath. Equally rare, Round-fruited Rush *J. compressus* (6–7) still occurs at Startops End; it has also only been seen recently at a single other site, near Ickleford. Within the developing carr, which in places is dominated by Common Osier, is one of the few county localities for Green-flowered Helleborine *Epipactis phyllanthes* (7–8). There are times, for example in 1989, when the demands for water to be diverted from the reservoirs into the canal system are particularly high. This causes levels to fluctuate, although large-scale changes have generally been less frequent in recent years. Regular falls and rises of water can create distinct zones of vegetation on the muddy shores of the reservoirs; the presence of Round-fruited Rush, high on the shore of Startops End, is associated with the quite frequent periods of inundation, while at the lower level there is a region that is normally inundated, but when drained develops an unusual community of dwarfed marginal species, with Gypsywort, Water Chickweed, Water Mint, Silverweed, Marsh Yellowcress, Amphibious Bistort, Orange Foxtail, and Pink and Blue Water Speedwell. At the bottom of this zonation, rarely free from water cover, is the only site in the county for the nationally scarce Mudwort *Limosella aquatica* (6–10). First discovered in 1910, this has only ever been sporadically observed, seeds apparently lying dormant for years awaiting just the right conditions for germination; several plants were seen at Wilstone Reservoir in 1989, when water levels were particularly low. The damp clay of the reservoir beds thus exposed at this time proved ideal also for the growth of great masses of Red Goosefoot *Chenopodium rubrum* (7–9).

Aldenham Reservoir, now part of the Aldenham Country Park to the west of Elstree, was hand-dug by French prisoners-of-war between 1795 and 1797 on what was then Aldenham Common, its original purpose being to maintain levels of surrounding rivers following the building of the Grand Union Canal. Today it is a popular country park with sailing, fishing, ornamental wildfowl and other recreational facilities. Dug into less calcareous deposits of the London Clay and now with rather turbid water and shaded and disturbed margins, Aldenham, like the nearby Hilfield Park Reservoir which was opened in 1957 to supply drinking water, has never attracted the same interest as Tring Reservoirs. Both are naturally less diverse, although possibly under-recorded. Amongst species to be found are Canadian and Nuttall's Waterweeds, Common Duckweed, the Water-starwort *Callitriche platycarpa*, Soft, Hard and Jointed Rushes, Cyperus Sedge, Reed-grass, Reed and Floating Sweet-grasses, watercress, Fool's Watercress, Branched Bur-reed, Water Mint, Water-plantain, Celery-leaved Crowfoot, Amphibious Bistort, Brooklime, Nodding and Trifid Bur-Marigold, Common Skullcap, Water Forget-me-not, Great Hairy Willowherb, Meadowsweet, Marsh Ragwort, Alder and willows. The muddy, sometimes submerged, margins of both Aldenham and Hilfield Park Reservoirs are possibly the sole county localities for the short, slender Needle Spike-rush *Eleocharis acicularis* (8–10).

10.10 Flooded Pits and Mineral Workings

Over centuries many small pits were dug, mainly by hand, into deposits of sand, gravel, brickearth, clay and Chalk to meet such local demands as parish road repairs, small-scale building and fertiliser. Some of these excavations became ponds but most, being rather shallow and dry, were quickly infilled, often with local rubbish, and returned to agriculture with little impact upon the landscape. After the First World War, there was a tremendous increase in requirements for concrete-constructed roads, bridges and buildings. To meet these, sand and gravel industries developed and expanded. Extensive deposits of Tertiary and Pleistocene sands and gravels in southern Hertfordshire were obvious resources for exploitation, especially as they were so close to London. Large-scale workings were opened up in the river terrace gravels of the lower Lea and Colne valleys and in the glacial plateau deposits between Watford and Ware, and as demands escalated after the Second World War, further workings were opened to supply a vigorous boom in building. Today quarrying continues, with improved mechanisation allowing faster and deeper excavations. In places some of the pits remain dry, often eventually being used for the disposal of 'non-toxic' refuse, covered with topsoil and returned to agriculture or otherwise developed. During and after quarrying, the dry, disturbed sands and gravels of such pits can be extremely interesting places, exhibiting a wide range of wild flower species including many annual 'weeds' (*see* Chapter 15) and many facets of succession.

Being in such permeable deposits, excavations near rivers, on spring sources or in areas of relatively high water-lines readily flood and may require considerable pumping operations to allow gravel or sand production to continue. Once pumping operations cease, pits soon flood, and over the past fifty years or so these have become the largest and most important addition to the semi-natural habitat of Hertfordshire, their amenity and wildlife conservation value to some extent compensating for the great loss of ponds in the wider countryside. In much of the Lea Valley below Ware, and the Colne Valley below Watford, gravel resources appear to be exhausted and strings of complex flooded workings have developed interesting wetland and other wildlife communities. In the Vale of St Albans and around Hertford, however, extensive quarrying continues and more is likely.

It is possible, by visiting recent, middle-aged and old pits, to see aspects illustrating the many ecological changes and full natural succession, or hydrosere, from uncolonised waters through lush submerged, emergent and marginal vegetation to the development of marsh, carr and damp woodland. Because they are supplied mainly from calcareous springs or groundwater filtering through sands and gravels, many pits have clear eutrophic water and a rich wildlife. Those with direct supplies from rivers, streams or surface water are noticeably less diverse because of inherent pollution. The river-terrace gravels of the Lea and Colne Valleys, originating from fluvial deposition, are naturally much clearer and contain less silt than those in the glacial, often more acidic deposits of the Vale of St Albans. Many sites, especially in the early stages of succession, are well known for attracting breeding and migratory wildfowl and wading birds which, probably, are responsible for introducing quite a number of plants. The proximity of lower-course rivers, canals and existing pits further facilitates rapid colonisation and spread of other species.

Water depth, steepness of banks and bottom substrates are important factors governing rates of colonisation and diversity of flooded gravel pit flora. Larger, deeper pits exhibit slower rates of colonisation. There are no data indicating that any of the county's extant pits are deep enough (about ten metres or more) to have significant thermoclines. Steep banks are relatively unstable, even in still water, and inhibit aquatic plant growth, although gently shelving margins may rapidly develop submerged and emergent vegetation. This may accelerate silting, leading to colonisation by reedbeds, sedges and rushes that hasten the formation of willow and Alder carr. Apart from potentially and probably introducing pollutants, inflowing streams and rivers will bring in more turbid, silt-laden water, and flooded pits with such sources have muddier, more unstable bottoms and less diverse flora and fauna. Many of the older pits, with areas of deeper and shallower waters, such as can be seen in the Lea and Colne Valleys, well illustrate a range of differing depths and plant colonisation, although a number of the potentially better sites have had their natural history interests reduced by fishing and water sports. Some are now amongst the county's most important nature reserves.

Lists of wild flowers associated with both wet and dry aspects of gravel pits can be very long. Changes in flora will occur as sites mature, with, in dry places, noticeable declines, as annuals, adventives and other open-ground species are replaced by more competitive and permanent grasses, herbs and shrubs. Few sites have had detailed long-term documentation and there is still much to be learned about the various phases of natural succession and the effects of management.

An area that has been the subject of extensive studies is Amwell Quarries, to the east of Great Amwell in the Lea Valley. Here two pits, now known as Hardmead and Hollycross Lakes, were dug for sand and gravel between 1973 and 1988 by St Albans Sand and Gravel Company Limited. In 1983 the company designated the site, including pits, river margins, marsh and a small plantation, for wildlife conservation, with limited public access. As excavations were completed some raw landscaping was carried out to create islands, spits, bays, shallows, marshes and flatter dry places and plant colonisation was largely allowed to proceed naturally. Dry areas were soon vegetated, and colonisation by aquatics and marginals continued apace, facilitated by the presence of the nearby pits, river, marshes and visiting waterfowl. By the end of 1988, some 190 species of bird and almost 300 species of wild flowers, a third of which were aquatics or marginals, had been noted. Other pits have been similarly assigned as wildlife conservation areas, notably by Redland Aggregates Limited.

At Amwell submerged aquatics include Canadian and Nuttall's Waterweeds, Spiked and Whorled Water-milfoil, Hornwort, Fan-leaved Water-crowfoot, Horned Pondweed and Broad-leaved Pondweed. Also found have been the particularly scarce and difficult to identify Small Pondweed *Potomageton berchtoldii*, Hair-like Pondweed *P. trichoides* and Lesser Pondweed *P. pusillus*. Of the floating aquatics only Common Duckweed has so far been noted, but other species may well be expected in sheltered bays. Yellow Water-lily possibly arrived from the nearby river, but White Water-lily is a certain introduction. Shelving margins are typically developing reed and sedge beds with Common Reed, Lesser and Great Pond-Sedges, Reed-grass, Branched Bur-reed and Reed Sweet-grass. Stands of Great Reedmace are present and this is the county's only gravel pit site for Lesser Reedmace. Some Tussock-sedge is thriving in swampy places and Mare's-tail may almost choke some shallows. Mixed and colourful emergent communities include watercress, Fool's Watercress, Water-starwort, Water-plantain, Nodding Bur-Marigold, Water Forget-me-not, Bulrush, Yellow Iris, Common Spike-rush, Water Chickweed, Amphibious Bistort, Brooklime, Blue and Pink Water-speedwell, Marsh Yellow-cress and Water Dock. Rather scarce, and only known from one other recent site at Smallford, Sea Club-rush *Scirpus maritimus* (7–8) was possibly introduced as seeds attached to the plumage of wildfowl.

Steeper banks are too well drained to support much marginal flora, but lower lying places include a good number of wild flowers that are also found in marshes or by slow-moving rivers and canals such as, Great Hairy Willowherb, Hemp Agrimony, Meadowsweet, Purple-loosestrife, Water Mint, Indian and Orange Balsams, Common Skullcap, Ragged Robin, Wild Turnip or Bargeman's Cabbage, Sweet Flag, Golden Dock, Silverweed, Ladies-smock, Gypsywort, Greater Yellow-cress, Water-pepper, Water-Figwort, Celery-leaved Buttercup, Common and Russian Comfrey, Marsh Woundwort, Marsh Speedwell, Butterbur, Hard, Soft, Jointed, Sharp-flowered and Blunt-flowered Rushes, Tufted Hair-grass, Yorkshire Fog and Glaucous Sedge. In more mature areas, natural succession is adding, and to a degree already subtracting diversity as scrub and carr develop with Alder, willows, osiers, Guelder Rose, Woody Nightshade and other shrubs and trees.

11

Arable Fields and Hedges

In its many guises farming has had profound effects upon our more *Appendices*
1.14, 1.15, 1.16 recent landscapes – references have already been made to prehistoric and subsequent clearances to create grasslands, arable fields and settlements. Indeed, few, if any, parts of Hertfordshire have remained untouched, in some way and at some time, by farming. The progress from early subsistence arable farming to agricultural big business has resulted in a long chronicle of habitat creation and loss, species upsurge and declines. As will be shown, some of the developments responsible for ecological change have been necessary to the maintenance or increase of the living standards for rising populations; others have perhaps been based upon more dubious motives. In particular, the scale of recent changes has brought about the whole question of agriculture into the arena of international debate and concern.

From the first of the wildwood clearances some seven thousand years ago, farmers have had to battle against 'nature'. Whenever and wherever land is broken for cultivation, a whole range of plants and animals is ready to exploit the new open habitats and compete with and for whatever crop is cultivated. A substantial group of wild flowers, the arable weeds, is completely dependent upon regularly cultivated land having adapted to need in open, disturbed conditions. For thousands of years, firstly by hand but more recently – and vastly more effectively – with the aid of potent chemicals, farmers have waged war against forms of wildlife that they perceive, correctly or otherwise, to affect the quality or productivity of their crops. Although some are perennials or biennials, most arable weeds are annuals or overwintering herbs. Weeds can be damaging to crops in several ways; if they are tall enough their shade reduces the amount of sunlight reaching the crop plants, and so reduces their yields; the roots of weeds reduce the amount of soil that a crop can exploit by using up water and soil nutrients; some weeds harbour pests and diseases of cultivated plants; some cause mechanical problems, for example by hindering tilling and harvesting, (restharrows derive their name from the action of their long, wiry roots in restricting the passage of harrow or plough through the soil) and some noxious species can render crops impure or even poisonous.

There is no doubt that many arable weeds must be regarded as highly successful colonisers, at least until comparatively recently. Many seem tolerant of a fairly wide range of environmental conditions. One factor responsible for the great success of many species is fruiting capacity; prodigious numbers of small, light seeds are produced, these are readily distributed by wind and, until more recent times, slipped through agricultural screening systems. A single plant of Groundsel may produce over a thousand fruits; for Mayweed the total may be over fifteen thousand, for Red Poppy nearly twenty thousand and for Prickly

Sowthistle up to twenty-five thousand. Many species have fruiting organs specially adapted to aid dispersal. Although small, seeds of a number of arable weeds are remarkably long-lived, sometimes with the capacity to remain buried for decades until the right conditions for germination occur. Other weeds have a great ability to reproduce vegetatively, even regenerating from small pieces chopped-up during cultivation. Nature's regenerative vigour, it seems, is still a match for today's most potent agricultural chemicals, although almost unimaginable losses have been incurred. Most arable fields today, given a respite from herbicides, would soon develop a respectable weed flora, although a good number of attractive and formerly widespread species would be missing, but without cultivation arable areas soon show signs of natural succession towards scrub and woodland or, if grazed, develop low-growing species associated with grasslands.

From very early times, boundaries of some form or another inevitably became intimately associated with developing agriculture. At first, these were probably earth banks or brushwood piled around margins of small fields to keep out wild animals or stock. Later, more permanent boundaries were constructed in the form of ditches, banks and live hedges, some of which survive as important features in the landscape today, for example as parish or estate boundaries. Less elaborate structures were probably used for minor demarcations, for example the narrow grassy baulks that separated the cultivation strips characteristic of mediaeval times. Nevertheless, all were important and often long-term features of the countryside, and provided diverse wild flower habitats. Although farming techniques and landscape 'planning' in the past two centuries or so have radically altered most of the Hertfordshire countryside, it is still possible to find traces of former farmscape patterns and glimpses of the past richness of arable wildlife.

Archaeologists have shown that, from about 3500 B.C., the human population of Britain underwent a fundamental sociological change, from a rather nomadic, hunting and gathering, way of life to what was to become a more settled existence, based largely upon cultivation and pastoral farming. These changes were initiated by the Neolithic farmers, who, on entering Hertfordshire, initially moved north-eastwards by way of the Chalk escarpment and later advanced up the major river valleys. Areas of wildwood were cleared for cattle, sheep and pigs and for the growing of primitive cereals such as oats, barley and wheat. Evidence suggests that at first a good many settlements may have been transient; once the soils were exhausted of nutrients, especially on sands, gravels, Clay-with-Flints and Chalk, they were abandoned and new fertile plots opened up from the wildwood. Abandoned fields soon reverted to tree cover and it is possible that some places went in and out of cultivation several times in these early centuries. Where grazing stock was retained, tree regeneration was inhibited and it was here that the semi-natural grasslands developed. It is probable that in a number of places, on deeper richer soils, such as those below the Chalk escarpment and on some of the clays of the dip slope, more permanent and expanding Neolithic settlement occurred. The full extent of forest clearance by this first wave of farmers may never be known, although it is possible that it may have been quite extensive with, at least, relatively open patterns of grazing land and small square or rectangular fields on much of the Chalk escarpment, its immediate environs and in some of the river valleys, long before the arrival of further settlers in the Bronze Age between 2000 and 650 B.C. Some quite steep slopes were also cultivated to produce distinct topographical features, termed lynchets, that are still visible in a few places today. Here cultivation across steep slopes accelerated solifluction downslope and loosened soil, over hundreds of years, piled up against a lower boundary or another cultivated strip to form the sharp breaks in slope. Sometimes these cultivated terraces were in groups of narrow fields, shown as 'strip lynchets' on maps, although not all are of very early origins and some it is thought may have grown grape vines for local production of wines, perhaps in Roman or mediaeval times.

As settlers moved from place to place, they carried stocks of cereal seeds to plant in the new fields, but amongst the crop seeds there would also have been transported seeds of other species, many originating in the ancestral continental homelands. So started the spread of arable weeds. Seeds of other species, formerly limited to sea cliffs, screes, shingle banks, dunes, river gorges and other open habitats, were blown in by the wind or dispersed by birds, and these too readily colonised the newly exposed farmlands. Godwin (1975) provides some succinct accounts of the patterns of change of the British flora and demonstrates the relationship between wildwood clearances and the arrivals of weeds and other ruderal species. His evidence, obtained particularly from contemporary peat deposits, shows that there were many weeds present before Neolithic times including the following species:

Parsley-piert, Rosebay Willowherb, 'Mouse-ear Chickweed', Creeping and Spear Thistles, Sun Spurge, Goosegrass, Toadflax, Scentless Mayweed, Ribwort and Great Plantains, Creeping Buttercup, several docks, Chickweed, dandelions, Coltsfoot, Field Pansy, Bladder Campion and Perennial Sowthistle

These were probably part of the native flora residing in habitats noted above and, no doubt some had long been present in open and disturbed patches amongst the wildwood, readily spreading into places laid bare by gales or fires. Early hunters and game would also have inadvertently carried some seeds during their wanderings. Studies of Neolithic deposits reveal a great upsurge in the relative amounts and diversity of arable weed pollen and other remains, together with some significant changes, particularly reductions, in remains of some forest species. Notable are many previously unrecorded weeds, evidence of introductions by the steadily increasing farming populations. Further introductions and increases have been detected throughout the Bronze and Iron Ages with the establishment of species such as

Common or Field Poppy, Common Fumitory, Wild Turnip, Charlock, Corn Spurrey, further docks, Mugwort, Black Medick, Red Deadnettle, Agrimony, Small Nettle, Fat Hen, hawkweeds, Oxtongue, Black-bindweed, Prickly Sow-thistle, Field Madder, Cornflower, White Campion, sandwort, Barren Brome and False Oat-grass.

127

Evidence suggests that during the Bronze Age not inconsiderable areas of Hertfordshire were patchworks of rectilinear field systems increasingly associated with hamlets and farms, with some domesticated stock maintained close to the settlements, arable fields on the outer margins, and the wildwood beyond. At the start of the Iron Age, about 650 B.C., much of the chalkland was under some form of agriculture and probably quite extensively cultivated on gentler slopes. Interpretation from surviving archaeological features, such as hillforts, and other evidence is increasingly suggesting a relatively high and well-organised contemporary human population. Development of iron-tipped ploughs may have made only marginal differences to cultivation on lighter soils but considerably eased breaking fallow or cultivation of newly cleared lands on some of the heavier clays.

It is difficult adequately to assess the extent to which the county had been settled and cultivated by the time of the Roman annexation of Britain in A.D. 43. It seems likely, that on the wetter heavy soils of Boulder Clay and London Clay at least, considerable tracts of wildwood remained with scattered remnants elsewhere. Roman occupation, with its military and social organisation, establishment of towns and networks of communications and improved farming techniques, especially heavy ploughs, brought some sweeping changes to the landscape. In places, Romans occupied and developed former Iron Age sites. Over centuries, there is some evidence of integration of the two races but also, that the native British population, although dependent upon the Roman economy, retained much of their own culture. There was expansion into, apparently, previously unoccupied areas. Agriculture flourished to supply local and increasing export markets, particularly with wool and cereals. Further extensive incursions were made into the wildwood, which itself was becoming increasingly managed; as Munby (1977) suggests, 'it is impossible to make any precise and comprehensive calculation of the full extent of Roman settlements in Hertfordshire, but it would be unwise to underestimate it'. Probably little more than 30 per cent of the county remained wooded, with the bulk of the woodland situated on the heavy clays and more acid soils of the east and south; indeed some of the woodland in the south was perhaps regenerated on once-cleared lands.

Much of the Roman countryside was a pattern of many small, squarish arable fields and pastures, farmsteads (villas), copses and small woods. Although many aspects of forest wildlife were in decline, plants and animals of open habitats flourished. Movements of garrison forces and supplies, especially from Europe, inadvertently or deliberately introduced or spread a great many new plants – weeds, adventives, cultivated herbs and garden plants – including

Greater Celandine, Opium and other poppies, Garlic Mustard, Corn Marigold, Woad, Goosefoot, Common Mallow, restharrows, vetches, Hemlock, Pignut, Ground-elder or Goutweed, Swine-cress, Deadly Nightshade, Betony, Henbane, Burdock, Field Gromwell, Goat's-beard, Hairy and Small-flowered Buttercups, sow-thistles, Scarlet Pimpernel, White Mustard, Flax, Walnut, Hemp, Fennel, and Radish.

Arguably, wildlife was possibly richer than at any other time, before or since, and it is difficult to imagine the tremendous diversity of plants and animals of forests, marshes, waterways, downland, flowery meadows and arable fields, perhaps bounded by living hedges.

Social unrest in Europe threatened the Roman Empire and, in A.D. 410, legions were withdrawn from Britain. For centuries before, small waves of northern Europeans, the Jutes, Angles and Saxons, had been forcibly or more passively infiltrating Britain, often intermingling with a declining British population and, at times, battling against Roman forces. The departure of the Romans left a power vacuum which was to be filled by the Anglo-Saxons and, later, in some parts of Britain, by Danes. Native British populations, economically devastated by the loss of Roman exports and organisation, were apparently easily dominated by the relatively few but powerful newcomers. In comparison with the rich archaeological heritage of the Romano-British times, remains relating to the six centuries of Saxon occupation are generally scarce and the period is popularly referred to as 'The Dark Ages'. However, continuing historical research is beginning to piece together a clearer picture of Saxon life, showing the many tribal conflicts, serious outbreaks of plague, new techniques in farming and significant developments in estate tenure and management.

Without the Roman markets at home and abroad and with some depopulation caused by outbreaks of disease, probably bubonic plague transmitted to humans via fleas carried on the native Black Rat, some arable lands became derelict, at least for a time. Scattered farmsteads and some larger settlements were abandoned, a number to disappear completely from the countryside beneath scrub and woodland. Despite these privations, it is unlikely that there was any significant increase in overall woodland cover of the county and, in general, 'Dark Age' communities flourished, with many native British peasant farmers still cultivating fields, coppicing woods and tending their cattle and sheep. Contrary to former beliefs, it now seems that early Anglo-Saxons, settling northern Hertfordshire, re-used some of the Romano-British sites, boundaries of their hamlets, with timber and thatch huts and adjacent fields, being situated within pre-existing enclosures.

Unlike the Romans, Anglo-Saxons were not military conquerors nor colonial administrators for a distant regime. They moved to Britain in distinct groups, to create new homelands in which most of the remnants of Roman civilisation were destroyed, and bases of language, society, institutions and government of the English race and nation were established. Essentially, the early English were peoples of small communities, probably at first based upon extended families, allied through tribal affiliations to regional kingdoms which would eventually integrate the native populations. Importantly, Saxon lords defined and created significant boundaries within the landscape, many of which survive today. Many farms, estates, villages and towns have their more permanent origins in 'The Dark Ages', some created from pre-existing Romano-British sites seized or traded by Anglo-Saxon warriors. Kingdoms were divided into *shires*, each of which was sub-divided into *hundreds* – originally groups of a hundred warriors, but later units of newly emerging villages and small towns in the same areas. It seems that by late Saxon times Hertfordshire had quite a large mixed population, living a mainly settled life of simple agriculture. The six centuries of Saxon rule were not, however, free from unrest and there were periods of substantial military conflict, especially in the vicinity of Ware and Hertford where, for a time, the Lea formed the boundary between lands held by the invading Danes to the north and the Saxon Kingdom of Wessex to the south. No doubt, such conflicts caused considerable disruption and movements of peasant farmers from some areas, allowing scrub and woodland to return.

The nature of the 'Dark Age' landscape of Hertfordshire is made a little easier to assess by some of the evidence contained within the Domesday Survey carried out by the Normans between A.D. 1080 and 1086. (*See below.*) It appears that areas in the north and east were more open, with arable land and pastures, than those in the south-west. It is suggested by Cantor (1982) that south-east Hertfordshire was one of the most intensively cultivated areas of Saxon Britain and that it is likely that little change occurred before the Domesday Survey. Some Saxon documents make references to dense forests, perhaps even on the chalklands, although these are rather vague and there seems to be no differentiation between forest and thick scrub. It is conceivable, as noted above, that population dispersal, resulting from wars with the Danes and the Norman Conquest itself, led to abandonment of some lands for several decades, thus allowing scrub to mature and secondary woodland to develop. During the more settled Saxon period, it is suggested, considerably less than 30 per cent of the county was wooded, the implication being that the population was reasonably large and there were extensive tracts of tilled or grazed land. Overall, there was probably little change in the diversity of wildlife from that of Roman times, but specialised wildwood species were in decline, whilst flora and fauna of open places continued to flourish and spread.

Anglo-Saxon boundaries of all sorts from small hamlet to shire, were often well defined both in documents and by features on the ground, such as rivers, streams, valleys, ridges, tracks, old trees and large boulders, plus specifically created banks and ditches. Living hedges, planted or formed by managing strips of scrub or wood, became new aspects of the landscape. These may have been formed from bushy, thorny shrubs to mark settlements and other territorial boundaries, to aid their defence or to prevent stock animals from straying onto cultivated fields. As communities developed, needs for defensive, administrative, economic and social organisation led to networks of new trackways linking hamlets, villages and small towns. Some of these trackways may have had origins in prehistoric times, for example the Icknield Way, which is a series of more or less parallel routes, that traversed the length of the Chalk escarpment. The enduring Roman roads, which were specially constructed and surfaced directly across the landscape, with little regard for terrain, mainly to facilitate rapid movements of troops and supplies between major settlements and garrisons, were largely incorporated into the Saxon systems. Much of the broader layout of the Saxon countryside still survives in places, particularly in country lanes, footpaths, 'green lanes', estate, parish and county boundaries.

Around many settlements, Anglo-Saxons and many later generations used what is termed an open-field system for arable farming. This involved one or more larger fields being cultivated in strips, with groups of strips all running in the same direction. Individual strips were of more or less equal area, usually half or third of an acre, but local variations in length or breadth might be dictated by local topography or soils. Groups of strips were called a *furlong*. Groups of furlongs, some at right angles to others, made up the field. In some cases, there were scores of furlongs of various shapes and sizes. It is thought that most villages had two large open fields, later some added a third. Each field was traversed by various access tracks and each strip bounded by a double furrow or narrow unploughed grass baulk. Contemporary ploughs, drawn by hand or oxen, were designed to turn the soil for crop growth towards the strip centre, producing a distinctive ridged effect which aided drainage. On heavier wetter lands, strips were often directed down or obliquely across slopes to improve overall drainage. In many open-field systems, tenure and management of strips were complex, with individuals owning or tending individual or groups of strips scattered throughout the fields. Perhaps this was initially designed to ensure an even balance of good and poor land throughout the community, and it has been suggested that the system evolved in those landscapes where there was no further room for expansion. Sometimes management was further complicated as landowners contracted land to tenants and sub-tenants or employed agents to oversee their holdings. In a three-field system, each year would generally see some forms of crop rotation with two fields in cultivation and one lying fallow, probably with grazing stock to control weeds and fertilise the ground through their droppings. With a two- and especially a single-, field system, fallowing could lead to all sorts of problems with stock animals, for, if not carefully controlled, they would readily stray onto growing crops of adjacent strips.

Strip-farming was apparently suited to these early times, with relatively small Saxon communities and, later, the bound serfs who worked the land for their Norman lords and lived at bare subsistence levels. Over the following centuries, as populations rose, towns developed and demands for higher agricultural productivity and efficiency increased, open-field systems became uneconomic and were replaced by an enclosed landscape of smaller hedged fields. With little recourse to the effects upon tenants and smaller landowners, some powerful landowners and noblemen simply and callously enclosed large areas for their own estates.

Strip cultivation in open fields extended and remained an overriding landscape feature throughout many parts of Hertfordshire. In southern parts of the county its full extent is rather uncertain; it was possibly never particularly widespread or perhaps largely destroyed by 16th century or earlier enclosures. In some northern parts the system commonly survived until enclosures of the 18th and 19th centuries, a few even into the early 20th century. In parishes on the Chalk escarpment north-east of Hitchin, remnants of the large open fields can still be seen – Bygrave near Baldock is a good example. In a few places, strip cultivation has been 'fossilised' beneath grassland or in woods; often called *ridge and furrow* it is likely that most such remnants are later than Anglo-Saxon; a fine series of Tudor origin can be seen at Norton Common and at the nearby Standalone Farm Centre, in Letchworth.

As already noted, Anglo-Saxon settlements were at first small and well distributed but, in each generation, land was probably cleared. It would take many centuries for each group of settlements to reach territorial limits but permanent, clearly defined, boundaries were being etched into the landscape, such as isolated and managed woods, banks and ditches, hedged trackways and, with the aid of large teams of oxen pulling heavy ploughs, the open fields themselves. Pasture-woods and coppices were developing their distinctive wildlife and some forest plants and animals were adapting to the, as yet scarce, but increasing, hedgerow habitat. From about Saxon times onwards, much of the remains of the wildwood vanished quite quickly and there was a rapid spread of grassland and arable wild flowers. Archaeological researches indicate that the Saxons brought in a few new crops, including Rye, Hemp or Cannabis, Flax and root crops, and certainly spread many wild flowers such as Field Scabious, Corn Marigold, cat's-ears, hawkbits, Corncockle and Goosegrass.

On 14 October 1066, William, Duke of Normandy, defeated Harold, last of the English kings at Hastings. For a few weeks, despite some stiff resistance, Norman invaders continued to advance northwards, until they reached Berkhamsted. Here, led by Archbishop Aldred of London, the English submitted to Norman rule, although stubborn resistance continued in the fens of East Anglia for another decade or so. William the First was crowned in Westminster Abbey on Christmas Day 1066, and another distinctive period of English history began, one which politically united the country under one central administration, the Crown. Normans, although invaders from France, were descended from Vikings who had settled in Normandy and developed a strong feudal society with French language and customs. Despite their military strength and successful conquest, they soon adopted the English language and many basic institutions. There was a gradual integration of English and Norman cultures.

Norman society was exceedingly well organised, skilled in all its aspects and governed by strictly enforced laws. It set about imposing a European feudal system upon the whole of Britain, the basis of which involved bonds of loyalty and military service, between the King, his lords and their servants or slaves – vassals. The overriding currency of this new order was land. Many surviving English landowners were ruthlessly displaced, usually without compensation, often into virtual slavery, and replaced by Norman overlords. The King was supreme landowner and granted lands for his knights or earls to occupy. In turn, these created beneath them, hierarchies of land and manor holdings occupied by bonded lords and vassals. Primogeniture – the handing down of intact estates to eldest sons (usually) of the family – became a lasting, and still controversial, British institution. To effect this great social revolution, the Normans relied upon sheer military power, creating a network of fortified strongholds throughout the countryside, the remains of some of which still survive, for example the 'castles' at Berkhamsted, South Mimms, Pirton, Great Wymondley, Walkern, Barkway and Anstey, and many moated sites.

To carry out his objectives, King William I required knowledge of the administration and distribution of Anglo-Saxon lands. In 1080, with typical Norman efficiency and using as a model a Saxon survey carried out by King Alfred the Great, he commissioned an appraisal of all lands and properties in Britain. Completed in 1086, this survey, which became *The Domesday Book*, provides a unique record of Saxon land ownership, indications of major land management and contemporary valuations. It also gives some insight into the overall picture of Saxon landscapes. Nearly every village we know today was recorded, around which stretched two or three open fields covering a few hundred acres or more. Beyond these were, in general, pastures, coppices, pasture-woods or remnants of wildwood which might have to be crossed before the next village was encountered. Areas of 'waste' were also recorded; these were probably lands deliberately devastated by the Norman armies, temporarily out of cultivation where scrub had spread or common land with no particular ownership. In the 12th and 13th centuries significant changes were to occur in landscape and social development in Hertfordshire.

Under Norman rule, populations increased, villages and small towns expanded and trade and ancillary services began to flourish. Commerce and money became much more important, with the development of market towns along an expanding network of roads. To keep pace, agricultural production increased at the expense of woodland and marginal areas, by further cultivation of heavy clays and downland and expansion of pasture land for stock and draught animals. Again, there must have been notable influxes of plants and animals into the open habitats, whilst the few final bastions of the wildwood, although possibly still reasonably extensive in the south of the county, would be showing signs of their final demise particularly in the decline and extinction of larger mammals and birds. Rabbits, introduced by the Normans as a source of readily available food and fur, inevitably escaped from enclosures or warrens and began to impose the effects of their close grazings upon grasslands, verges and woods. There is a little evidence which suggests that, in places, parts of open-field systems were enclosed with new patterns of boundary banks, ditches or hedges to form smaller workable fields around farmsteads.

Profiting from their feudal repression of the English peasantry, the Normans developed great wealth. They built many substantially moated and fortified houses and the creation of well-wooded hunting parks (*see* Chapter 6) exacerbated hunger for land in other places. Towns began to flourish and small local industries prospered. Increasing trade brought better maintenance of highways and improved communications between major settlements. Not without trials, tribulations and some bloodshed, there was a growth of the organised Church as monastic orders established themselves in the countryside.

New monasteries and churches were built, and built more substantially, and many of their occupants set about improving the quality of everyday life. In time, the Church came to the forefront in resurgences of art, literature and education. These, together with improvements in trade and economy heralded demands from the largely oppressed population for freedom from bondage, including payment for duties, that is wages. Slowly social changes occurred; most importantly, some of the peasantry were able to buy freedom and acquire their own lands. The relative prosperity of the later 12th and 13th centuries was overshadowed by events of the 14th century which briefly halted the expanding ex-ploitation of the landscape. By the beginning of the 14th century royal taxation and currency crises were crippling much of the countryside, which itself appears to have been significantly overstretching natural resources, causing disruptions to communities. To meet the demands of increased urbanised populations, unproductive military forces and courtiers, as well as their own requirements, many rural communities were forced into cultivating marginal lands, such as those on the thin poor soils of sands, gravels and Chalk. These soon became exhausted of nutrients and crops failed. It is possible that, with a large labour force and such struggles to obtain some crop yields, arable fields received great attention, including spring and summer weeding and there may have been some diminution in local abundances of arable weeds. Living standards for subsistence farmers were pitifully low.

Between 1314 and 1325, Britain suffered such poor weather that the period is often referred to as 'The Little Ice Age'. A series of cold wet summers resulted in devastatingly poor harvests and outbreaks of disease in stock, notably an epidemic called *sheep murrain*. Compounded by a great drought in 1341, famine was widespread, and there seems to have been substantial abandonment of less productive lands. Adding to, and overshadowing, the miseries of these events were a series of plagues that swept through much of the countryside in 1348, the 1360s, 1370s and later. It is estimated that this bubonic plague – the 'black-death' – wiped out between 30 and 40 per cent of the population of England. Although this pestilence affected lords and servants alike, it was particularly rife amongst peasantry, already weakened by famine. As Rutherford Davis (1973) shows, the after-effects of famines and plagues had significant effects upon the landscape of Hertfordshire. Many settlements were totally abandoned and most were radically depopulated, especially in the longest exploited districts of north Hertfordshire, around Tring and St Albans. Black-death affected virtually every community. Inevitably some land 'tumbled down' to scrub and probably secondary woodland.

With so few to work it, land values plummeted. This soon facilitated changes in ownership and the development of new social orders. Survivors of the plagues, such as manorial officers, merchants, lawyers, churchmen, and freemen who had been able to build up capital, were able to buy land, sometimes large areas. Associated with this rediffusion of lands and wealth were cultural changes. Aspects of the underlying English civilisation began to break through. Only a few of the great Norman lords were able to hold their lands for any length of time and slowly the feudal system was abolished. New autocratic dynasties were evolving. Rather suddenly, because of acute shortage of labour, many peasants found they could command higher wages, perhaps even become wealthy enough to purchase their own lands. Waking up to the reductions in profits and potential threats to their holdings, some larger landowners reacted by reducing the extent of their cultivated or demesne lands, turning them over to pastures for sheep and cattle, or by creating systems whereby lands were leased to peasants. A new class of peasant farmers emerged, many of whom would, in time, also be rich enough to purchase lands.

Characteristic of the period were moves towards less labour-intensive, more profitable pastoral farming, reducing the extent of open fields. Almost certainly by the 15th century, Chalk downland and the acid heaths and grasslands had expanded to their fullest extent and there were many parts of Hertfordshire with patterns evolving of small hedged meadows, pastures and arable fields. A good deal of the county, especially on the heavier clay soils of the east, was to be enclosed in this way during mediaeval times, no doubt with much dealing, aggravation and ruthlessness. Wishing to set their seal upon newly acquired estates, many landowners set about building substantial residences, gardens and 'amenity' parks. After about 1450, there was a trend for the wealthier landowners throughout England to enclose large tracts of land within which strip cultivation would be replaced by more profitable sheep or cattle grazing. Peasant farmers were often cruelly evicted from their homes and fields. Sometimes most of the population of a whole parish were removed. It seems that Hertfordshire escaped much of this misery, for the proximity to developing London assured a ready market for the county's staple product – corn.

By the close of the mediaeval period much of Hertfordshire's landscape was again under arable cultivation with, away from the chalk downs and acid heaths, a good deal of small piecemeal enclosure taking place. Probably all the wildwood, *sensu stricto*, had gone by 1500, although some extensive yet well defined and managed woods, with wildwood origins, characterised southern and central parts. As in earlier times, a great number of arable weeds bedecked arable fields and, for the next four hundred years or so, were to cause endless problems for farmers, reducing yields, polluting crops and impeding cultivation. However, overall populations of many species were most likely showing some signs of reduction, as early enclosures progressed, grasslands increased and towns expanded, and populations of hedgerow wild flowers were probably further increasing.

The early 16th century saw considerable social unrest; the un-believably cruel repercussions of the Reformation had far-reaching effects; poverty and homelessness were widespread, many of the victims being dispossessed priests and monks; many estates changed hands; often, unconcerned new owners evicted tenants and peasants to extend enclosures for parkland and grazing. However, in the wake of the mediaeval disasters populations began to rise quite rapidly and, in the later 16th and early 17th centuries, the countryside was again more peaceful and contributing to a fairly stable and improving national

Plate 12 (*Top*) Once common and most troublesome, Corn Marigold *Chrysanthemum segetum* has become one of our rarer arable weeds; (*Bottom*) in recent decades, fields of Oil-seed Rape *Brassica napus* ssp. *oleifera* have become a familiar part of the landscape (near Nuthampstead)

136

Plate 13 (*Top*) Where unaffected by herbicide sprays and inappropriate cutting regimes, road verges on the Chalk support a diverse and colourful flora (Wilbury Hill, near Letchworth); (*Bottom*) This ancient 'green lane' near Austage End, Preston, retains some of the flavour of traditional countryside

137

economy. To supply its own needs and the seemingly ever-insatiable requirements of London, Hertfordshire would have had a 'busy air' about it. According to season, fields and meadows would be full of workers tilling, harvesting, hay-making, hedging, ditching, tending to stock and carting crops and materials. Others would be coppicing woods and attending to a welter of ancillary tasks, crafts and services. Wealth was brought back into the county, particularly by politicians, Court officers, merchants and courtiers, who acquired and built up estates with fine houses and landscaped parks. There were innovations in agricultural technology, and crops such as carrots, turnips, new grasses and clovers were introduced. Clover was found to be especially useful, for it enriched the soil and led to the initiation of temporary grasslands or *leys*, where arable fields could be put under grass with clover and used as pasture for a few years, then with rejuvenated soil, returned to arable, undoubtably with some losses in arable weed flora.

New parks and estates left some indelible marks on the landscape but, as mentioned above, a series of greater changes was beginning in the wider landscape, as enclosure became a more common practice. Some, possibly quite extensive, enclosures had been carried out since the 13th century and, on a small scale, earlier. From the 16th century onwards, enclosures with small fields and well managed hedges were to become more typical features of the landscape. Largely because of the dictates of local economics, early enclosure in Hertfordshire was piecemeal and most often on the fertile, corn-producing, heavy clay lands. Munby (1977) shows how careful fieldwork has revealed the relationships between ancient open-field boundaries and patterns of enclosure hedges, for example around Knebworth, Harpenden and Kings Langley. Despite the traumas of the English Civil War, when forces were recruited from largely agriculturally orientated local communities to fight for the opposing causes, enclosures continued. Again, these were generally on fertile soils where corn-growing predominated and there was little, if any, effect in those places on Chalk, sands and gravels, where sheep grazing was important. With more settled times after the Civil War, this piecemeal or manorial enclosure gathered momentum to create a very varied but increasingly 'manicured' landscape. It is evident that much of Hertfordshire was enclosed in this way, for such was its charm that 18th and early 19th century travellers and writers were moved to record such impressions as 'the garden of England for delight'; ' the beauty of this prospect'; ' – a planted garden'; 'What – under the name of pleasure-grounds, can equal these fields of Hertfordshire'; and 'a most exquisitely beautiful, cultivated, hedgerow'd Country'.

Because they probably followed pre-existing, often sinuous, boundaries, it seems that it was very much the well managed, early-enclosure hedges which produced the aesthetic beauty of the countryside. Other contemporary writers relate how hedges were carefully tended by local craftsmen; regular *plashing* (a skilled operation which involved thinning a hedge followed by selective bending down of partially cut branches and interweaving with twigs for stability) was generally undertaken on a twelve-year rotation with probably annual trimming;

this ensured the primary function of most hedges in keeping straying stock under control. But also, as in most of the resourceful countryside, the hedges full economic potential was realised, with cuttings providing fuel, fencing and some building materials and berries and nuts being harvested for food or home-made beverages. Standard trees were allowed to grow in places as timber resources.

The structure and species composition of most of the early hedges are usually more diverse than those of 18th century and later enclosures. Some may have been formed from already existing scrub or woodland, but most were planted, and, with careful regard to establishment costs and potential returns, it was prudent for landowners to create mixed hedges, using locally obtained saplings. Dependent upon soils Blackthorn, Woodland and Common Hawthorn would be selected for basic thorny, stockproof barriers. Hazel, Hornbeam, Ash and Field Maple, which layer and coppice well, might be added to provide fuel and underwood for craftsmen. Winter cattle fodder could be produced by elms which, together with oaks and Ash were frequently left to mature and felled for timber. In places, particularly central Hertfordshire, Holly is characteristic either as a main hedgerow component or as small trees standing above hedge lines – some farmers thought it unlucky to slash or lay Holly and these attractive reminders of the past remain, their current shapes very much the artifacts of local berry-gathering for Christmas decorations. Other trees and shrubs were possibly planted and many would naturally colonise the hedgerow habitats.

Older hedges, which tend to weave across the countryside are often quite thick with some, perhaps, resulting from ancient boundaries or management of strips left by woodland clearance, termed assarts, might be 12 metres across. Hedges formed in the 19th century and later seldom exceed widths of two metres, whilst those of mediaeval or Tudor age normally fall somewhere between. In general, trees are scarce in Victorian and later hedges; regularly spaced oaks and Ash are often found in hedges of Georgian age and, as noted above, are frequent as coppice or pollards in earlier examples. Species-rich hedges, especially when associated with banks, ditches, trackways sunken by centuries of traffic and old boundaries, suggest antiquity.

Throughout much of Hertfordshire it is possible to make an approximate estimate of the age of a hedge by applying a simple theory evolved by Dr Max Hooper in 1974. Although subject to some controversy, this theory is based upon the premise that older hedges are richer in species of trees and woody shrubs and that a new species is likely to invade each century. Field investigation is simple, involving no more than counting the total number of tree and woody shrub species in a 30-yard sample length of hedge. Species typical of Hertfordshire's hedges are noted in the checklist of wild flowers (*see* Appendix 1.14), but it should be remembered that, for date estimation, certain woody climbers, such as Ivy, brambles, Wild Clematis, Hop and White Bryony, should be ignored. If possible, several samples should be taken along each hedgerow. Broadly speaking, Hooper's theory states that one species of tree or woody shrub will be present in a hedge for each century of its existence; mediaeval to Saxon hedges should therefore have eight or more species, Tudor hedges five to seven and Victorian hedges one or two.

Obviously care is needed in the final interpretation of data acquired by such fieldwork; for example, acidic soils are naturally species-poor, whilst calcareous soils can be very species-rich. The field studies are best backed up by documentary research, especially detailed studies and comparisons of old maps, estate documents and enclosure and tithe awards. Nevertheless it has been demonstrated in parts of the county that Hooper's methods do allow coarse estimates of hedgerow dating and thus assist determinations of periods of enclosures.

By using documentary evidence and extensive field surveys, Gilbert Burleigh and I found a very close correlation between species diversity and the Saxon, Tudor and Victorian hedges on the Boulder Clay in Clothall parish, east of Baldock (Burleigh and Sawford, 1977). More extensive studies have shown that care must be exercised in dealing with certain kinds of hedges, for example, where hedges have been developed from scrub growth on lynchets or railway embankments, especially on naturally species-rich calcareous soils. It is quite possible to find a hedge with ten or more species of trees or woody shrubs along an abandoned railway line that has perhaps only been in existence for just over a century.

Ancient hedges, notably those that originated from woodland clearances or assarts, often preserve at least some aspects of the woodland ground flora, with species such as Bluebell, Dog's Mercury, violets, Yellow Archangel, Greater Stitchwort, Wood Anemone, Cow-wheat and Lesser Celandine among invasive hedgerow specialists like Red Campion, Wood Woundwort, Lords-and-Ladies, Garlic Mustard, Hedge Parsley and Hogweed. Tudor-enclosure hedges have significantly fewer woodland indicators and there are virtually none in the later enclosures. Many hedgerows have associated ditches which add some wetland aspects to their flora. (*See* Chapter 10.5.) Reference to the checklist of characteristic species Appendix 1.14, will reveal that the sheltered-edge habitats created by hedges are potentially very diverse. But, as will be shown, more recent trends in agriculture have resulted in great reductions in the numbers of hedges in the countryside and a widespread decline in traditional management of remaining ones, with resultant losses and changes in flora. Especially noticeable has been the eutrophication effects of agricultural chemicals promoting the considerable spread of a few vigorous hedge-bottom species such as Cow Parsley, Stinging Nettle, Goosegrass, some docks, False Oat-grass and Barren Brome.

For three centuries or so, following the black death, despite short-term sometimes violent upheavals, everyday life in the Hertfordshire countryside seems to have progressed quite gently. Up to the late 18th century new crops and farming techniques were slowly introduced. To meet the growing demands of an increasing national population and, as has been shown, to improve local agrarian economics, extensive piecemeal enclosures had been carried out in the south and west of the county. Throughout the 17th century great interest had focussed on the development and cultivation of new and improved crops, and on mechanisation and fertilisers for both farmers and market gardeners. Stock-breeding produced more specialised and productive strains of cattle, sheep and pigs. Heavy horses were replacing oxen as the power to work the land and for other haulage. Inefficient hand-broadcast seeding gave way to the mechanised seed drill invented by Jethro Tull in 1701. Apart from seeding in straight, widely spaced rows, this device, importantly, allowed cultivation and easy weeding between the rows.

Weeds were, however, to remain problematic for farmers, and many went to great lengths and employed laborious techniques to remove seeds from grain crops. One widely used technique involved winnowing the entire crop by hand, relying upon wind to carry away chaff and lighter weed seeds; after this, grain was thrown across the floor of a threshing shed using a *casting spade*; lighter seeds or *tailings* would fall nearer the thrower and could be swept away; finally the crop residue or *headings* would be sieved in meshed riddles to further separate crop from weed seeds. Although some reductions in arable weeds must have been effected by these arduous methods, contemporary accounts indicate that the arable fields were still emblazoned with an abundance of colourful and troublesome wild flowers. Mixed farming and new crop rotations were introduced. The use of a *root break*, such as turnips, instead of a rather wasteful fallow year, helped alleviate the age-old problem of providing winter feed for stock.

Many arable developments were to prove impracticable or even impossible on lands where open-field systems persisted and the new selectively bred stock could not be allowed to graze communally upon common lands. As Britain entered the Industrial Revolution cities and towns expanded, and there was an urgency, nationally, to increase food production. This would involve expansion of both arable and stock farming and radical changes in those lands where farming was inefficient, notably where strip cultivation remained in open fields. Governments of the day reacted by establishing policies that, by law, enforced enclosures of open fields and commons. In Hertfordshire this was carried out mainly by private Acts of Parliament between 1766 and the final decades of the 19th century and about 20 000 hectares, almost 12 per cent of the county, were subjected to Parliamentary Enclosure. Although there were many variations, these enclosures, in general, created distinctive patterns of fairly large rectangular fields with new, often straight, hedge-and-grassy-margined road verges, which paid little attention to the former boundaries. Typically, fields were margined with thin hedges, planted up with Common Hawthorn and occasionally trees at regular intervals. Although significantly affected by later changes, much of the landscape east of the Chalk escarpment from Pirton to Royston and Barley bears the hallmarks of 'planned' Parliamentary Enclosures. It is interesting to compare this landscape with the more irregular field margins, sinuous mixed hedges, still open greens and winding roads of the 'ancient' countryside to the south. A few places escaped enclosures; for example around Hinxworth, Bygrave and the western portion of Clothall parish, many of the large open fields, with some strip cultivation, survived until the early years of this century. In this rolling, little-hedged countryside it is still possible to gain some feeling of the openness of the mediaeval landscape, with compact villages and a few outlying farms. Straight, species-poor hedges and unfenced roads are characteristic of the later enclosures; linear conifer plantations are later additions to the landscape, serving as wind-breaks to shelter soil, crops and game birds.

Parliamentary Enclosures, especially of those areas where strip cultivation survived, were not without considerable wrangling and disputes. They were carried out under the control of the Enclosure Commissioners who, using maps specifically produced for the purpose, often parcelled up lands rather ruthlessly and redesignated them in more compact units. Sometimes this meant that landowners had to build new farmhouses or cottages for their tenants. In some places tenants were forcibly evicted as land came into new ownership, and there were instances of acute poverty and homelessness leading to a not in-significant movement of labour from the land to seek employment in the developing industrial centres. Each owner was required to enclose his new allotment of lands within a specified time, often within a year. Consequently, hundreds of miles of new ditches and hastily planted hedges were added to the landscape, usually in straight lines to conform with instructions set out in Enclosure Awards.

It was usual practice to excavate a ditch, about a metre deep and a-metre-and-a-half wide, throwing soil up to form a low bank upon which was planted one or two rows of seedling Common Hawthorn or *quickset*. Where it was necessary to protect the developing hedge from stock, temporary hurdles, post-and-rail fencing or dead brushwood fences were used. Much of the raw materials for this would have been plundered from surviving woods and copses. Quickset grew fast and within a few years could be managed to produce effective stock-proof barriers. Because of their relative youth, Georgian and Victorian Parliamentary Enclosure hedges are found to be generally poor in trees and woody shrubs, seldom with more than one to four species per 30-yard length. Associated hedgerow flora is also often of low diversity, especially in terms of woodland elements, although in places, for example where a hedge has been created on former calcareous grassland, flora may still be quite rich. Most later hedges are thin and narrow-banked, if banked at all, and lack evidence of coppicing. However, their widespread addition to the landscape allowed for a great expansion of the invasive, sheltered margin species noted above. In suitable places, aquatic and freshwater-margin wild flowers occupied ditches, including elements of headwater, marsh and wet grassland species. (*See the relevant chapters.*)

Away from northern Hertfordshire, much of the landscape had been enclosed prior to the 17th century and Parliamentary Enclosure was mainly directed towards relatively small areas of common grazing (manorial waste) and woodland. As detailed above (Chapter 9.5) some extensive tracts of 'waste' escaped enclosure, largely on account of their underlying, agriculturally poor, soils. These remain as the 'commons' for example about Wheathampstead, Harpenden, Aldbury, Berkhamsted and Kings Langley.

By the end of the 19th century and out of centuries of change, the basis of Hertfordshire's continuing farmscape and distribution of wildlife had

Figure 11.1 *Large, intensively cultivated fields occupy much of the Chalk of northern and western Hertfordshire (Wilbury Hill, near Letchworth)*

been laid. At that time, because of the survival of many facets of the past together with more recently developed habitats, there was considerable landscape variety and wildlife diversity. Three major rural types would have been distinguishable, the hedged, larger, open fields of the north-east, the commons of the west and, in between, the 'ancient' countryside of small fields, sinuous hedges and narrow lanes. Economic and social deveopments were beginning to bite more deeply into the rural landscape. Out of the industrial boom, population growth, expanding towns, new railways, roads and canals of the 19th century came yet further needs to improve agricultural efficiency. Man and animal power were gradually to be replaced, first by steam and later by petrol-, and diesel-propelled machinery. New crops and strains were continually being developed and introduced. The more recent increases in bright yellow Oilseed Rape can hardly have escaped notice, but many other, older, crop changes have been less detectable. Cultivation regimes changed, as did technologies, many of which had more than small effects upon arable wild flowers; for example, at the end of the 19th century, threshing machines were developed that winnowed chaff from grain, at the same time removing lighter seeds of weeds. Chemical fertilisers and, later, herbicides and pesticides became part of everyday farming to ensure greater crop yields. Hedges were removed and grasslands ploughed to create the patterns of larger fields, in which the bigger more powerful machines could operate efficiently, that dominate much of today's farmscape. Agriculture itself has become 'industrialised' with 'factory farming' and highly efficient 'production lines'. The impact of mid- to late 20th century farming has been overwhelmingly severe on landscape and wildlife although, as so often in the past, lucrative to many of its exponents. As has already been shown again and again, many wild flower habitats have been and continue to be destroyed or degraded as a result of agriculture, including the arable lands themselves.

It is likely that, until the beginning of the 20th century, the overall diversity of arable weed species had increased quite considerably since Roman and Anglo-Saxon times. Over the centuries some species were lost, some reduced in their distribution but many others gained. The beauty of 19th century cornfields was frequently described in contemporary literature, depicted in paintings and recorded by the county's early botanists. Reference to the early county floras, Webb and Coleman (1843), and Pryor (1887), will reveal that many now rare or extinct wild flowers of arable lands were then quite common and widespread, including Corncockle, Cornflower, Common Gromwell, restharrows, Great Dodder, Night-flowering Catchfly, Mousetail, Corn Buttercup, Corn Marigold, Thorow-wax, Great Pignut, Shepherd's-needle, Venus's Looking-glass, Spreading and Knotted Hedge-parsley, Annual Larkspur, Round- and Sharp-leaved Fluellen, Corn Bedstraw, Darnel and other grasses. (*See* Appendices 1 and 2.) As outlined above, many of these were, throughout history, serious pests and troublesome to cultivation. Added to the native species were, during the 19th century and until comparatively recently, a wide range of foreign weeds from many parts of the world, although seldom were these of more than local interest. These aliens arrived via the wool waste or *grey shoddy* which some farmers annually applied to fields as a slow-acting organic manure. Although treated with hot alkali and dilute suphuric acid prior to application, shoddy still contained many viable seeds and a good number of, albeit usually temporary, new species were added to the county lists. This practice gradually ceased with the development of chemical fertilisers, which together with improved seed-screening techniques, herbicides and cultivation regimes have so effectively eliminated or reduced the arable weed flora. Some aliens are still found occasionally as a result of imported grain being badly screened; others are inadvertently introduced in imported seed stocks sold for wild bird food; yet a third source of aliens is so-called 'wild flower mix' seed. Occasionally, such seed may also contain some of what are now our rarer wild flowers and care has to be exercised in the acceptance of records that may have their origin in such circumstances.

Since the Second World War and the introduction of highly intensive agricultural practices, arable wild flowers have been declining at an unprecedented rate, even such persistent species as Charlock, poppies, Scentless Mayweed, Goosegrass, Wild Oat and Barren Brome, although still widespread and common, have shown signs of considerable declines in general abundance. Potent, once somewhat indiscriminate but now more selective, weedkillers have exacted a tremendous toll. Some species have been ousted as the chemical balances of soils have been altered, usually towards increased alkalinity, from frequent, often excessive, applications of lime and mineral fertilisers. Years of stubble-burning must also have had effects upon soil chemistry and destroyed vast quantities of weed seeds. The scale of change in the countryside, particularly that of arable cultivation, has had significant impact upon the public image of farmers, to some extent overshadowing the considerable efforts and expenditure that some farmers and landowners put into caring for their landscape and wildlife. As we have seen, farming has grown from the day-to-day subsistence support of individual families and small communities to long-term provision for a highly populated industrial nation with international requirements and obligations. Without many exceptions, farmers and landowners have had to enter the world of business and ensure profit from their capital investment. This of course is land, and aims have more recently been very much directed or even forced towards maximum returns from this investment – hence most of those landscape changes and wildlife losses so much regretted by naturalists.

It seems, with hindsight, that at least a significant proportion of these changes and losses could and should have been avoided. Some environmental disasters, such as the long-term effects of certain agricultural chemicals, were perhaps unforeseeable accidents, and it is easy to apportion blame to farmers for being mercenary in their approach to quick profits, although, in some instances, these were dictated or facilitated by, now questionable, national and international policies and actions. Naturalists and conservationists could be blamed for not studying and realising the full extent of the changes that were taking place and for not organising their forces to voice and act upon their concerns. It is the role of the conservationist, (and this should include everyone with concern over the environment in which they themselves live), to maintain as great a 'natural' diversity as possible, to ensure not only the survival of rare species but also that common species remain common. To achieve this goal obviously requires maintenance and management across the whole spectrum of wildlife habitats, a task which falls heavily upon landowners and farmers, who, of course, may justly expect sympathetic national policies and incentives and full co-operation from conservationists. Although little of the past is likely to be recaptured, there is still much that can be done to save and improve what remains, especially if the motivation and incentives from central and local government are compatible with the increasing general environmental awareness and public concern to maintain our 'natural' heritage.

Recent land-use analyses show that just over half the total area of Hertfordshire is under intensive arable cultivation and dominated by large fields. From the checklists of arable wild flowers (*see* Appendix 1.15), it can be seen that a good number of species can still be found in the county but in most fields these are confined to narrow field margins, and corners too awkward for cultivation where chemical sprays and stubble-burning are least effective. Occasionally, possibly through long-buried seeds being brought to the surface by deep ploughing, or, more probably, as a result of uneven herbicide application or the use of poorly screened seed stock, there may temporarily be a good display of arable weeds; some less well-kept local authority allotments are also

145

Figure 11.2 *Arable field margin on the Boulder Clay, with Field Bindweed, Common Marrow, Common Toadflax and Pineappleweed*

havens for these wild flowers. A field hazed red with poppies or dotted golden with Corn Marigold may reflect these circumstances and give impressions of past landscapes that many of us yearn for but know to be an impossible dream. Now enlightened, most people would savour such sights, accepting their transience, but all should direct their attention towards ensuring that the species concerned, in these and all other habitats, do not disappear. Already this century, about twenty species of arable weeds have become extinct (*see* Appendix 2), a good number are on the verge of local extinction and all but a few show signs of considerable decline. (*See* checklist of arable rarities, Appendix 1.16.) To some, it may seem an anathema to propose the establishment of arable weed 'reserves', but there is a very real need and many species are as much a part of the county's heritage as the orchids of the downs or spring flora of coppiced woods.

There is a glimmer of hope in some recent and potentially far-reaching developments linked with Britain's membership of the European Community. Because of the wine 'lakes' and grain and butter 'mountains', that is over-production in some spheres of agriculture, the European Community announced in June 1987 a range of measures to reduce and rationalise productivity amongst the farmers of Europe, notably in cereals and beef. In turn, it is said, the cost of the Common Agricultural Policy, to the Community and to the taxpayer would be reduced. To effect these measures, member states would be expected to initiate schemes encouraging less intensive farming – *extensification* – or take lands out of production – *set-aside*.

These directives could involve large areas of land, and their implementation is still in its infancy; individual landowners will employ different solutions, which may or may not be conducive to wildlife conservation. It seems that extensification has the potential to reduce the extremely high rate of loss in semi-natural habitats on farmland that have occurred since the 1940s, but, as always, with a close regard to economics some farmers are already reacting against the spirit of the policies by replacing cereals and cattle with new regimes such as increased sheep grazing on newly created grass leys and Red Deer farming and Flax, Sunflower and Evening Primrose cultivation. Others are considering or developing alternative land uses including recreation and forestry. Set-aside, which appears to be finding some favour in Hertfordshire, with whole fields or wide margins – *headlands* – being taken out of intensive cultivation, pastures less heavily grazed or fertilised and hedges allowed to develop, possibly offers more benefits for wildlife conservation. Through early, positive and organised consultations between the conservation movement and farmers and landowners, and with planning and perhaps some financial compensation, many existing places of wildlife interest and importance can be preserved and improved. Some set-aside areas could have a special wildlife conservation interest created within them. It is possible that reductions in cultivation will have a deleterious effect upon arable weeds, although there may be ways of ensuring 'planned' ploughing of certain set-asides or of creating the much needed 'arable weed reserves' noted above.

Extensification and set-aside may perhaps be only temporary expedients related to European crop demands and it is still uncertain whether any long-term benefits will accrue from them, particularly in landscape and wildlife. Some unsprayed, fallow headlands are showing signs of an improving arable weed flora although not infrequently a number of wild flowers have been introduced to provide food for game birds. It is virtually certain, however, that we shall never again see whole cornfields ablaze with colourful arrays of arable wild flowers unless these have been deliberately introduced into soils unadulterated by chemicals and where old cultivation techniques are practised without regard for possible profits, at least from the crop. But what an attraction this could be! Perhaps, somewhere in the expanding 'leisure and interpretation' industry, there will emerge someone prepared to initiate such a project, which would not only reveal much about the everyday heritage of the past but also significantly aid wildlife conservation!

Figure 11.3 *With far reaching agricultural changes, many arable fields may be set-aside as wildlife fallow, converted to grasslands or developed for income-generating leisure pursuits such as golf courses (near Puckeridge)*

12

Wild Flowers of Trackways, 'Green Lanes' and Road Verges

Well defined game trails, as well as a variety of other trackways, would *Appendix* have been significant, sometimes enduring, features of the prehistoric *1.17* wildwood. As has been suggested in earlier chapters, the first nomadic hunters would have used these as part of their day-to-day lives, following the herds of game animals, periodically encamping by major trails and penetrating the wildwood along minor tracks in search of their quarry. No doubt some routes became increasingly used and certain places traditional camp sites, although most evidence of this has long disappeared. Archaeological evidence from Mesolithic times, about 10 000 to 4500 B.C., indicates some trading, in stone tools and weapons and probably also food and animal skins, between small and scattered human groups. This suggests some early forms of settlement, communication and supply networks, possibly more sophisticated than yet realised. Certainly, during the following Neolithic times, evidence reveals the development of more permanent and enlarging settlements with, probably, major and minor trackways through the wildwood linking many corners of Hertfordshire. There is no real evidence that allows a full interpretation of the nature of such tracks, but they were presumably unmetalled, grassy or muddy swathes flanked in most places by dense forest. From other parts of Britain, archaeological investigations have shown that wooden structures were laid down to facilitate the crossing of extensive marshy areas. These pioneering routes were ideal for the colonisation and spread of open-ground and grassland wild flowers.

Discoveries of artifacts, particularly stone tools and weapons, from Neolithic sites indicate quite advanced levels of trading between settlements in many parts of Britain, and possibly also Europe. Despite many later changes, archaeologists and historians consider that the general alignments of many of these trade routes survived in long-distance highways, some even perpetuated in modern roads. One such example, now known as 'The Icknield Way' and probably the most ancient track system in the county, follows the line of the Chalk escarpment from Royston to Tring, and linked Norfolk with south-west England. Mainly traversing dry open downland, between wetter thickly forested soils of Gault Clay and Boulder Clay, The Icknield Way would have been a wide series of more or less parallel trackways. Lower routes, for example that stretch, now known as 'Ashwell Street' from Melbourn in Cambridgeshire through Ashwell, thence westwards to Radwell and Ickleford, provided easier passage in summer and autumn. Higher routes, although often steeper and more tortuous, were considerably drier in winter and spring. The vast amounts of archaeological evidence

149

attest to the long-term importance of these routes, but it must not be assumed that other major track systems were absent in the Neolithic. Increasingly, there is a realisation that Neolithic settlements of some substance were scattered across Hertfordshire, with links to The Icknield Way and other contemporary tracks, some perhaps surviving in the complex of lanes which pattern today's countryside.

One of the best remaining stretches of The Icknield Way can be seen to the north of Lilley, where it passes over Telegraph Hill and for a while forms the county boundary with Bedfordshire. For centuries its margins were flanked by Chalk downland, and some good relics of this flora may still be seen, especially at Telegraph Hill. Here generations of foot, hooved and, later, wheeled traffic have deeply incised into the soft Chalk to create an attractive 'hollow-way'. As will be shown below, such relics of former and once widespread habitats, especially grasslands, once typified most highway, and railway, verges, although more recent changes are obscuring or destroying them. Even on this section of The Icknield Way, which in view of its historical and wildlife importance is probably Hertfordshire's premier heritage site, overgrowth from scrub is threatening to destroy some of the flora. Lower down the hill, especially towards the Hitchin to Barton-le-Clay road, boundaries to the track can be seen with banks and, now unkempt, tall species-rich hedges containing some interesting wild flowers, notably extensive colonies of the low-growing Moschatel, which, together with some other woodland species, is indicative of antiquity.

Well before the Roman invasions, Hertfordshire is likely to have been well endowed with fairly comprehensive systems of major and minor trackways, linking settlements, providing access to woods and fields and facilitating the transport of all manner of goods. As Rackham (1986) demonstrates, some parts of the population may have been particularly mobile – he cites itinerant pedlars and strings of working pack horses. Invention of iron-tyred wheels in the Iron Age allowed long-distance transportation of heavy timber and building stones, with some early bridge construction and, no doubt where necessary, surfacing and maintenance of roads. Conquering Romans adopted, improved and added to this road system. Significantly, they imposed long, characteristically more or less straight highways upon the landscape, linking strategic garrisons or settlements by the shortest possible routes along which soldiers and military supplies could be rapidly moved. Paying little heed to terrain or land ownership, and expertly surveyed by military engineers, these, and some of the improved Iron Age routes, further opened up access for future settlements. Some forged lasting major highways that still link London and the north.

Where necessary, major and possibly some minor Roman roads, were metalled with locally obtained materials such as gravel or Chalk, from small pits, new features in the landscape. With organisation typical of the Roman occupation, upkeep of roads was strictly assigned by state and local legislation to contractors and landowners. The new roads were typified not only by their straightness, but also by their construction, many, though not all consisting of an *agger* – the raised bank bearing the metalled road – margined by two ditches; widths ranged from a few metres to thirty metres or so across. Unless avoidable by short detours, difficult terrain was crossed by bridges, specially constructed fords, cuttings and embankments. The open ground created along these roads soon attracted weeds and grassland wild flowers, and no doubt helped the wider establishment of species the Romans themselves introduced from Europe, for example sowthistles, vetches, Corn Marigold, Scarlet Pimpernel, Common Mallow. (*See* Chapter 11.) Large numbers of domestic stock, including cattle, sheep, goats, pigs and geese, would have been herded along these roads, and their grazing, together with that of cavalry and pack horses, would have led to the establishment of grassy verges. In places, beyond the bounds of the highway, relicts of wildwood or developing scrub might have been managed to form hedges marking estate or field boundaries.

As Munby (1977) showed, the Romans occupied many existing Iron Age sites as well as founding a wide range of new settlements throughout Hertfordshire. Complexes of roads linked important administrative and military centres, notably Verulamium (St Albans) and London, particularly by way of Akeman Street, Ermine Street, The Great North Road and Watling Street. Larger communities developed around major crossroads, for example Braughing on the intersection of Stane Street and Ermine Street, Baldock where Stane Street joins The Icknield Way and Tring at the crossing of The Icknield Way and Akeman Street.

Reference to Ordnance Survey maps will show that many of these early roads remain in the landscape, sometimes as parts of much altered major trunk roads, sometimes just as footpaths or in the form of bridleways, byways and roads now used as public paths, some of which are generally referred to as 'green lanes'. Once perhaps busy traffic routes, green lanes have, for various reasons, not been incorporated into the more recent metalled road systems and, in certain cases, remain as historical 'monuments', giving an insight into past landscapes as well as providing excellent wildlife habitats. There are fine stretches, of Roman origin, to be found near Ardeley, Clothall and Hertford Heath, although the flora and fauna have changed considerably since the withdrawal of regular traffic, especially stock movements, and extensive lengths have been invaded by shrubs, trees and elements of woodland ground flora. Inevitably, through the centuries, stretches of even important Roman roads have been lost, particularly during the relatively recent expansion of arable farming. With careful fieldwork, it is however possible still to detect the lines of some routes. For example, the Roman road from Great Chesterford, in Cambridgeshire, to Braughing remains quite clear until just inside Hertfordshire, near Brent Pelham. Then virtually all traces have been destroyed by ploughing, except through part of Great Hormead Park, an ancient wood, where a substantial agger survives and upon which subtle differences in woodland flora can be determined. These variations perhaps relate to original soil disturbance, although more likely they are indicative of the use of the highway over centuries.

As new and enlarged settlements came into being, so existing highways were improved and new ones created to meet their local and regional needs. There is ample evidence to suggest that in later Anglo-Saxon times, at least, many highways were adequately maintained and capable of carrying relatively high volumes of traffic. Long strings of pack horses were used to pull quite large wagons, or transport heavy materials such as timber, building stones, ironwork and loads of grain, as well as more fragile everyday items like pottery or foodstuffs, not just across Hertfordshire but also to most parts of the country. With the wildwood diminishing, patterns of minor lanes were added to the landscape, linking outlying farmsteads to towns and villages and providing access to fields and woods. It is probable that, as suggested by Rackham (1986), nearly all woods, commons, meadows, houses, barns, fields and furlongs had access for vehicles. Also, innumerable other rights of way and footpaths criss-crossed the countryside. To mark boundaries and inhibit trespass, from both humans and stock, banks, ditches and hedges slowly became an integral part of the roadside landscape. The permanence of roads and lanes, from Saxon times onwards, is testified by their increasing usage as definitive land boundaries in official documents. The serpentine nature of present country roads and lanes may often be traceable back to circuitous meanderings between Saxon land holdings. Following Roman precedents, the care of roads was for centuries vested in a variety of public and private authorities; manorial courts were particularly concerned with local maintenance, such as ditch-clearance, removal of obstructions, hedge-trimming, surfacing, bridge-mending, ownership, minor realignments and encroachments onto the highway. Increasingly, small pits were opened up to provide local materials for surfacing and repairs.

Road improvements and modifications were undertaken over the centuries to cope with increased traffic. Major highways were widened so that horse-drawn wagons and coaches could pass each other and roadside facilities, such as inns, coaching houses and stock folds, established for the convenience of travellers. Wayside inns, sometimes seemingly out of place and isolated on country roads, or unnecessarily abundant along the trunk roads of today, were vital staging-posts for rest and refreshment when travel was considerably slower and certainly less comfortable than it is today. Along certain stretches of the highway, widths of verges were defined by the Crown, sometimes in an attempt to reduce the nefarious activities of highwaymen. King Edward I stipulated that, where the 'King's road' passed through a wood, trees and bushes must be cut down for sixty feet on either side; other statutes ordered similar clearances of up to two hundred feet or the construction of marginal trenches to improve safety of travellers between market towns. The remains of some of these measures can still be found along certain roads.

Despite the far-reaching effects of the Reformation, with dissolution of the monasteries in the 1530s, great changes in land tenure and recorded declines in highway management in the 16th and 17th centuries, road transport continued to increase, with considerable innovations in the public carriage of goods and passengers. Highway verges flourished, now, often, as well established grasslands reflecting much of the flora of adjacent meadows, pastures, downs and heaths, grazed and fertilised by passing stock and draught animals. Many weeds were also present in disturbed and rutted places. To avoid conflict with increased and faster-moving traffic, to circumnavigate towns or, later, to evade tolls, certain minor trackways were used as *drove roads*, along which slow-moving and often large herds of stock could be driven to new farms or major markets. Often with wide grassy margins for grazing, patterns of drove roads stretched for long distances across the countryside until quite recent times. Geese, bound for London from Norfolk, were once herded through eastern Hertfordshire. A sunken track across the eastern part of Therfield Heath, apart from once carrying countless wagon loads of barley to Royston, for the malting of 'Royston Fine Ales', also saw the passage of, probably, hundreds of thousands of sheep and cattle on their way to Royston Market; in 1916 over 24 000 animals used this route for what was possibly their last journey. Throughout history, the open, disturbed nature of track and roads encouraged the spread and colonisation of weeds. Seeds and fruits would be widely distributed by muddy hooves or wheels or by attachment to fur and clothing as well as blown in by wind. Even into the early 20th century, most roads had loose, dusty or muddy surfaces, and, as depicted in many contemporary paintings and photographs, were characterised by colonies of weeds, flowery verges and well maintained hedges.

It is evident that there were not inconsiderable rigours associated with long-distance and even local travel in the 17th and 18th centuries. The neglect of roads, noted above, and the fact that each parish was generally responsible for the, apparently time-consuming and expensive, upkeep of its own roads, brought matters to a point where Parliamentary intervention was necessary. Acts were passed with the intention of achieving planned and radical improvements, many of which have formed the basis of modern communications. Together with the navigations, the later railways, industrial and urban expansions, increases in arable farming and greater social changes, these developments have ultimately combined, as will be shown, to all but destroy the beauty and richness of the once traditional Hertfordshire road verge.

From 1663, particular stretches of major roads, which now form much of the main or A-road system, were designated as *turnpikes* and put into the hands of registered Turnpike Trusts. These bodies had reponsibilities for the acquisition of lands for road improvements and, for management, and powers to erect gates and levy tolls upon users. *Turnpikers* set about road-surfacing, realigning sharp bends, reducing steep gradients and establishing milestones. Progress was generally slow and not without a good deal of racketeering and despite the changes, there are many contemporary accounts vilifying the often atrocious conditions of turnpikes, which largely resulted from increasing volumes of traffic. Iron-wheeled mail coaches and heavy wagons, pulled by teams of up to eight heavy horses, would have caused considerable rutting, especially in wet seasons. In 1725 Daniel Defoe related how the course of The Great North Road between Baldock and Stevenage was so bad that travellers actually left the road, by courtesy of local farmers who strategically placed gates and men to collect voluntary payments, and travelled across fields to avoid mud and holes so deep that 'no horse could wade through'.

Between 1712 and 1769, fifteen different Turnpike Trusts were set up in Hertfordshire, administering most of the contemporary main roads. Eventually, they brought considerable improvements for traffic, but not without the loss of significant stretches of what would have been ancient and, presumably, botanically interesting verges. New cuttings and embankments to a degree compensated for this loss but, along the major routes, the passage of grazing animals would have been much reduced and most of the control of overgrowth would subsequently be by rabbits. During the 18th century efficient and wide-ranging stage-coach and freight-wagon services were established. These employed thousands of people, particularly in the ancillary and support services, and attracted investments which brought increased prosperity to many towns and villages. This was, perhaps, the heyday for meadows and pastures which provided hay and grazings for the great numbers of horses involved. But, as will be shown in the next chapter, the coming of the railways in the mid-19th century was rapidly to sound the death knell for both horse-drawn transport and stock-droving, and the end of these, compounded by other developments arising from the Victorian age of invention and industrialisation, not least the design and ultimate application of motor vehicles, made it inevitable that road verges would lose much of their original purpose and undergo dramatic wildlife reductions.

As shown above (Chapter 11), in those parishes affected by Parliamentary Enclosures, new roads, often ignoring former boundaries, were added to the landscape and many old roads, tracks and paths leading to the furlongs of open fields disappeared. Enclosure roads tend to be characterised by their straightness, although maps will often reveal places where one parish failed to link its lanes to those of its neighbour, with resultant kinks at parish boundaries. To link into the newly planned countryside, some old roads were realigned or narrowed – Enclosure Awards often set out detailed specifications for roads, including minimum widths. Some were quite wide, but general policy, at the close of the 18th century, was to stipulate a width of about forty feet for inter-village roads, with ditches on both sides and a paved carriageway down the centre of some twelve to fifteen feet. (Despite this stipulation most roads remained unsurfaced until the 20th century.) The width specification left about twelve feet of mainly grass verge on either side of the carriageway to allow coaches to pass or to detour waterlogged sections in winter. Landowners were ordered to plant hedges defining their boundaries with the edge of the highway and to prevent stock from straying.

In a countryside worked virtually entirely by man and animal power, and with most of the natural resources managed and utilised, hedges, ditches and road verges would have been carefully tended and where possible brought into the rural economy. Road verges provided grazing for passing livestock, as already mentioned, wider areas might also be used on a more permanent basis, and hay crops could be obtained by farmers and villagers. Centuries of this kind of management created and maintained hundreds of miles of grassy verges, with rich wild flower communities frequently separated from adjacent fields by well maintained ditches and neatly trimmed hedges.

Into the 20th century, Hertfordshire's complex of roads and lanes reflected facets of origination and change back to prehistoric times. As the natural and semi-natural environment was destroyed, degraded or changed, road verges and hedges became increasingly important to wildlife, especially for many species of woods and grasslands, as their premier habitats were lost to arable and urban expansion. Throughout the 20th century, a host of new roads has been added to the county's landscape, from urban streets to broad motorways; there has also been considerable widening and realignment of older roads. Despite reductions in the extent of footpaths, green lanes and some minor roads, much remains to attract the interest of both historians and naturalists, but it must be emphasised that, from the viewpoint of the latter, reductions and losses of wildlife are approaching disastrous proportions. Pre-eminently, the increasing use of vehicles fuelled by polluting hydrocarbons and lead heralded faster, more economic and, eventually, widely available transportation requiring broader, better-surfaced highways. First most major, then many minor, roads were widened, with consequent loss of verge width. Subsequently most became surfaced with, mainly, tarmacadam, applications of which caused their own forms of disturbance and pollution. Improved surfacing generated more traffic and attracted people from towns out into the countryside, to live or for pleasure. A positive benefit of this was that greater mobility accelerated natural history studies in the county, but, on the debit side, increasing pressures and disturbances were placed upon the countryside through various leisure and recreational activities, particularly at local beauty spots. The fact that the burden of maintenance and surfacing of roads was borne largely by local authorities, resulted in lengths of tracks and lanes remaining 'unadopted' because of insufficient funding for works. Little used, many either became overgrown or have disappeared beneath arable cultivation.

Replacement of animal power by motorised transport obviously reduced the effects of grazing and hay-making along road verges. However, the presence of abundant rabbits helped retain most stretches free from too much overgrowth until the outbreaks of myxomatosis from the early 1950s onwards. Rabbit populations were reduced very rapidly and, within a few years, almost all verges were showing marked signs of deterioration. In the 1960s and 1970s considerable lengths of verges were cut by local authorities and landowners, but this was noticeably a declining practice in many places in the 1980s. Cutting can be useful in terms of wildlife conservation but it cannot really replace grazing and most mowing regimes are inadequate to retain traditional swards of fine-leaved grasses and diverse herb communities. For conservation of most typical species, the timing and periodicity of cutting are vital, and variable according to the type of grassland being managed. Removal of aftermath is essential to prevent changes in soil micro-habitats, such as increased water retention and eutrophication, which accelerates the spread of a few vigorous species of coarse grasses, tall herbs and scrub.

Plate 14 (*Top*) Oxeye Daisy *Leucanthemum vulgare* is a common species of recently disturbed Chalk verges and banks; (*Bottom*) Field Poppy *Papaver rhoeas* and Scentless Mayweed *Tripleurospermum inoderum* produce large numbers of seeds and rapidly colonise new sites, although here they were sown as a cosmetic exercise on a recently completed road verge (Watton-at-Stone bypass)

Plate 15 (*Top*) Ivy Broomrape *Orobanche hederae*, parasitic on Ivy *Helix hedera* and one of Hertfordshire's rarest wild flowers; (*Bottom*) Oxford Ragwort *Senecio squalidus*

157

Wider changes in agriculture are also reflected in the present depauperate state of most road verges. If present, hedges are frequently neglected, overshading and invading verges, sometimes right up to the highway. Particularly evident in the more open countryside, for example on the historically unhedged chalklands, are many examples where farmers have ploughed out floristically rich verges, and arable land now ends within centimetres of the surfaced roads. The legality of such actions is questionable, for, throughout history, the ownership of verges has been vested in various local authorities or *common-right* owners. Similarly, other forms of encroachment, including fencing, hedge-removal, digging and even certain cutting, mowing and grazing regimes, may well be illegal. It is also unfortunate that, in some places, quite inappropriate tree-, shrub- and bulb-planting schemes are spoiling the nature of verges, especially in areas of traditionally open countryside.

Almost everywhere, there is evidence amply illustrating the effects of agricultural chemicals leaching from adjacent lands. Herbicides have exacted a great toll, not just from farming for, until comparatively recently, highway authorities regularly, and seemingly indis-criminately, used chemical sprays to control weeds along miles of road verge. Results of this can be seen in the scarcity of more interesting low-growing flora and the widespread tall, rank and species-poor herbage that is so characteristic today. Fertilisers are just as damaging, and their leaching also tends to promote the growth of just a few vigorous species. Today, only a very few traditionally flowery road verges survive, often on sites protected from agricultural pollution by thick hedges, ditches or favourable slopes of the gound; depending on local soils, and management, they will contain many fine-leaved grasses and colourful mixtures of largely low-growing herbs, which may include such species as Cowslip, Meadow and Bulbous Buttercups, Bird's-foot Trefoil, Agrimony, Salad Burnet, Stone Parsley, Burnet Saxifrage, Sheep's Sorrel, Common Toadflax, Marjoram, Betony, Wild Thyme, Wild Basil, Self-heal, Hoary Plantain, Field Scabious, Common Daisy, Dog Daisy, Black Knapweed, Greater Knapweed and its parasitic broomrape, Mouse-ear Hawkweed, Goat's-beard, Bee Orchid and Common Spotted-orchid, Twayblade and, where there are ditches, wetland species.

In contrast, the flora characteristic of most of our road verges, though rich, contains a high proportion of annuals that invade disturbed areas; as the checklist (*see* Appendix 1.17) shows, the few rarities that remain are usually to be found in the least disturbed places. Typically, the verges of Hertfordshire are eutrophic, suffering from lax or non-existent management and swept by wind and spray from passing vehicles. Commonly they are dominated by tall, tangled, coarse grasses and a few vigorous herbs, notably False Oat-grass, Barren Brome, Couch-grass, Cock's-foot, Creeping Bent, Hedge Garlic, Cow Parsley, Hogweed, Rough Chervil, Common Sorrel, Curled and Broad-leaved Docks, Stinging Nettle, Goosegrass, Black Horehound, Common Ragwort, Yarrow and Creeping and Spear Thistles. Encroachment by trees, shrubs and climbers is also evident, and long stretches have been taken over by Common Hawthorn, Blackthorn, Elder, brambles, Wild Clematis, roses, Ash and oaks. Frequently verges are disturbed through trenching, and certain arable weeds or pioneer species may flourish until ousted by grasses; it is not unusual to see flushes of a single species such as the scarlet Field Poppy, golden Oil-seed Rape, or, on Chalk, golden-eyed, snowy white Dog Daisy.

Amongst the most recent additions to the county's road network are the broad motorways, dual carriageways and by-passes. Many of these have extremely wide verges, often seeded with 'specialised' grass-mixes calculated more to rapid hiding of construction scars than to production of wildlife habitats of any quality. Some of the seed-mixes contain native species of grasses and herbs, others a variety of alien or non-local varieties. The long-term benefits of these newly created verges appear to be few, when judged against the importance of the well-maintained older verges, which they will probably never replace. As has been stated, correct management regimes are essential and, in the context of many of the new verges, very expensive to carry out. Already, the spread of a few coarser grasses and scrub encroachment are evident along extensive stretches of such roads. In places, for example on roundabouts and at major junctions, over-zealous cutting, as on urban verges, creates a short turf enhanced with but a few cropping-tolerant wild flowers such as Common Daisy, dandelions, Autumnal Hawkbit, Self-heal, Yarrow and plantains (if herbicides are not used). A particular feature apparent along many major roads on the first metre or so of the verge, is a narrow strip of the tufted, perennial, greyish-leaved Reflexed Saltmarsh-grass. Colonisation by this normally maritime species has been promoted by residues from winter salting of the carriageways.

Some thirty years ago Charles Elton, one of the founders of modern ecological thought and study, described road verges as 'the last big nature reserve'. Even in those days, verges were often all that remained of the once widespread heaths, downlands, meadows and pastures. As we can now easily see by travelling around the countryside, little survives of 'the last big nature reserve'. Even more disturbing is that, to date, not a single 'roadside nature reserve' exists in Hertfordshire, despite the knowledge that some scarce habitat types are represented and that a number of notable and rare species have main, some their only, colonies on road verges of declining quality.

Information kindly supplied by the Highways Department of Hertfordshire County Council shows that at the end of 1989 Hertfordshire's highways totalled some 4500 km. Of this, 95 km are motorways, trunk roads and significant through-routes or primary roads, 151 km main distributor roads linking primary roads, 179 km secondary distributor roads between main towns and linking to the main road grid and 1244 km major local roads. A further 2773 km constitute the networks of urban links, streets, country lanes and other public highways, including some unmade roads and green lanes. In addition there are about 425 km of public footpaths giving access to the county's countryside. Inevitably road construction will increase, in particular, and it seems fairly certain that the always difficult east-to-west communications across the county will be improved through the building of at least one major road system. Although no detailed surveys have been undertaken, it is estimated that there are approximately 3000 km of road-verge habitat in Hertfordshire (perhaps doubled if one includes both sides of roads), including about 80 km of green lanes. Of this, in excess of 80 per cent has lost its potentially rich wild flower interest, and most of the remainder is showing signs of serious degradation.

A few stretches of the county's road verges still support reasonable elements of flora indicative of their former character, although most, if not all, have ample evidence of deterioration in habitat quality. Chalk downland relicts are amongst the best represented, mainly along the margins of roads traversing the escarpment about Tring and Berkhamsted, in the Hexton area and between Hitchin and Reed. Heathy verges occur around Aldbury, Berkhamsted, Chorleywood, Bricketwood, Chipperfield, Wheathampstead, Harpenden, Hertford and Hoddesdon, many representing some of the last grassland elements of the now much overgrown commons. A few waysides and greens on the Boulder Clay still retain interesting aspects of meadow flora, especially near Ardeley, Sandon, Meesden and Little Hadham.

There are other road verges of importance because of the antiquity of their hedges, quality of ditch flora or as woodland relicts. Similarly, many of the unmetalled green lanes can be of considerable wildlife conservation value, but few retain their traditional characters of wide grassy tracks, flanked by well maintained ditches and hedges. Hedge removal, reductions in width, scrub overgrowth, flooding from un-maintained ditches, erosion by unsuitable traffic and illegal tipping and ploughing are widely in evidence. One of the most disgraceful examples of neglect and misuse can be seen on The Icknield Way, where it descends from Wilbury Hill at Letchworth towards Ickleford. Once, in places, fifteen metres or so wide, with margins rich in chalkland wild flowers, this historic trackway has been reduced by, probably illegal, incursion from cultivation to little more than a narrow muddy path, margined by coarse grasses and ragged shrubs. The nationally rare Great Pignut does fortunately survive but its future must be regarded with concern. Many other green lanes have floras more typical of scrub and woodland margins. Some of the more interesting stretches can be found near Ardeley and Clothall on the Roman Stane Street, on tracks leading from Munchers Green and Wood End also near Ardeley, in Violets Lane at Furneux Pelham, in Sparksfield Lane near Great Hormead, in Wood Lane at Pirton, in Long Lane near Bendish, in Coleman Green Lane, in Hornbeam Lane at Essendon, along Ermine Street between Martins Green and Hertford Heath, and in parts of Wood Lane near Ware.

13

Wild Flowers of Railways

The Industrial Revolution gave rise to a national demand for improved communications with faster and more economic transportation of larger volumes of goods and people, especially between London and the rest of Britain. In reponse to this and with the improving development of one of man's most useful inventions – the steam locomotive – came the great 19th century boom in railway construction which made the Industrial Revolution possible and changed the face of the country. Hertfordshire was in the forefront of railway mania and six main lines passed through the county, linking London to the north, the midlands and East Anglia. The first, from Euston to Birmingham via Watford, Hemel Hempstead and Tring, was opened for traffic in 1837; the second, the (now) Liverpool Street to East Anglia line had been constructed before 1850 through Cheshunt, Broxbourne and Bishop's Stortford, with a branch line to Ware and Hertford; the third opened in 1850 the Great Northern Line, from Kings Cross to the north, which was routed via East Barnet, Hatfield, Welwyn and Hitchin, from where branch lines diverged to Royston, Cambridge and Bedford; in 1920 a loop was added to the Great Northern linking Cuffley and Stevenage; the fourth the Midland line, from St Pancras to Bedford and Derby through St Albans, was opened in 1868 with a branch to Hatfield; the fifth, the Metropolitan line, from the City of London, reached Rickmansworth in 1887 and two years later Chorleywood, and the last main line, the Great Central from London to Leicester and Nottingham, opened in 1899; running jointly with the Metropolitan through Hertfordshire, it had stations at Moor Park, Rickmansworth and Chorleywood. Branch lines were also constructed, connecting Watford to Rickmansworth, Welwyn to Luton and Ware to Buntingford.

Appendix 1.18

The coming of the railways halted further canal building and, despite fierce opposition, quite rapidly replaced much of the major stage coach and heavy wagon commerce. Some horse-drawn services remained, feeding passengers and goods to the newly built stations, until replaced by motorised transport in the early decades of the 20th century. The decline in horse power was widley reflected in the loss of large areas of meadows and pastures no longer required for hay-making and grazing. Emphasis put upon railway construction also seriously reduced the importance and maintenance of roads, and it was not until after the development and increasing use of the motor car, from the 1920s onwards, that significant road improvements were made in the countryside.

The impact of the Industrial Revolution and the railways upon the landscape of Hertfordshire was to be dramatic. At the beginning of the 19th century most of the now major towns were little more than villages; for example Watford had a population of about 3500, St Albans 3000,

Hitchin 3100 and Barnet 1250. In 1840 London was about four miles across, today it exceeds twenty-five miles. The far-reaching effects of this expansion have effectively breached the borders of Hertfordshire, putting pressures upon much of the countryside. Railways facilitated a 'mushrooming' of commuter settlements, particularly in the south of the county, and the establishment of overflow populations in new towns such as Letchworth and Welwyn Garden Cities, Stevenage and New Barnet. (*See* Figure 13.1.) As shown in earlier chapters, Hertfordshire's proximity to London had, over centuries, been responsible for many great changes in the landscape, from the supply of firewood out of coppices and expanding arable cultivation to provide ever-growing demands for food, to the creation of parks, estates and great houses for the capital's nobility and businessmen. Apart from great swathes of new housing across the countryside, further widespread landscape and social changes followed the coming of the railways. As villages grew into towns, which coalesced to form largely still expanding, conurbations, they attracted services and industries that placed further strains upon the dwindling countryside. Increasing numbers of homes for commuters and workers had gardens, which replaced traditional countryside with cultivated plants from many corners of the world. It is perhaps fortunate that some branch lines closed when they did, inhibiting the land speculation and development of the earlier parts of the 20th century. Some of the areas left remote by railway closure have since been serviced by improved roads, and now bear scars of the inevitable effects of development.

Despite the ever-increasing power of locomotives, steep gradients needed to be avoided by railway constructors. Where possible, routes followed fairly level, stable ground, following valleys and, generally, gently curving around higher terrain, with embankments, cuttings, tunnels and bridges built and marshes drained only where necessary. Hertfordshire's railways were constructed mainly by manpower, and they incorporate some great monuments to Victorian design, ingenuity, technology and tenacity; for example, Tring cutting required the removal of one-and-a-half million tons of Chalk; several men died and many were injured whilst forging tunnels; and Cubitt's forty-arched, brick-built viaduct stands more than thirty metres above the valley of the Mimram near Welwyn Garden City.

Railway construction and its aftermath destroyed much countryside but, in its wake, created a number of new and eventually important habitats for wildlife. For construction, quite wide swathes of land were acquired by the various railway companies, not all of which would be disturbed, notably the margins of the permanent way. Together with the new embankments and cuttings, many of these would, in time, link into and through towns and to extensive sidings and marshalling yards, forming corridors for the colonisation and spread of many forms of wildlife.

The bare rock or soils of cuttings and embankments soon became colonised, first by successions of weeds, and then by the spread of more permanent species of wild flowers from adjacent habitats, notably grasslands. Very steep banks, as can still be seen today, are slow to

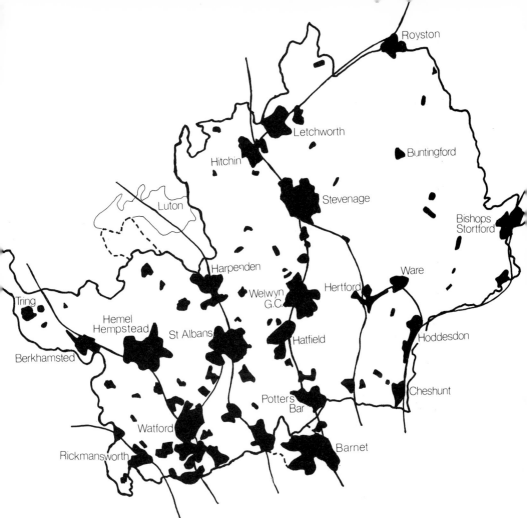

Figure 13.1 *Map showing present railway systems and major built-up areas of Hertfordshire*

colonise; because shrubs and trees are to a degree inhibited here, these sometimes maintain a few of the more important aspects of relict flora. In their heyday, many railway banks were places of great beauty, especially on Chalk substratum, with snowy drifts of Oxeye Daisy, golden expanses of Kidney Vetch, Bird's-foot-trefoil and Hop Trefoil, with Cowslip, vetches, ragworts, Greater Knapweed, Hardhead, Field Scabious, Common Toadflax, Agrimony, Harebell, Lady's Bedstraw and many others. As has been shown above in connection with the chalk downlands, the aspect of a slope has considerable influence upon flora; south-facing banks and cuttings are thus often floristically richer than those facing north.

Until about the 1960s, most railway banks were characterised by communities of grasses and herbs of better-drained grasslands, their species composition generally being determined by the local geology in cuttings and in embankments by the nature of the construction material used – this was often imported from nearby cuttings or from local pits

163

specifically opened for the purpose. Reference to the checklists of wild
flowers in previous chapters, firstly of arable weeds and then of heath
and drier grasslands, especially the Chalk, will provide something of
an insight into the range of species that, perhaps at times or in many
cases more permanently, graced the county's railsides. (It should be
pointed out, that in the past, as today, access to railways was restricted
for obvious safety reasons, and our knowledge about the former flora
of these habitats is therefore far from complete.) There were many
parallels with the floras of road verges, although past management of
railway banks was, generally, never quite so intense, and low tussocky
grassland with taller herbs predominated. The open nature of railway
banks and busy goods yards is strikingly apparent in photographs
taken during the 'steam age' and contrasts sharply with the situation
today.

Before the economic constraints of the post-Second World War years
and replacement of steam by other forms of motive power, railway banks
were kept relatively free of overgrowth. Most stretches of line were
maintained by linesmen, – as individuals or teams. These cared for the
permanent way, repaired fences, bridges and other structures and,
where necessary, removed encroaching scrub and trees. 'Until
decimated by outbreaks of myxomatosis from the 1950s onwards,
tremendous populations of rabbits kept many banks open, their grazings and soil disturbance being particularly important for creating and
retaining patches of fine-leaved grasses and lower-growing herbs. Then
there were the erratic , but significant, lineside fires of dry seasons,
caused by errant sparks and hot cinders from passing steam locomotives. These, and sometimes deliberately started fires that were part of
line-side management, helped prevent the build-up of litter from coarser
grasses and restricted the spread of brambles, Wild Clematis and scrub.
A consequence of such fires was the notable spread of the tall,
rose-flowered and gossamer-seeded, Rosebay Willowherb or Fireweed,
a once rather scarce native plant.

As indicated above, national economic problems and, in particular, the
development of improved road networks brought shifts from rail to road
transportation which were soon evidenced in an alteration and deterioration in the nature of most, if not all, of the railway flora. Reductions
in lineside manpower and the rapid transition, in the 1960s, from steam
to cleaner and more efficient diesel, and later electric, motive power
facilitated the rapid and uncontrolled overgrowth of coarser grasses,
scrub and trees which had largely started a decade or so before with the
demise of rabbits. The legacy of these changes can be viewed today. As
trains speed along (*see* Figure 13.2) most of what is seen from carriage
windows is mile after mile of banks shrouded in scrub, small oak, Ash,
Sycamore and birch trees, extensive bramble thickets, tumbling masses
of Wild Clematis or roses, and pink hazes of Rosebay Willowherb. Long
stretches are now virtually secondary woodland. Only here and there
are fleeting breaks where more open vegetation survives, and this, more
often than not, is rough tussocky tall grassland usually dominated by
False Oat-grass. It is only upon the steepest, often near vertical, cuttings
that some of the once typical railside flora can be glimpsed.

Little of interest remains on the sites of the branch lines, which were mainly closed by the Beeching 'axe' of the 1960s. Many stretches have been developed for housing or returned to agriculture. North of Ickleford, a botanically interesting cutting and the old trackbed of the abandoned branch line from Hitchin to Bedford was infilled by the dumping of domestic refuse in 1978 and 1979 and then returned to agriculture, despite vociferous opposition from local residents and wildlife conservation organisations. What survives of the branch lines is now largely overgrown, with characteristics similar to those of green lanes, although relict track ballast, which once supported sleepers and rails, can have noticeable local effects upon flora, with a few typical species still to be found. (*See below.*) Examples of these changes can be readily seen along the route of the line formerly linking Hertford, Welwyn Garden City and Luton, where stretches have been acquired by Hertfordshire County Council and are now managed for informal recreation and known as Cole Green Way and Ayot Greenway. Here margins are mainly dominated by Common Hawthorn, Blackthorn, Elder, Dogwood, roses and brambles with some oaks, Ash and Sycamore. Some grassy margins and ballast from the trackbed still support a few aspects of railway flora, with occasional Dog Daisy, Cowslip, Bird's-foot-trefoil and Coltsfoot and, in trampled places, lichens, mosses and low-growing herbs and annuals. Were it not for management, passing walkers, cyclists and horses, even this would soon be lost in a tangle of scrub. One of the last and once most important of the abandoned branch-line embankments was that at Cadwell near Ickleford, just south of the cutting noted above. Constructed from Chalk and topped by ballast, this still had a particularly diverse flora and fauna until 1983. The owner, in the face of intense and informed opposition, then decided to turn the site into a 'conservation area'. With bulldozers, the banks were stripped of their open scrub and relict Chalk flora and replaced with seeded grasses and planted shrubs. Their were many casualties, not least the destruction of the county's last site for Curtis' Mouse-ear Chickweed *Cerastium pumilum*, a nationally uncommon species, that flourished on the old ballast.

Ballast, the foundation giving support to sleepers and rails, could be formed from a wide variety of materials. Vast quantities of gravel, industrial slag and a wide range of other rock types were used, some locally obtained and some imported from quarries in many parts of Britain. The laying of ballast was to create extensive cross-country habitats for wild flowers, that penetrated and expanded to the hearts of towns and cities, especially into marshalling yards and sidings. Apart from its potentially diverse origins, the effects of which have never been fully studied, railway ballast, by design, is exceptionally well-drained, unyielding and open and therefore generally attractive only to a rather limited, specialised and almost unique flora. As the railways expanded in the 19th century, botanists were soon noting additions to local floras with some variations which could be related to different types of traffic. One species, whose spread has become legendary in the annals of railway botany is Oxford Ragwort. Specimens of this were brought from volcanic slopes in southern Europe to the Botanic Garden at Oxford in the 18th century. Quickly naturalising, it soon spread to many limestone walls of that city and thence, in the later 19th century, to local railway sidings and ballast. Being light and having a long *pappus* (dispersal parachute), the seeds were subsequently easily distributed and rapidly spread to germinate on ballast along lines throughout lowland England, and no doubt, this distribution was helped by the wind currents from passing trains or by seeds being carried on wagons and coaches. Oxford Ragwort was first noted in Hertfordshire during 1921 and has since become common, especially in the south of the county, spreading into towns and colonising gravel pits; in northern areas, its distribution still relates quite closely to the railways. A number of other species exhibited notable railway-assisted increases, including Sticky Groundsel and Groundsel, both of which are closley related to, and may hybridise with, Oxford Ragwort. Similar spreads can be assigned to such species as Canadian Fleabane, Michaelmas Daisies, Rosebay Willowherb, evening-primroses, Coltsfoot, Wall Rocket, Oxeye Daisy, Weld, Common Toadflax, Wall Pepper, mulleins, Herb Robert and Hedgerow Cranesbill which still, to varying extents, occur in the harsh ballast habitat. Occasionally, although less frequently than in the past, records of essentially maritime wild flowers are made, with species such as Strapwort, Sea or Dark-green Mouse-ear Chickweed and Early Scurvy-grass. These most probably relate to ballast being imported from coastal places. Sidings and goods yards became well known for unusual floras, particularly adventives and aliens carried in via trucks and their loads. Over the years many new species were added to the county list.

The permanent way was always well managed and, with regular re-ballasting, was kept relatively free from overgrowth although certain annuals in particular continued to flourish. More recent utilisation of weedkillers, often sprayed from specially equipped trains, has significantly reduced trackbed floras. There have been further reductions with the advent of containerised goods wagons, and economic cutbacks have seen the decommissioning and re-development of many sidings and goods yards. In more recent years, increases of Buddleia, brambles and a few tall herbs such as Canadian Fleabane, Michaelmas Daisy and Goldenrod have become features of less frequently used sidings. As will be seen from the checklists of railway flora (*see* Appendix 1.18), some tracksides and sidings still provide good hunting grounds (obviously only to be used with the permission of the relevant railway authorities) and may still reward careful study with more than a few botanical gems!

An additional railway feature worth searching is old brickwork of bridges, walls, tunnel entrances, platforms and engine sheds; here colonies of mosses and lichens, as well as a few, sometimes uncommon, ferns are often supported. It seems that the railways played an important part in extending the distribution of a number of ferns, including several quite rare species; perhaps aided by the slipstream of trains, the light fern spores may have been carried long distances to find suitable sites for germination on moister brickwork in shaded or north-facing situations, most frequently where water regularly seeps through. In the past, ferns were often associated with certain places where water condensed from the emissions of stationary steam locomotives. Quite a number of wild flowers, including a few specialised species, may also be found growing, in sunny and shaded aspects, from cracks and crevices between bricks, often in the barest of soils. Amongst the more frequent occurrences may be Shepherd's Purse, Whitlow Grass, Procumbent Pearlwort, Herb Robert, Wall Pepper, Ivy, Pellitory-of-the-Wall, Ivy-leaved Toadflax, Oxford Ragwort, Sticky Groundsel, Goundsel, Feverfew, Wall Lettuce, Fern Grass and Wall Barley. (*See also* the checklist for wild flowers of old walls, Appendix 1.20.)

Figure 13.2 *Rabbit grazing and erratic fires formerly kept linesides free from overgrowth*

14

Wild Flowers of Urban Areas

Appendices
1.19, 1.20

There is a wealth of wild flowers to be discovered in the variety of towns and villages throughout Hertfordshire. Many habitats are provided by old and new buildings, open spaces and parks, public and private gardens, churchyards and cemeteries, urban verges, derelict sites, waste dumps, old pits and sewage farms. In addition, most urbanised areas will retain some facets of woodland, grassland, rivers, ponds, hedges and other semi-natural habitats already described.

14.1 Towns and Gardens

Most urban situations especially more recent conurbations, are typified by relatively closely spaced buildings and extensive paved areas with disrupted and accelerated drainage. Between these, most of the open space has been artificially created and is intensively managed in the form of gardens, parks or street verges. In many places, pollution levels for plants can be very high; vehicle-exhaust gases, fallout from domestic and industrial fuels, rubber dust and salt from roads, particles washed out from building materials, chemical herbicides and fertilisers can be very damaging to plant tissues. Nevertheless (and despite the best intentions of planners, developers and individuals over-zealous in their display of civic pride!) a wide variety of wild flowers will become temporarily or permanently established, even in the most built-up of the county's towns. Indeed, in the hearts of some of the most historic settlements an extremely diverse flora has developed, including some fairly uncommon species of long-standing.

Window-boxes, flower-beds, gutters and cracks and crevices in buildings and pavements soon become colonised by the wind- or bird-carried seeds of opportunist weeds like Groundsel, Shepherd's-purse, Oxford Ragwort, Rosebay Willowherb, Pineappleweed, Greater Plantain, Stinging Nettle, Field Bindweed, docks, Common Mallow, Annual Meadow-grass, Common Couch and Wall Barley. Various ferns may occupy shady, damp places. Even in new developments it is not at all unusual to come across species which seem entirely out of place; these perhaps are survivors from the habitats that were there before or may have been brought in with the topsoil. The occasional plants of species such as Lady's Bedstraw, Bird's-foot-trefoil, clovers, violets and Red Fescue-grass are frequently found springing up from gaps in tarmac, kerb-stones and pavements. Here and there a real surprise may be met with; for example at Letchworth a Bee Orchid flowered on a well-mown street verge, and a plant of Twayblade turned up in a narrow crevice between paving slabs and the wall of the town's main museum. Shrubs and trees renowned for their invasive properties include Elder, Sycamore, sallows, Woody Nightshade, Aspen, brambles and, more recently, Buddleia, which was not introduced into this country until the end of the last century.

Street trees add further diversity, although in many instances the species or varieties used are alien or planted for quick growth, ornamental qualities, drought or pollution tolerance rather than for any wider ecological benefits. Native species such as oaks, birches, Ash, Beech, Rowan and Whitebeam, are better than aliens (*see* checklist, Appendix 1.18) in their wildlife value, providing greater ranges of associated invertebrates. However, both alien and native trees of the streets create cover, food and breeding sites for birds and mammals as well as often forming 'green corridors' linking town with countryside. Similarly, although usually sown with a limited number of grass species, greenswards increase variety with intensive-cutting- and trampling-tolerant grasses such as Perennial Rye-grass, Timothy, Smooth Meadow-grass, Red Fescue and Creeping Bent. Unless exterminated by large doses of herbicide, a few low-growing herbs will establish themselves in these short swards with, most commonly, Great Plantain, Daisy, dandelions, Self-heal, Autumnal Hawkbit, Yarrow, Creeping Buttercup, Red and White Clovers. A little searching will reveal some less intensively managed or undeveloped corners in most urban areas, and these may hold a surprising number of species, notably those of grasslands, arable lands and larger waste areas. (*See* checklists, Appendix 1)

With such large-scale reductions in the semi-natural habitats of the Hertfordshire countryside, urban gardens are becoming more and more important havens for wildlife. Many gardeners, with a concern for wider environmental consequences, are thinking carefully about the usage of chemicals on their 'patch'. Some, at least in parts of their gardens, are cultivating trees, shrubs and flowers with wildlife conservation very much in mind. It is becoming increasingly common to find, even in the smallest of gardens, ponds, rough corners left for weeds, beds sown with wild flower seed mixes, patches of less regularly cut grasses and hedges planted up with selected native shrubs alongside the more formal lawns, neatly clipped hedges and flower-beds bedecked with plants from all corners of the world. The selling of potted native plants such as Primrose, Cowslip, Devil's-bit Scabious, Cuckoo-flower, Marjoram, knapweeds and Yellow Iris is now quite widespread and it is easy to form a conservaion area in a garden. Older, well established gardens, especially those in villages, will tend to attract more wildlife; for example, certain woodland wild flowers will colonise shrubberies and groves of trees and wetland species may spread into ponds via wind-blown or bird-transported seeds. As buildings and walls mature and decay, they may become suitable habitats for further, sometimes specialised, species.

Even the most assiduous of gardeners, if so motivated, will have great difficulty in completely abolishing all wild flowers. Particularly persistent are Goosegrass, Field Bindweed, Groundsel, Creeping Cinquefoil, Ground Elder, Scarlet Pimpernel, Common Couch and Creeping Bent. Many other arable weeds may also crop up from time to time and it is not unusual for various uncommon aliens to arrive seemingly spontaneously, perhaps from poorly screened packeted seeds or from wild bird seed. Unmanaged gardens, like building sites, yards or any other uncultivated or derelict places, soon show signs of plant colonisation, first come annual and biennial weeds and then perennials. (*See* checklist, Appendix 1.19.)

When looked at closely, most lawns often have more herbs than grasses. Some may in fact be relict grasslands resulting from development on former meadows or pastures or, more frequently, the importation of grass turves, quite probably of non-local origin. In south Hertfordshire, for example, around Cuffley, some garden lawns contain significant elements of the acidic grassland and heath upon which the estates were built, with Harebell, Tormentil, Field Woodrush and occasionally, traces of Heather. Before, and contributing to, the virtual demise of ancient pastures and meadows, it was quite common for gardeners to take delivery of grass turves, for laying down as lawns, containing a great variety of grasses, Cowslip, buttercups and even the occasional orchid. Herbicides, lawn foods and frequent close mowing very soon eradicate most of the herbs, but, even on the best managed bowling- and golf-green quite a number of herbs may well be recorded. One species in particular has benefited from intensive grass-management in Hertfordshire; this is the low, creeping Slender Speedwell. Native to the Caucasus, this was introduced into Britain as a rockery plant and was first noted as an escape in the county in 1952. Since then, it has become naturalised, fairly well distributed and difficult to control. Fruiting is very rare in Britain and reproduction is vegetative, with tiny, cut-up fragments capable of forming new colonies.

Allotments are somewhat akin to the ancient form of strip cultivation, with varying crops under differing degrees of management and, often, separated by grassy paths or narrow banks. Some of these, especially but not entirely in rural areas, are good wild flower refuges, particularly for weeds. At some sites, one may find the last bastions of certain once common arable weeds, together with uncommon casuals and aliens. Amongst the more interesting allotment weeds noted in recent years have been such scarce species as Prickly-headed Poppy, Sowbane, Annual Mercury and several fumitories (*See* checklist, Appendix 1.19.)

14.2 Public Parks, Recreation Grounds, Churchyards and Cemeteries

The better examples of these urban spaces are derived largely from original countryside. Although often significantly degraded later by intensive management, weed-control, added plantings and other developments, many retain some characteristics and species of the former habitats. A number of the county's more important sites, with public access and good surviving semi-natural habitats, have been referred to in previous chapters, for example Wilbury Hill and Norton Common at Letchworth, Oughtonhead Common near Hitchin, Monks and Whomerley Woods in Stevenage, Ashwell Springs, Therfield Heath near Royston, Sherrardspark Wood at Welwyn Garden City, Gustardwood Common, Harpenden Common, Hertford Heath,

Broxbourne Woods, Northaw Great Wood, Patmore Heath near Albury, Bricketwood Common, Croxley Common Moor, Roughdown Common near Boxmoor, Whippendell Woods and Cassiobury Park near Watford, Chorleywood Common, Tring Reservoirs and parts of the Ashridge estate. Some of these premier sites may fall into the category of urban or public open spaces but they are all largely atypical, for most public green spaces including parks, recreation grounds, sports fields, school fields and burial grounds, are intensively managed and formalised. Apparently for public benefit, grasslands are short-mown and, at times, treated with herbicides and fertilisers, with the result that communities are usually reduced to a few grass species and low-growing herbs, little different from the street verges noted above. Often groups of alien conifers and ornamental hardwoods are planted, and 'Lakes' are stocked with fish, such as carp; these, together with introduced wildfowl, soon assure the loss of any botanical interest.

Fragments of former habitats do still occur and are well worth detailed recording, especially now that there is a greater awareness of how much has been lost. If a good factual case is presented to them, local authorities, landowners and other custodians should be increasingly persuaded to care for these last relics of a vanishing heritage. With grasslands, it may be necessary to examine short turf in close detail and be able to recognise non-flowering grasses and herbs in order to acquire data. Less intensively managed margins of recreation fields, sports grounds, roughs of golf courses and many village greens may well repay such examination for, despite frequent cutting, many of the species noted in the various grassland checklists may still be found. Recent studies on parts of the semi-rough at Letchworth Golf Club and regularly mown turf at Norton Common have revealed two of the best patches of Boulder Clay grassland remaining in the county, with probably the only remaining small colonies of the once fairly common and widespread Sulphur Clover. A recent lapse in the mowing of a recreation field at Weston facilitated the flowering and discovery of another very rich neutral grassland. Subsequent formalisation of management agreements should ensure the long-term survival of this site.

Gilbert White, one of the greatest founding fathers of British natural history studies, advocated the importance of studying one's own parish. Today, this dictum is just as valid as it was in the 18th century, perhaps more so for, like charity, conservation can be said to begin at home and all should seek to ensure the integrity of their own local sites of wildlife conservation interest. All too often small sites and larger ones are neglected, swept away by development, or degraded. Well-meaning but ecologically ill-founded enhancement schemes, like tree-planting on verges and greens, addition of ornamental bulbs or shrubs to verges, unsuitable grass-cutting regimes, encouragement of too many wildfowl to ponds and an almost obsessional keenness for unnatural tidiness, all help to reduce wildlife diversity. Perhaps, organisations giving local amenity grants or awards, for example 'The Best Kept Village' competition, should take more account of wildlife as an integral as well as aesthetic part of our everyday heritage! Information and communication are vital in these respects and it will be up to the local naturalist to gather information and then to communicate it to the relevant bodies. (*See* Appendix 3.) Wild flower data has always been and will continue to be the most important, although not always the sole, basis for wildlife-conservation activities on a local as well as a county-wide scale. Perhaps more widespread public expressions of support would lead to some of our public open spaces being more suitably managed for wildlife. This would make a positive contribution to the 'green-ness' said so often by politicians and the media to be increasing.

As well as providing habitats for many weeds and garden flowers, most churchyards and cemeteries are of considerably wider wildlife conservation value. Some will be found to contain interesting fragments of former habitats amongst the more formal, well-tended and ornamentally planted areas. Old hedges, groves of trees and scrub patches may all have ancient origins. Of particular note are swards of relatively unimproved grassland, which are often all that remains to give any clues to the past landscapes of meadows and pastures into which the church and cemetery were introduced. Because of their antiquity, parish churchyards in towns can produce interesting records of native as well as adventive flora. At Baldock, the uncommon Fiddle Dock, thought by some 19th century botanists to be peculiarly characteristic of churchyards, still occurs. Nearby, a specimen of Pokeweed *Phytolacca americana* (6–9), native to North America, was recently found.

Amongst the many rural churchyards in Hertfordshire are still several where, either by fortunate accident or concerned design, overall management is less intensive or more sensitive. Here, vestiges of floristically rich habitats survive, notably the grasslands mentioned above – two of the finest esxample can be seen at Little Hormead and Ardeley, although there are others which, with a little planning and more sensitive approaches to management, might become just as interesting. Freed from applications of herbicides and fertilisers and with conservative mowing, many of the characteristic elements of grassland floras will flourish in churchyards. (*See* relevant checklists, Appendix 1.) Together with adjacent trees, shrubs and plant-covered tombs and walls , patches of such flower-rich grass, encouraged between narrower mown paths and burial plots, can provide not just botanical interest but also add great aesthetic appeal – 'God's acre', it is said, should be a 'paradise' – a place of spiritual refreshment, with signs of resurrection, as well as a burial ground. Even in some of the more intensively managed churchyards, close inspection may produce quite long lists of plants. Church walls and tombstones are well known as habitats for lichens, mosses and, sometimes, ferns, the influence of changing geology affecting distribution of some species. As will be seen below, a variety of flowering plants may also colonise these exacting habitats. One species of particular note is Ivy Broomrape *Orobanche hederae* (6–7). This was unexpectedly discovered, in a churchyard in northern Hertfordshire in 1984, parasitic upon Ivy tumbling over a few ancient limestone tombstones and by an adjacent gravel drive. These are the only colonies of this normally maritime plant ever known from the county, and the only location in the whole of the eastern part of Britain, north of the River Thames. It is possible that seeds may have been introduced long ago, clinging to the tombstones, which were perhaps hewn from quarries on the Isle of Portland in Dorset where the species is still fairly common.

One of the most typical species found as a shrub or small tree in many churchyards is Yew *Taxus baccata* (3–4). Some specimens are reputed to be of great age, possibly a thousand years or more, although these have relatively new trunks arising from decayed originals. Archaeological evidence suggests close links between individual trees or groves of Yew and Man, from prehistoric shelters to more modern churchyards. Some authorities propose that certain rituals or ceremonies were associated with the tree. The reasons behind the almost traditional presence of Yew in churchyards is uncertain, unless the trees were there, possibly as sacred groves in pre-Christian times, before the churches were established. It is possible, because of their longevity, that the trees were sown as symbols of immortality. Other theories speculate that yews near the church door could afford shelter for those awaiting a service, handy boughs to decorate the church at Easter, and/or evergreens to place on coffins and in graves, as was once the custom. There is no evidence to suggest that consecrated ground produced yew timber for mediaeval bowstaves. Whatever the human intention was in providing yews, winter birds, especially thrushes, avidly gorge the conspicuous scarlet fruits or *arils*, although the highly poisonous seeds are voided.

14.3 Wild Flowers of Walls

However well it is constructed, masonry cracks and crumbles through weathering and, if not soon repaired, can provide a toe-hold for plants to move into. In general, the further the deterioration of stone or brickwork, the greater the degree of colonisation, although the geological origins of materials used will affect both the diversity and abundance of species. Older bridges, walls and roofs should present better hunting grounds for the botanist in Hertfordshire, especially where local, mainly soft and calcareous, materials have been used. However, a relatively dry climate precludes much of the lushness so typically associated with the mural floras of western Britain, but, as will be seen from the checklist in Appendix 1.20 the county's buildings and walls can nevertheless support a considerable diversity of flowering plants.

Apart from churches and the structures associated with railways and waterways already mentioned, many older buildings, in towns as well as villages, can provide suitable conditions for the temporary and more permanent establishment of both opportunist weeds and very specialised species. Examples of the latter include cliff-dwellers, such as Pellitory-of-the-Wall, Rue-leaved Saxifrage, Wall Lettuce and Wall-Rue, that have taken advantage of man-made rock-crevice habitats. Occasionally small trees and shrubs, such as Elder, Common Hawthorn, Holly, Yew and increasingly, the introduced Buddleia, gain a foothold. The chemical nature and toughness of bricks, building stones and roof tiles will greatly influence the nature of the colonising flora. Notable comparisons of this can be made throughout much of Hertfordshire.

Obdurate flint-faced walls have an exceedingly depauperate flora, whilst some other walls, constructed from locally made and readily weathered lime-rich bricks and mortar, may support quite long lists of wild flowers.

Moisture demanding mosses, most ferns and certain flowering plants, such as Pellitory-of-the-Wall, Mind-your-own-business and some stonecrops, are more restricted to shady damp places. Other species are adapted to survive in very exposed, dry, nutrient-deficient situations. Some, like Wall Pepper, have specialised water-retaining tissues and many, typically annuals, flower and fruit early, thereby avoiding the driest and hottest periods of the year. Not infrequently, seeds of common wayside plants manage to germinate in cracks and crevices on walls or roofs but, because of the harsh, often changeable, conditions, are usually short-lived or dwarfed, sometimes with noticeable colour differences in the leaves. The most frequent wild flowers of walls are annuals, such as Shepherd's-purse, Groundsel, Common Mouse-eared Chickweed and sandworts, which grow fast and produce light easily distributed and hardy seeds.

A few walls remain in the county that are worthy of some conservation status, for example at Hitchin Priory, Baldock churchyard and Hertford Castle, and no doubt more will be found with detailed surveying. The major threats to old-wall and roof flora comes from rebuilding and repointing, especially if the whole structure is treated at one go. Modern mortars and materials, harder and often chemically different from those of the past, provide less suitable substrates for colonisation and most of our mural flora is showing considerable signs of decline. Uncontrolled overgrowth from creepers, including Honeysuckle, Ivy and brambles, can soon shade out more interesting species. Acid rain destroys many lichens, mosses and ferns but can benefit some of the more pollution-tolerant wild flowers by dissolving limy mortar and bricks to create new habitats.

15

Wild Flowers of Waste Areas

Today, the term 'waste' is used to encompass many different kinds of sites, mainly temporary and usually subject to disturbance, for example derelict building sites, spoil heaps, dumps and urban refuse tips which, not infrequently, infill disused and nominally dry mineral workings. Often the floras of such places appear to be rather mundane, with little more than dense patches of nettles, thistles, ragworts, Field Poppy, Rosebay Willowherb, Coltsfoot, brambles and other common annual and biennial weeds. However, most sites are worth a closer look for, over the years, areas of waste have been most productive in adding interesting records to the county lists, including native and especially alien species. For example, flourishing colonies of Common Spotted-orchids and Southern and Early Marsh-orchids were recently discovered on fly-ash tips at Rye House power station near Hoddesdon; on sites awaiting development at Hitchin Deadly Nightshade crops up frequently, a survivor from times when it was cultivated in surrounding fields to supply the town's pharmaceutical industry, and similarly, Hop may not be infrequent where breweries once operated; Cornflower was found on dumped soil by the M25 near London Colney in 1986 and a fine colony of Salsify *Tragopon porrifolius* (6–8) appeared on a new roundabout at Hertingfordbury in 1985. Even without the urban refuse tips, which will be described below, a considerable diversity of wild flowers can possibly be expected from waste places including many facets of habitats already examined, particularly arable weeds, plants of disturbed road verges, urban flora and scrub, and especially species in these groups whose fruits and seeds have facilities for wide dispersal by wind or birds.

Throughout Hertfordshire it is possible, in abandoned Chalk, sand and gravel pits, to see various stages of vegetational succession from virgin soil to scrub and secondary woodland. Many aspects of these have been detailed in preceding chapters, although a number of factors may affect the nature of individual sites, for example, underlying geology, availability of seed sources and whether or not there is dumping or management. Although probably initially colonised by typical pioneer species such as Kidney Vetch, Bird's-foot-trefoil, Yellow-wort, Harebell, Ploughman's Spikenard, Fairy Flax, Salad Burnet and Red Fescue, many old Chalk workings without cutting or grazing rapidly develop scrub cover, with little real intermediate grassland stage. Unless landscaped or used as tips, disused sand and gravel workings can attract a colourful, but generally rather limited, array of pioneering species, including tall communities of Ragwort, Rosebay Willowherb, hawkbits, thistles, and sowthistles. More calcareous substrates are rather richer with, quite commonly, Wild Carrot, Common Toadflax, Weld, melilots and Coltsfoot. Damper places will support Great Hairy Willowherb,

Appendices 1.21, 1.22

Plate 16 (*Top*) Coltsfoot *Tussilago farfara*, one of the earliest wild flowers in bloom, readily colonises disturbed ground; (*Bottom*) Rapid loss of the attractive and once common Cornflower *Centaurea cyanus* should serve as a reminder of how vulnerable many other wild flowers are to extinction

Water Figwort, Gypsywort and Hard Rush. Arable weeds and casuals will inevitably also occur, some sites holding county rarities. (*See* checklist, Appendix 1.21.) The early colonisation helps to add humus to raw soils and open communities of annuals and biennials are slowly replaced by, generally species-poor, tussocky grasses, neutral to acid in character, depending upon underlying deposits and water regimes. An interesting feature of several sites over recent years has been the development of Bee Orchid colonies, some of which number hundreds of flowering spikes. Unless controlled, scrub encroachment and establishment of secondary woodland will follow, usually at a rather slower rate than for Chalk exposures. Common Hawthorn, Blackthorn, Elder, Ash, Pedunculate Oak and Sycamore are typical on more neutral soils, whilst on more acid soils predominant species will include brambles, Gorse, Broom, birches, Aspen and Sessile Oak; wetter places will favour sallows.

Throughout history, small hand-dug pits were very much a feature of the landscape. Chalk and Chalky Boulder Clay were excavated for marling adjacent fields; sand, gravel and brickearth pits provided materials for road-mending and local building. When abandoned, many of these various pits became convenient places for the dumping of unwanted farm or village rubbish – some parish pits have provided local historians with considerable information from amongst centuries of accumulated rubbish, allowing fairly accurate interpretations of the everyday lives of our forbears. Generations of botanists were also attracted to these pits, and their findings added a variety of unusual plants to county lists, including, culinary, medicinal, garden and agricultural species, whose roots or seeds germinated with many common ruderals amongst the cast-out rubbish. With the advent of more organised refuse collections, the majority of small pits became covered with scrub or were infilled, top-soiled and returned to agriculture or otherwise developed. Here and there, a few of these small pits remain with relatively open conditions and a little of the interesting flora may still survive. Near Dane End, to the east of Stevenage, some recent disturbance resulted in the germination of long-dormant seeds of Vervain and Henbane, both now rather scarce species in Hertfordshire. Amongst the developing calcareous grassland and scrub at Hexton Chalk Pit can be found Purple Toadflax, Common Broomrape, Alkanet, Ground Elder and the very rare Slender Tare, survivors from dumping before the site was declared a nature reserve in 1973.

Two factors that have had a recent and profound impact upon the list of flora for Hertfordshire have been the extensive sand and gravel workings in the southern portion of the county and the subsequent infilling of drier sites with vast amounts of domestic refuse. In addition to invasions from native species, as noted above, a great array of casuals and aliens have been introduced amongst the rubbish. This is evidenced in the checklists of our 'waste' flora, (*see* Appendix 1.21) which are far from complete and only reveal a relatively small proportion of the species involved; a full list of aliens and adventives might well exceed the combined totals for all semi-natural habitats in the county. Certainly, 'dump' species have given our flora a most cosmopolitan flavour and its study requires a knowledge of world-wide wild flowers, fruits and vegetables. There are a few botanists who make a speciality of exploring refuse dumps, and new, sometimes 'one-off', records of bird-seed aliens, exotic fruits, garden 'throw-outs', foreign vegetables and many annual weeds are constantly being added to the county flora. The majority of these alien plants have always been very transient, and controlled largely by climate and the ultimate filling, topsoiling and development of sites. Today, dumps are less productive because of the rapid rates of filling and compacting by bulldozers. Nevertheless, active dumps can repay detailed searching – permission should, of course, always be sought from the appropriate authority before any such searching is done. There will be many of the common and widespread weeds such as Common Couch-grass, Coltsfoot, Field Bindweed, Hemlock, Hoary Cress, Fat Hen, Horse Radish, ragworts, docks, Mugwort, Scentless Mayweed, nettles and brambles. More typical garden escapes and throw-outs include Goldenrods, Michaelmas Daisies, Buddleia, Japanese Knotweed and Honesty. There may be garden vegetables, herbaceous cultivars and outcasts from greenhouse, dining table and animal feeds.

Domestic refuse generates heat as it decays and, particularly in warmer summers, may allow germination and even flowering of such exotics as melons, gourds, dates, groundnuts (peanuts), soya beans, Squirting Cucumber, cereals, grasses and southern temperate and sub-tropical flowers, although frosts usually prevent further establishment. Waste from the cages of pet birds has been responsible for the introduction of perhaps thirty or more, mainly Mediterranean, weeds, including Millet, Sunflower, Gold of Pleasure, Narrow Thorow-wax, Hemp (Cannabis) and Cowbane.

In a similar way, sewage farms that still retain sludge beds into which treated sewage is pumped to settle and dry, can develop interesting aspects to their flora. Some fruit and vegetable seeds inevitably slip through various screening processes and may germinate in the nutrient-rich sludge, a common example being tomato seeds, whose viabilities are enhanced by passage through human digestive systems – some sewage farms have been renowned for their fine crops of 'wild' tomatoes! In drier places, the high nitrate levels are indicated by dense masses of common weeds such as Stinging Nettle, Mugwort, Ground Elder and the poisonous Hemlock.

Whether or not most of the exotic and alien flora should be regarded as a serious part of the county flora is arguable. However, such occurrences should continue to be recorded and monitored for, as has been shown in several preceding chapters, apparently casual introductions, since prehistoric times, have become established and important components of semi-natural habitats.

16

The Future for Hertfordshire's Wild Flowers?

Since early Man first set foot in Hertfordshire there have constantly been great changes in the countryside and its wildlife. As detailed in previous chapters, until comparatively recently there has been a long history of sensitive land uses which, although sweeping away the natural forest cover of the region, yielded a rich legacy of varied semi-natural habitats supporting a great diversity of flora and fauna. The key to this richness lay in the dependence of largely immobile people on their local areas to provide the bulk of their subsistence requirements. They therefore managed the resources of the land, particularly the renewable elements carefully, creating, albeit often unwittingly, flower-rich grasslands, wetlands and coppiced woods.

Expanding populations and new technologies from the 19th century onwards have radically transformed everyday life and all but obliterated the varied mosaic of the old countryside; it has been estimated that since about 1940, when there was a noticeable acceleration in the rate of change, there have been more loss, pollution and neglect of wildlife habitats – especially those semi-natural habitats we have now come to treasure – than at any other time throughout history. There have been some gains, both in species and habitats, but these are mostly short-term.

The very fact that declines and losses in our wild flowers can be identified highlights our debt to the pioneering botanists of the past and to those who continue to record in the field. (*See* Chapter 1.) The warnings inherent in the compendium of the past and present data in this work should be enough to raise more than passing concern for the current state of Hertfordshire and wider environments. If many of our historically typical wild flowers are to remain, together with their associated communities, conservation is vital now.

Some good work is already being undertaken, through the auspices of both voluntary and public organisations, but only about one per cent of the total 163 415 hectares of the county is under any form of conservation protection or management. Most nature reserves, Sites of Special Scientific Interest and other 'protected' areas are too small, and often too isolated, to support most of the typical communities adequately. Management resources are so small, thinly spread or financially impoverished that necessary cutting, grazing or other maintenance regimes cannot be adequately implemented. It is apparent that pressures from agriculture, development and pollution will continue to escalate in the countryside, putting an even greater emphasis upon the need for concerted conservation.

Farmers, landowners and local authorities must accept much more responsibility in their determination of what is to be conserved. But conservationists must not underestimate their role, particularly in gathering the all-important basic data regarding species lists from defined sites and overall species distribution. Without such data to compare with past records in the light of historical and current land development and management, sound wildlife conservation cannot adequately be carried out. In fact ill-informed conservation measures may well be deleterious. Efforts must be made at every level to persuade public and politicial opinion of the importance to be attached to the remains of our natural heritage. More support must be given to the county's conservation movement to ensure that conservation policies are well founded and effectively executed. The face of Hertfordshire's landscape is as it is and most of our wild flowers exist where and as they do because of Man's activities, and only Man can ensure their future. There is no time left for complacency. Any losses of traditional wild flowers and areas of semi-natural habitat must be seen as a degradation of our own environment.

In this book as in *The Butterflies of Hertfordshire* (Sawford, 1987), I have had to feature some depressing facts. There are some brighter aspects, not least that a still reasonably varied flora survives despite

Figure 16.1 *Good local conservation! (Village green at Wood End, near Ardeley)*

Figure 16.2 *Without appropriate habitat management, many of Hertfordshire's rarer wild flowers may soon be extinct (Snake's-head* Fritillaria meleagris)

all the traumas the Hertfordshire countryside has suffered over millennia. It is my fervent hope that this guide will stimulate the reader to take a more active role in recording and, above all, conserving Hertfordshire's wild flowers in their appropriate habitats.

Appendices

Contents

Appendix 1

1.1 Checklist of Characteristic Flora of Ash/Maple Woods

Trees and Shrubs

Ash	*Fraxinus excelsior* (4–5)	
Field Maple	*Acer campestre* (5–6)	
Pedunculate Oak	*Quercus robor* (4–5)	
Hazel	*Corylus avellana* (1–4)	
Common Hawthorn	*Crataegus monogyna* (5–6)	
Midland Hawthorn	*C. laevigata* (5–6)	
Spindle	*Euonymus europaeus* (5–6)	
Blackthorn	*Prunus spinosa* (3–5)	
Wild Plum	*P. domestica* ssp. (4–5)	
Elder	*Sambucus nigra* (6–7)	
Dogwood	*Cornus sanguinea* (6–7)	
Wayfaring Tree	*Viburnum lantana* (5–6)	on more calcareous drier soils
Guelder Rose	*V. opulus* (6–7)	on damper soils
Crab Apple	*Malus sylvestris* (5)	
Apple	*M. domestica* (4–5)	escape which may hybridise with Crab Apple
Holly	*Ilex aquifolium* (5–8)	on drier soils
Whitebeam	*Sorbus aria* (5–6)	on highly calcareous soils and scarce
Grey Willow	*Salix cinerea* (3–4)	
Goat Willow	*S. caprea* (3–4)	
Red Currant	*Ribes rubrum* (4–5)	
Black Currant	*R. nigrum* (4–5)	
Gooseberry	*R. uva-crispa* (3–5)	
Snowberry	*Symphoricarpos albus* (6–9)	occasionally planted or escaped alien
Oregon Grape	*Mahonia aquifolium* (1–5)	occasionally planted or escaped alien

Woody scramblers or climbers

Brambles	*Rubus fruticosus* agg. (5–9)	
Dewberry	*R. caesius* (6–9)	
Honeysuckle	*Lonicera periclymenum* (6–9)	
Wild Clematis	*Clematis vitalba* (7–8)	

Ground flora

Lesser Celandine	*Ranunculus ficaria* (3–5)	
Wood Anemone	*Anemone nemorosa* (3–5)	
Dog's Mercury	*Mercurialis perennis* (2–4)	
Sweet Violet	*Viola odorata* (2–4)	
Early Dog-violet	*V. reichenbachiana* (3–5)	
Common Dog-violet	*V. riviniana* (4–6, rarely 8–10)	
Primrose	*Primula vulgaris* (12–5)	
Oxlip	*P. elatior* (4–5)	very rare, one site in north-east Herts and a few, recently discovered, near Berkhamsted

185

Appendix 1.1

Hybrids have been recorded between Oxlip and Primrose, Cowslip and Oxlip, and Cowslip and Primrose (the False Oxlip)

Bluebell	*Hyacinthoides non-scripta* (4–6)	
Early-purple Orchid	*Orchis mascula* (4–6)	
Common Spotted-orchid	*Dactylorhiza fuchsii* (6–8)	
Twayblade	*Listera ovata* (6–7)	
Greater Butterfly-orchid	*Platanthera chlorantha* (5–7)	rare and declining
Herb Paris	*Paris quadrifolia* (5–8)	rare and declining
Bugle	*Ajuga reptans* (5–7)	
Enchanter's Nightshade	*Circaea lutetiana* (6–8)	
Goldilocks	*Ranunculus auricomus* (4–5)	
Lords-and-Ladies	*Arum maculatum* (4–5)	
Wood Forget-me-not	*Myosotis sylvatica* (5–6)	restricted as a native to the Ash valley
Herb Bennet or Wood Avens	*Geum urbanum* (6–8)	
Red-veined Dock	*Rumex sanguineus* (6–8)	
Ground Ivy	*Glechoma hederacea* (3–5)	
Ivy	*Hedera helix* (9–11)	
Stinging Nettle	*Urtica dioica* (6–8)	
Cow Parsley	*Anthriscus sylvestris* (4–6)	
Green Hellebore	*Helleborus viridis* (3–4)	scarce
Stinking Helleborine	*H. foetidus* (3–4)	garden escape, rare
Snowdrop	*Galanthus nivalis* (1–3)	introduced and naturalised
Winter Aconite	*Eranthis hyemalis* (1–3)	introduced and naturalised
Wood Small-reed	*Calamagrostis epigejos* (7–8)	rare and declining
Giant Fescue	*Festuca gigantea* (6–7)	
Hairy Brome	*Bromus ramosus* (7–8)	

Damper, open rides, margins, glades, ditches and pond margins

Annual Meadow-grass	*Poa annua* (1–12)	
Cock's-foot	*Dactylis glomerata* (5–8)	
Bearded Couch	*Elymus caninus* (7)	
Creeping Soft-grass	*Holcus mollis* (6–7)	
Yorkshire Fog	*H. lanatus* (6–9)	
Wood False-brome	*Brachypodium sylvaticum* (7)	
Tufted Hair-grass	*Deschampsia caespitosa* (6–8)	
False Oat-grass	*Arrhenatherum elatius* (6–7)	
Wood Sedge	*Carex sylvatica* (5–7)	
Thin-spiked Wood-sedge	*C. strigosa* (5–6)	local
Pendulous Sedge	*C. pendula* (5–6)	local
Remote Sedge	*C. remota* (6)	local
Hard Rush	*Juncus inflexus* (6–8)	
Creeping Jenny	*Lysimachia nummularia* (6–8)	
Hairy St John's-wort	*Hypericum hirsutum* (7–8)	
Common Figwort	*Scrophularia nodosa* (6–9)	

Water Figwort	*S. auriculata* (6–9)	wetter situations
Marsh Thistle	*Cirsium palustre* (7–9)	
Angelica	*Angelica sylvestris* (7–9)	
Water Starwort	*Callitriche stagnalis* (5–9)	
Brooklime	*Veronica beccabunga* (5–9)	
Water Mint	*Mentha aquatica* (7–10)	
Corn Mint	*M. arvensis* (5–10)	scarce
The hybrid between Water and Corn Mint	*M.* × *verticilliata*	has been recorded
Greater Burnet-saxifrage	*Pimpinella major* (6–7)	local in north-east and south-west
Stinking Iris	*Iris foetidissima* (5–7)	scarce
Nettle-leaved Bellflower	*Campanula trachelium* (7–9)	local in north of county
Giant Bellflower	*C. latifolia* (7–8)	rare, mainly in Buntingford area

1.2 Checklist of Characteristic Flora of Oak/Hornbeam Woods

Trees and shrubs

Pedunculate Oak	*Quercus robor* (4–5)	
Sessile Oak	*Q. petraea* (4–5)	
Sessile/Pedunculate Oak hybrid	*Q. petraea* × *robor*	
Hornbeam	*Carpinus betulus* (4–5)	
Field Maple	*Acer campestre* (5–6)	
Ash	*Fraxinus excelsior* (4–5)	
Silver Birch	*Betula pendula* (4–5)	on lighter drier soils
Downy Birch	*B. pubescens* (4–5)	more tolerant of damper conditions
Aspen	*Populus tremula* (2–3)	usually invasive into cleared areas
Wild Cherry	*Prunus avium* (4–5)	usually on deeper soils
Rowan	*Sorbus aucuparia* (5–6)	on acid soils
Wild Service Tree	*S. torminalis* (5–6)	occasional, usually as a single tree on clay soils in central, south and south-east Herts
Hazel	*Corylus avellana* (1–4)	
Holly	*Ilex aquifolium* (5–8)	
Alder Buckthorn	*Frangula alnus* (8–11)	rare in wetter woods of south Herts
Cherry Laurel	*Prunus laurocerasus* (4–6)	introduced, occasional
Rhododendron	*Rhododendron ponticum*	introduced and spreading in some localities at expense of ground flora
Heather	*Calluna vulgaris* (7–9)	occasional on acid soils in more open places
Butcher's Broom	*Ruscus aculeatus* (1–4)	rare, mainly on dry soils of south Herts

Appendix 1.2

Woody scramblers and climbers

Brambles	*Rubus fruticosus* agg. (5–9)
Raspberry	*R. idaeus* (6–8)
Honeysuckle	*Lonicera periclymenum* (6–9)

Ground flora

Bluebell	*Hyacinthoides non-scriptus* (4–6)	
Dog's Mercury	*Mercurialis perennis* (2–4)	
Wood Anemone	*Anemone nemorosa* (3–5)	
Enchanter's Nightshade	*Circaea lutetiana* (6–8)	
Lords-and-Ladies	*Arum maculatum* (4–5)	
Common Dog-violet	*Viola riviniana* (4–6, rarely 8–10)	
Herb Bennet or Wood Avens	*Geum urbanum* (6–8)	on damper soils
Greater Stitchwort	*Stellaria holostea* (4–6)	on heavier soils
Three-veined Sandwort	*Moehringia trinerva* (5–6)	on heavier, richer soils
Ivy	*Hedera helix* (9–11)	
Yellow Archangel	*Lamiastrum galeobdolon* (5–6)	especially frequent on Clay-with-Flints
Pignut	*Conopodium majus* (5–6)	mainly on acidic soils
Wood Sorrel	*Oxalis acetosella* (4–5)	most frequent on London Clay and Clay-with Flints
Yellow Pimpernel	*Lysimachia nemorum* (5–9)	more often in open areas on London Clay and Clay-with-Flints
Violet Helleborine	*Epipactis purpurata* (8–9)	rare
Broad-leaved Helleborine	*E. helleborine* (7–10)	scarce, mainly on London Clay
Toothwort	*Lathraea squamaria* (4–5)	scarce, mainly on Clay-with-Flints
Purple Toothwort	*L. clandestina* (4–5)	introduced, naturalised in Stevenage area
Ramsons	*Allium ursinum* (4–6)	scarce
Wild Strawberry	*Fragaria vesca* (4–6)	on drier soils
Barren Strawberry	*Potentilla sterilis* (4–5)	on drier soils
Bitter Vetch	*Lathyrus montanus* (4–7)	very rare on gravels
Opposite-leaved Golden saxifrage	*Chrysosplenium oppositifolium* (4–7)	scarce; mainly in wet woods on London Clay and gravels in Lea Valley
Lily-of-the-Valley	*Convallaria majalis* (5–6)	rare in south of county
Wild Daffodil	*Narcissus pseudonarcissus* (2–4)	in damper woods of central Herts
Moschatel	*Adoxa moschatellina* (4–5)	rare on gravels and decalcified Boulder Clay
Foxglove	*Digitalis purpurea* (6–9)	on acid soils
Cow-wheat	*Melampyrum pratense* (6–9)	on acid soils
Slender St John's-wort	*Hypericum pulchrum* (6–8)	on acid soils
Trailing St John's-wort	*H. humifusum* (6–9)	uncommon on acid soils
Wood Speedwell	*Veronica montana* (4–7)	in open places on acid soils
Heath Speedwell	*V. officinalis* (5–8)	in open places on acid soils

White Bryony	*Bryonia cretica* ssp. *dioica* (5–9)	
Black Bryony	*Tamus communis* (5–7)	
Wood Club-rush	*Scirpus sylvaticus* (6–7)	very rare, only site on damp soil at Cowheath Wood
Hairy Woodrush	*Luzula pilosa* (4–6)	
Heath Woodrush	*L. multiflora* (4–6)	more restricted to woods on London Clay and gravels
Great Woodrush	*L. sylvatica* (5–6)	more restricted to woods on London Clay and gravels
Pale Sedge	*Carex pallescens* (5–6)	rare on neutral soils around Stevenage
Wood False-brome	*Brachypodium sylvaticum* (7)	
Wood Melick	*Melica uniflora* (5–6)	on drier soils
Wood Meadow-grass	*Poa nemoralis* (6–7)	
Wood Millet	*Milium effusum* (6)	
Common Bent	*Agrostis capillaris* (6–8)	on drier soils
Wavy Hair-grass	*Deschampsia flexuosa* (6–7)	occasional on acid soils
Fine-leaved Sheep's-fescue	*Festuca tenuifolia* (5–6)	rare on acid soils
Hairy Brome	*Bromus ramosus* (7–8)	
Bracken	*Pteridium aquilinum*	common on dry soils
Male Fern	*Dryopteris filix-mas*	frequent in damper places
Lady-fern	*Athyrium filix-femina*	occasional on damp soils

Rides and clearings

Common Centaury	*Centaurium erythraea* (6–9)	
Red Campion	*Silene dioica* (5–6)	on soils tending towards acidity
White Campion	*S. latifolia* ssp. *alba* (5–9)	
Hybrid between Red and White Campion	*S. dioica* × *latifolia*	where ranges overlap
Devil's-bit Scabious	*Succisa pratensis* (6–10)	
Betony	*Stachys officinalis* (6–9)	
Lady's Mantle	*Alchemilla filicaulis* ssp. *vestita* (6–9)	uncommon
Marsh Cudweed	*Gnaphalium uliginosum* (7–9)	often in damp, rutted tracks
Heath Cudweed	*G. sylvaticum* (7–9)	possibly extinct, last record in Harmergreen Wood in 1979
Imperforate St John's-wort	*Hypericum maculatum* (6–8)	rare, mainly in south on damp soils
Greater Bird's-foot-trefoil	*Lotus uliginosus* (6–8)	in damp areas
Water Pepper	*Polygonum hydropiper* (7–9)	in damp areas
Water Purslane	*Lythrum portula* (6–10)	scarce in damp areas
Small-flowered Willowherb	*Epilobium roseum* ((7–8)	scarce on damp acid soils
Square-stemmed Willowherb	*E. tetragonum* (7–8)	on damper soils
Broad-leaved Willowherb	*E. montanum* (6–8)	on base-rich damp soils
American Willowherb	*E. ciliatum* (6–8)	introduced
Rosebay Willowherb	*Chamaenerion angustifolium* (7–9)	frequent in cleared or burnt areas

Appendix 1.3

Wood Groundsel	*Senecio sylvaticus* (7–9)	sometimes a feature in cleared sites on acid soils
Wavy Bitter-cress	*Cardamine flexuosa* (4–9)	in woods on London Clay
Hard Rush	*Juncus inflexus* (6–8)	on damper soils
Soft Rush	*J. effusus* (6–8)	on damper soils
Compact Rush	*J. conglomeratus* (5–7)	on damper soils
Pill Sedge	*Carex pilulifera* (5–6)	rare on acid soils

1.3 Checklist of Characteristic Wild Flowers of Beech Woods

Trees and shrubs

Beech	*Fagus sylvatica* (4–5)	
Wild Cherry	*Prunus avium* (4–5)	in deeper soils
Whitebeam	*Sorbus aria* (5–6)	in south-west Herts but scarce as tree
Ash	*Fraxinus excelsior* (4–5)	
Sycamore	*Acer pseudoplatanus* (4–6)	introduced, naturalised and invasive
Spurge Laurel	*Daphne laureola* (1–4)	mainly on chalk
Wayfaring Tree	*Viburnum lantana* (5–6)	mainly on Chalk
Wild Privet	*Ligustrum vulgare* (6–7)	most frequent on Chalk

Ground flora

Yellow Bird's-nest	*Monotropa hypopitys* (6–8)	very rare, mainly in south-west
Bird's-nest Orchid	*Neottia nidus-avis* (6–7)	very rare, declined from sites on Boulder Clay and now restricted to Chalk near Tring and Great Offley
Fly Orchid	*Ophrys insectifera* (5–7)	scarce on Chalk
White Helleborine	*Cephalanthera damasonium* (5–6)	frequent on Chalk
Narrow-leaved Helleborine	*Epipactis longifolia* (5–7)	possibly extinct, last record near Sarratt in 1925
Narrow-lipped Helleborine	*E. leptochila* (6–8)	very rare, near Tring
Green-flowered Helleborine	*E. phyllanthes* (7–8)	very rare, near Tring and Welwyn Garden City
Broad-leaved Helleborine	*E. helleborine* (7–10)	scarce
Sweet Woodruff	*Galium odoratum* (5–6)	mainly in well-established woods
Wood Sanicle	*Sanicula europaea* (5–9)	
Wood Spurge	*Euphorbia amygdaloides* (3–5)	
Wall Lettuce	*Mycelis muralis* (7–9)	
Common Wintergreen	*Pyrola minor* (6–8)	very rare, four sites mainly in south-west Herts
Coral-wort	*Cardamine bulbifera* (4–6)	very rare, near Chorleywood

Dog's Mercury	*Mercurialis perennis* (2–4)	
Bluebell	*Hyacinthoides non-scriptus* (4–6)	
Wood Sorrel	*Oxalis acetosella* (4–5)	
Goldilocks	*Ranunculus auricomus* (4–5)	
Hairy Violet	*Viola hirta* (4–5)	
Early Dog-violet	*V. reichenbachiana* (3–5)	
Common Dog-violet	*V. riviniana* (4–6, rarely 8–10)	
Slender St John's-wort	*Hypericum pulchrum* (6–8)	on acid soils
Wild Strawberry	*Fragaria vesca* (4–6)	
Barren Strawberry	*Potentilla sterilis* (4–5)	
Ivy	*Hedera helix* (9–11)	often abundant in plantations and secondary woods
Herb Bennet or Wood Avens	*Geum urbanum* (6–8)	on damper soils
White Bryony	*Bryonia cretica* ssp. *dioica* (5–9)	
Black Bryony	*Tamus communis* (5–7)	
Wild Clematis	*Clematis vitalba* (7–8)	
Giant Fescue	*Festuca gigantea* (6–7)	
Wood Melick	*Melica uniflora* (5–6)	
Wood False-brome	*Brachypodium sylvaticum* (7)	
Hairy Brome	*Bromus ramosus* (7–8)	
Wood Barley	*Hordelymus europaeus* (6–7)	

1.4 Checklist of Characteristic Chalk Grassland Wild Flowers

NB *Certain rarities, excluded here, are detailed in Appendix 1.5.*

Upright Brome	*Bromus erectus* (6–7)	often dominant
Red Fescue	*Festuca rubra* (5–7)	often abundant
Sheep's Fescue	*F. ovina* (5–7)	limited distribution in more open situations
Quaking Grass	*Briza media* (6–7)	probably introduced by early settlers, also known as 'Totty-grass', 'Shaking-shivers' or 'Doddering Dillies'
Crested Hair-grass	*Koeleria macrantha* (6–7)	on drier soils
Crested Dog's-tail	*Cynosaurus cristatus* (6–8)	also in other old grasslands on basic and acid soils
Meadow Oat-grass	*Avenula pratensis* (6)	uncommon, restricted to downs with short turf, apparently lost from southwest Herts

Downy or Hairy Oat-grass	*A. pubescens* (6–7)	fairly widespread in unimproved calcareous grasslands
Yellow Oat-grass	*Trisetum flavescens* (5–6)	common
False Oat-grass	*Arrhenatherum elatius* (6–7)	spreading in many sites, difficult to control and inhibiting to other flora
Smaller Cat's-tail	*Phleum pratense* ssp. *bertolonii* (7)	in wide range of old pastures
Timothy	*P. pratense* ssp. *pratense* (7)	in less heavily grazed areas, often cultivated for fodder
Flattened Meadow-grass	*Poa compressa* (6–8)	bare open places such as dry banks and pit margins
Fern Grass	*Desmazeria rigida* (5–6)	bare open places such as dry banks and pit margins
Cock's-foot	*Dactylis glomerata* (5–8)	tussocky, increases as grazing declines
Glaucous Sedge	*Carex flacca* (5–6)	common in most grasslands
Spring Sedge	*C. caryophyllea* (4–5)	scarce, restricted to short turf
Dandelion	*Taraxacum* agg.	complex apomictic group with, in Britain, over 130 microspecies, about half of which are known in Herts
Cowslip	*Primula veris* (4–5)	frequent
Hairy Violet	*Viola hirta* (4–5)	restricted to calcareous soils
Bulbous Buttercup	*Ranunculus bulbosus* (5–6)	frequent in most calcareous pastures and verges
Wild Strawberry	*Fragaria vesca* (4–6)	declining, mainly on scrubby banks
Common Bird's-foot-trefoil	*Lotus corniculatus* (6–9)	common
Hop Trefoil	*Trifolium campestre* (5–9)	restricted to calcareous soils, common
Lesser Trefoil	*T. dubium* (5–10)	common on many soils
Black Medick	*Medicago lupulina* (4–8)	common
Common Restharrow	*Ononis repens* (6–9)	reasonably frequent in unimproved grasslands on calcareous soils
Spiny Restharrow	*O. spinosa* (6–9)	rare, on damper Chalk soils and calcareous peat, also on acid soils at Hertford Heath
Sainfoin	*Onobrychis viciifolia* (6–8)	once extensive as fodder crop, readily colonises open Chalk banks and verges
Horseshoe Vetch	*Hippocrepis comosa* (5–7)	restricted mainly to short turf, declining
Kidney Vetch	*Anthyllis vulneraria* (6–9)	mainly on open, disturbed Chalk, declining
Common Milkwort	*Polygala vulgaris* (4–7)	common
Common Rock-rose	*Helianthemum nummularium* (5–9)	common
Salad Burnet	*Sanguisorba minor* (5–9)	often abundant
Dropwort	*Filipendula vulgaris* (5–8)	scarce in ancient calcareous grasslands in north Herts
Large Thyme	*Thymus pulegioides* (7–8)	occasional

Wild Thyme	*T. praecox* (5–8)	rare, first noted for Herts in 1950, now known in about ten localities, but not in south-west
Squinancywort	*Asperula cynanchia* (6–7)	short-turfed or disturbed Chalk
Fairy Flax	*Linum catharticum* (6–9)	common
Fragrant Orchid	*Gymnadenia conopsea* (6–8)	limited, generally small colonies
Pyramidal Orchid	*Anacamptis pyramidalis* (6–8)	not infrequent, tolerant of shade
Twayblade	*Listera ovata* (6–7)	occasional, more frequent in damper habitats
Common Spotted-orchid	*Dactylorhiza fuchsii* (6–8)	a variable and quite common species in several habitats
Bee Orchid	*Ophrys apifera* (6–7)	populations fluctuate, a rapid coloniser of certain disturbed sites, including new road verges
'Wasp' Orchid	*O. apifera* ssp. *trollii*	a rare variant noted in recent years from near Great Gaddesden and Hexton
Stemless Thistle	*Cirsium acaule* (7–9)	limited to unimproved calcareous grasslands and a good indicator of antiquity
Musk or Nodding Thistle	*Carduus nutans* (5–8)	casual on disturbed soils
Carline Thistle	*Carlina vulgaris* (7–10)	restricted to short Chalk turf, one of the best indicators of antiquity
Greater Knapweed	*Centaurea scabiosa* (7–9)	restricted to calcareous soils
Common Knapweed	*C. nigra* (6–9)	found in many grasslands on basic to acidic soils
Tall Broomrape	*Orobanche elatior* (6–7)	restricted to Chalk, mainly road banks of north Herts, parasitic on Greater Knapweed
Lesser Broomrape	*O. minor* (6–9)	mainly on calcareous soils, parasitic on clover and other plants, (but only Ground Ivy has been noted as other host in Herts), uncommon and declining
Devil'sbit Scabious	*Succisa pratensis* (6–10)	occasional
Field Scabious	*Knautia arvensis* (6–9)	on most calareous soils
Small Scabious	*Scabiosa columbaria* (7–8)	limited to Chalk, particularly in short turf
Clustered Bellflower	*Campanula glomerata* (6–10)	frequent
Harebell	*C. rotundifolia* (7–9)	on unimproved, dry grasslands and acid heaths
Burnet Saxifrage	*Pimpinella saxifraga* (7–8)	common
Wild Carrot	*Daucus carota* (7–9)	mainly in rough or ungrazed places
Wild Parsnip	*Pastinaca sativa* (7–8)	mainly in rough or ungrazed places

Hogweed, Keck or Cow Parsnip	*Heracleum sphondylium* (6–9)	spreading as downs are ungrazed or neglected
Cow Parsley	*Anthriscus sylvestris* (4–6)	spreading as downs are ungrazed or neglected
Rough Chervil	*Chaerophyllum temulentum* (6–7)	spreading as downs are ungrazed or neglected
Lady's Bedstraw	*Galium verum* (7–8)	common
Hedge Bedstraw	*G. mollugo* (6–9)	in poorly grazed places, a very variable species group whose taxonomy is still under debate
Agrimony	*Agrimonia eupatoria* (6–8)	common
Autumnal Hawkbit	*Leontodon autumnalis* (6–10)	common
Rough Hawkbit	*L. hispidus* (6–9)	more restricted to calcareous soils, common
Hairy Hawkbit	*L. taraxacoides* (6–9)	more limited to drier, unimproved grasslands
Smooth Hawk's-beard	*Crepis capillaris* (6–9)	common
Rough Hawk's-beard	*C. biennis* (6–7)	scarce and declining, on Chalk road verges in north Herts; also recorded from Watford, Borehamwood and Hemel Hempstead area on differing soil types
Beaked Hawk's-beard	*C. vesicaria* ssp. *haenseleri* (5–7)	introduced in 1874, spreading in open and disturbed calcareous soils
Milk- or Sow-Thistle	*Sonchus oleraceus* (6–8)	in disturbed soils
Spiny Milk- or Sow-Thistle	*S. asper* (6–8)	in disturbed places
Mouse-ear Hawkweed	*Hieracium (Pilosella) pilosella* (5–10)	locally common in dry open places
Goat's-beard	*Tragopogon pratensis* (6–7)	common
Oxeye Daisy	*Leucanthemum vulgare* (6–8)	common, often abundant in disturbed calcareous soils
Ragwort	*Senecio jacobea* (6–10)	common
Hoary Ragwort	*S. erucifolius* (7–8)	most frequent on Chalk
Ploughman's Spikenard	*Inula conyza* (7–9)	in open, especially disturbed sites
Common Valerian	*Valeriana officinalis* (6–8)	in rough grassy places
Wild Basil	*Clinopodium vulgare* (7–9)	common
Marjoram	*Origanum vulgare* (7–9)	mainly in ungrazed places
Eyebright	*Euphrasia nemorosa* (7–9)	fairly widespread, also occasionally in wood margins, rides, acid grasslands, scrub
Eyebright	*E. pseudokerneri* (7–9)	scarce, restricted to shorter turf on Chalk
Yellow-wort	*Blackstonia perfoliata* (6–10)	mainly on old, disturbed Chalk downs, pits and open banks; decline in southwest associated with rabbit loss
Common Centaury	*Centaurium erythraea* (6–9)	very occasional
Felwort	*Gentanella amarella* (8–10)	often abundant in short turf

Common Toadflax	*Linaria vulgaris* (7–10)	common in rough grassland
Hoary Plantain	*Plantago media* (5–8)	common
Ribwort Plantain	*P. lanceolata* (4–8)	common

1.5 Chalk Downland Rarities

Because of their physical characteristics and historical management over several millennia, chalk downlands evolved to support a wide variety of specialised plants. As we have seen, more recent withdrawals of sheep grazing, with consequent overgrowth of coarser grasses and scrub, coupled with losses through ploughing and other developments have dramatically reduced the extent of downland and its wild flowers in Hertfordshire. Reference has already been made to several scarce and uncommon species, but there is also a considerable portion of the county's downland flora which is designated rare or very rare. A number of species are now restricted to just one or two sites, in which some have total county populations of less than ten plants; all must be regarded with the utmost concern if local extinction is to be avoided. Five of the twenty-four full species listed below, including one known introduction, are of such national rarity, that is they are native British species recorded nationally in fifteen or fewer ten-kilometre squares since 1930, that they are listed in the *British Red Data Book – Vascular Plants* (Perring and Farrell, 1983).

Burnt or Dwarf Orchid	*Orchis ustulata* (5–6)	always scarce on a few short-turfed downs; last confirmed sighting of two plants at Therfield Heath in 1988
Musk Orchid	*Herminium monorchis* (6–7)	two sites, near Pirton, with a small colony, and near Great Offley where a single plant was found in 1987
Frog Orchid	*Coeloglossum viride* (6–8)	not uncommon in calcareous pastures in 19th century, now just three colonies, two on Chalk in south-west with about 80 and 5 plants respectively; third colony in Boulder Clay meadow with less than 5 plants
Hybrid between Frog and Common Spotted-orchid	× *Dactyloglossum mixta*	a single plant reported in 1972 at Sheethanger Common
Hybrid between Common Spotted-orchid and Fragrant Orchid	× *Dactylogymnadenia cookei;*	a single plant near Pirton in 1979
Autumn Lady's-tresses	*Spiranthes spiralis* (8–9)	used to flourish, often with Frog Orchid; only recent sightings are a site near Berkhamsted with 7 plants in 1974 and 1 in 1979, and at Therfield Heath with 2 in 1969 and 1 in 1979

Appendix 1.5

Early Spider-orchid	*Ophrys sphegodes* (5–6)	nationally rare; introduced to edge of Chalk pit in east Herts about 1960, small colony still flourishes
Green-winged Orchid	*Orchis morio* (5–6)	a few plants at Sheethanger Common and near Pirton are the only colonies now known for the Chalk
Southern Marsh-orchid	*Dactylorhiza majalis* ssp. *praetermissa* (6–7)	better known in base-rich marshes, small colonies have been recently recorded at Wiggington, Roughdown Common and near Baldock
Spotted Cat's-ear	*Hypocharis maculata* (6–8)	a national rarity, restricted to Therfield Heath with about 5 plants
'Dandelion' microspecies	*Taraxacum acutum*	a national rarity with, probably, the sole extant population restricted to Therfield Heath; formerly also known from Norfolk
Pasque Flower	*Pulsatilla vulgaris* (3–5)	once known from Aldbury Nowers, near Hexton and Arbury Banks at Ashwell, now restricted to Therfield Heath where strong population survives
Perennial Flax	*Linum perenne* (6–7)	a national rarity; a few plants discovered at Therfield Heath in 1978 survived until at least 1987
Lesser Meadow-rue	*Thalictrum minus* ssp. *minus* (6–8)	fairly common on parts of Therfield Heath and small colony on Chalk road-verge near Sandon, where it was first noted about 1843 and rediscovered in 1974
Bastard Toadflax	*Thesium humifusum* (6–8)	small colonies restricted to short turf on Therfield Heath
Field Fleawort	*Senecio integrifolius* (6–7)	lost from the south-west, small colonies about Hexton and reasonable populations at Therfield Heath
Purple Milk-vetch	*Astragalus danicus* (5–7)	never known from the south-west, Therfield Heath remains its stronghold although small colonies occur on banks of Icknield Way near Hexton and near Ashwell

Woolly-headed Thistle	*Cirsium eriophorum* (7–9)	most records are from the Hexton area, although it has been noted at Hartham Common, near Brent Pelham and Great Offley in recent years
Common Gromwell	*Lithospermum officinale* (6–7)	mainly restricted to tracksides and rabbit scrapes in Hexton area, but recent reports from Hinxworth and near Easneye
Hound's-tongue	*Cynoglossum officinale* (6–8)	always scarce and associated with disturbances, such as rabbit scrapes and pits; formerly known from south-east Herts; recent records from near Hexton and Reed
Viper's-bugloss	*Echium vulgare* (6–9)	found sparingly on light dry soils of disturbed Chalk, sands and gravels
Wild Candytuft	*Iberis amara* (6–8)	once not uncommon on disturbed areas; demise of rabbits has resulted in local extinction in south-west and reductions elsewhere; much declined populations survive near Hexton, railway banks near Baldock, a bank by Priors Wood near Ayot St Lawrence and Church Hill at Therfield Heath
Great Pignut	*Bunium bulbocastanum* (6–7)	a national rarity; the Middle Chalk of North Herts is at the centre of national distribution and about ten colonies are known, some supporting good populations, nearly all on road or track verges; apparently extinct in south-west Herts; once a fairly abundant arable weed
Chiltern Gentian	*Gentianella germanica* (9–10)	almost exclusively restricted to a few sites in the Wiggington, Aldbury and Great Gaddesden area; introduced into sites near Essendon and Hertford; hybrids with the closely related Felwort have been recorded

197

Appendix 1.6

Tor-grass	*Brachypodium pinnatum* (7)	this species is often locally dominant on some downs in southern England but, in Herts, it has only been reliably recorded sparingly, between 1950 and 1970, from below Therfield Heath, near Pirton, and on railway banks near Standon and Letchworth
Purple-stemmed Cat's-tail	*Phleum phleoides* (6–7)	a national rarity mostly confined to the breckland of Suffolk and Norfolk; first recorded for county at Hertford in 1840; only extant site is Wilbury Hill near Letchworth where it has been known since about 1843
Juniper	*Juniperus communis* (5–6)	once reasonably common, now four sites, Roughdown Common with 'several bushes', Sheethanger Common with three bushes in 1982, Chipperfield Common with a single bush in 1988 and, the main locality on acid soils, at Gustardwood Common, where about 25 bushes remain, most of which show signs of senescence or are overshaded

1.6 Checklist of Characteristic Wild Flowers of Largely Unimproved Neutral Grasslands

*Species marked * are useful indicators of well-established sites*

Perennial Rye-grass	*Lolium perenne* (5–8)	often dominant or co-dominant with Crested Dog's-tail on heavy soils in old pastures, also frequently sown in modern leys
Italian Rye-grass	*L. multiflorum* (5–9)	introduced in 1830 as fodder crop; now frequent in leys
Crested Dog's-tail	* *Cynosaurus cristatus* (6–8)	often co-dominant
Creeping Bent	*Agrostis stolonifera* (6–8)	common

198

Common name	Scientific name	Notes
Black Bent	*A. gigantea* (6–8)	frequent on lighter soils
Common Bent	*A. capillaris* (6–8)	on acidic soils
False Oat-grass	*Arrenatherum elatius* (6–7)	common
Cock's-foot	*Dactylis glomerata* (5–8)	common
Yorkshire Fog	*Holcus lanatus* (6–9)	common
Smaller Cat's-tail-grass	*Phleum pratense* ssp. *bertolonii* (7)	common on more basic soils
Timothy	*P. pratense* ssp. *pratense* (7)	common in less heavily grazed areas, often sown in leys
Annual Meadow-grass	*Poa annua* (1–12)	common
Smooth Meadow-grass	*P. pratensis* (5–7)	common on damper soils
Rough Meadow-grass	*P. trivialis* (6)	common on damper soils
Meadow Fox-tail	*Alopecurus pratensis* (4–6)	common on richer soils
Red Fescue	*Festuca rubra* (5–7)	common
Meadow Fescue	*F. pratensis* (6)	on heavier soils
Tall Fescue	*F. arundinacea* (6–8)	more restricted to damp soils
Sheep's Fescue	* *F. ovina* (5–7)	rare, in open situations
Sweet Vernal-grass	*Anthoxanthum odoratum* (4–6)	often abundant on neutral to acidic soils
Soft Brome or Lop Grass	*Bromus hordeaceus* (5–7)	common
Meadow Barley	* *Hordeum secalinum* (6–7)	declining on heavy clay soils
Wall Barley	*H. murinum* (6–7)	common in drier disturbed and waste places
Quaking Grass	* *Briza media* (6–7)	on mainly drier calcareous soils, uncommon
Downy Oat-grass	* *Avenula pubescens* (6–7)	uncommon on calareous soils
Yellow Oat-grass	* *Trisetum flavescens* (5–6)	fairly frequent
Hairy Sedge	* *Carex hirta* (5–6)	quite frequent on heavy and wet soils
Glaucous Sedge	* *C. flacca* (5–6)	often common
Spiked Sedge	* *C. spicata* (6–7)	occasional on damper, less basic soils
Grey Sedge	* *C. divulsa* (6–7)	similar distribution to Spiked Sedge
Field Wood-rush	* *Luzula campestris* (3–6)	often frequent
Adder's-tongue	* *Ophioglossum vulgatum*	a fern, declining in damper basic sites
Yarrow	*Achillea millefolium* (6–8)	common
Sneezewort	* *A. ptarmica* (7–8)	damper more acidic sites, mainly in south-east
Agrimony	* *Agrimonia eupatoria* (6–8)	common
Lady's-mantle	* *Alchemilla filicaulis* ssp. *vestita* (6–9)	rare
Daisy	*Bellis perennis* (3–10)	common
Musk or Nodding Thistle	*Carduus nutans* (5–8)	occasional on disturbed soils
Common Knapweed	* *Centaurea nigra* (6–9)	common and widespread
Greater Knapweed	* *C. scabiosa* (7–9)	fairly frequent on calcareous soils
Centaury	* *Centaurium erythraea* (6–9)	on open acidic soils
Field Mouse-ear Chickweed	* *Cerastium arvense* (4–8)	rare, in dry calcareous or acid soils
Dusty Miller or Snow-in-Summer	*C. tomentosum* (5–8)	occasional as garden escape
Common Mouse-ear Chickweed	*C. fontanum* (4–9)	common and widespread

199

Sticky Mouse-ear Chickweed	*C. glomeratum* (4–9)	very common and widespread, especially in disturbed places
Sea Mouse-ear	*C. diffusum* (5–7)	very rare in dry gravelly or sandy places
Little Mouse-ear Chickweed	*C. semidecandrum* (4–5)	very rare on sandy soils
Creeping Thistle	*Cirsium arvense* (7–9)	common, often abundant in disturbed, poorly managed and over-grazed sites
Spear Thistle	*C. vulgare* (7–10)	similar distribution to Creeping Thistle
Marsh Thistle	* *C. palustre* (7–9)	common in moist areas
Stemless Thistle	* *C. acaule* (7–9)	rare, in short turf on calcareous soils
Wild Basil	*Clinopodium vulgare* (7–9)	reasonably common at some sites on calcareous soils
Pignut	* *Conopodium majus* (5–6)	on more acidic soils, especially in central and south Herts
Common Spotted-orchid	* *Dactylorhiza fuchsii* (6–8)	local on moister, neutral to calcareous, soils
Bee Orchid	*Ophrys apifera* (6–7)	occasional, usually in short open turf; may colonise recently disturbed areas
Early-purple Orchid	* *Orchis mascula* (4–6)	scarce, in richer less intesively grazed pastures
Green-winged Orchid	* *O. morio* (5–6)	very rare, four of its six known sites are damp neutral grasslands, fortunately protected as nature reserves or SSSIs, but populations are rather small
Frog Orchid	* *Coeloglossum viride* (6–8)	very rare, only one site in Boulder Clay pasture, with less than five plants
Wild Carrot	*Daucus carota* (7–9)	fairly common on calcareous soils
Eyebright	*Euphrasia nemorosa* (7–9)	scarce, on drier acidic soils
Dropwort	* *Filipendula vulgaris* (5–8)	very rare, only one site, in Chalky Boulder Clay pasture
Snake's-head or Fritillary	* *Fritillaria meleagris* (4–5)	very rare, probably now only two small colonies on damp soils near Northaw and at 'Park Grass', Rothamsted where it was probably introduced in 19th century
Lady's Bedstraw	*Galium verum* (7–8)	frequent
Hedge Bedstraw	*G. mollugo* (6–9)	frequent on calcareous soils
Dyer's Greenweed	* *Genista tinctoria* (7–9)	uncommon in slightly acid pastures and acid heaths
Petty Whin or Needle Furze	* *G. anglica* (5–6)	in similar situations to Dyer's Greenweed but scarcer

Small-flowered Crane's-bill	* *Geranium pusillum* (6–9)	not uncommon in drier grasslands on gravelly soils in central and south-east Herts
Dove's-foot Crane's-bill	*G. molle* (4–9)	widespread on dry soils
Cut-leaved Crane's-bill	*G. dissectum* (5–8)	common
Long-stalked Crane's-bill	* *G. columbinum* (6–7)	very rare in dry open basic grassland, only two recent records from near Great Offley in 1978 and Batchwood in 1981
Ground Ivy	*Glechoma hederacea* (3–5)	common on damper soils
Mouse-ear Hawkweed	*Hieracium (Pilosella) pilosella* (5–10)	locally common on drier, open soils
Perforate St John's-wort	*Hypericum perforatum* (6–9)	fairly common except on on Boulder Clay
Cat's-ear	*Hypochoeris radicata* (6–9)	common except on calcareous soils
Field Scabious	*Knautia arvensis* (6–9)	common on calcareous soils
Meadow Vetchling	* *Lathyrus pratensis* (5–8)	common and widespread
Grass Vetchling	*L. nissiola* (5–7)	scarce in rough grassland
Autumnal Hawkbit	*Leontodon autumnalis* (6–10)	common
Rough Hawkbit	*L. hispidus* (6–9)	frequent on more calcareous soils
Hairy Hawkbit	*L. taraxacoides* (6–9)	more local on base-rich soils
Oxeye Daisy	*Leucanthemum vulgare* (6–8)	common particularly on calcareous soils, often abundant in recently disturbed places
Common Toadflax	*Linaria vulgaris* (7–10)	common in rough grassland, especially on more calcareous soils, although scarce on Boulder Clay
Fairy Flax	* *Linum catharticum* (6–9)	fairly common, especially on calcareous soils
Twayblade	*Listera ovata* (6–7)	occasional
Common Bird's-foot-trefoil	*Lotus corniculatus* (6–9)	common
Greater Bird's-foot-trefoil	*L. uliginosus* (6–8)	scarce, in damp places mainly on London Clay
Narrow-leaved Bird's-foot-trefoil	*L. tenuis* (6–8)	very rare, only 3 recent records, two of which are from disturbed places, the third is from rough pasture near Mill Green
Black Medick	*Medicago lupulina* (4–8)	common
Red Bartsia	*Odontites verna* (6–7)	common on more calcareous soils
Common Restharrow	* *Ononis repens* (6–9)	fairly common on calcareous soils
Burnet Saxifrage	*Pimpinella saxifraga* (7–8)	common, especially in short turf
Ribwort Plantain	*Plantago lanceolata* (4–8)	common
Hoary Plantain	* *P. media* (5–8)	frequent on calcareous soils

Common Milkwort	* *Polygala vulgaris* (4–7)	occasional on more calcareous soils
Heath Milkwort	* *P. serpyllifolia* (5–8)	rare on acidic soils
Silverweed	*Potentilla anserina* (6–8)	common in damper places
Creeping Cinquefoil	*P. reptans* (6–9)	common, sometimes abundant
Cowslip	* *Primula veris* (4–5)	fairly common on more basic and calcareous soils
Selfheal	*Prunella vulgaris* (6–9)	common
Creeping Buttercup	*Ranunculus repens* (5–8)	common
Meadow Buttercup	*R. acris* (5–7)	common
Bulbous Buttercup	* *R. bulbosus* (5–6)	common on more calcareous soils
Lesser Celandine	* *R. ficaria* (3–5)	occasional in damper more basic soils
Yellow Rattle	* *Rhinanthus minor* (5–7)	occasional
Common Sorrel	*Rumex acetosa* (5–6)	common
Sharp Dock	*R. conglomeratus* (7–8)	common in damper places
Curled Dock	*R. crispus* (6–10)	common in rough places
Fiddle Dock	*R. pulcher* (6–7)	rare, dry places, only eight recent records including Sarratt Bottom and Windmill Hill, Hitchin
Red-veined Dock	*R. sanguineus* (6–8)	fairly common in rough grassland
Common Annual Pearlwort	*Sagina apetala* (5–8)	occasional in bare places on drier soils
Procumbent Pearlwort	*S. procumbens* (5–9)	common in bare places on damper soils
Betony	* *Stachys officinalis* (6–9)	occasional on lighter soils
Salad Burnet	* *Sanguisorba minor* (5–9)	common, especially on calcareous soils
Meadow Saxifrage	* *Saxifraga granulata* (4–6)	uncommon on base-rich soils
Ragwort	*Senecio jacobea* (6–10)	common, notably in poorly managed and over-grazed places
Hoary Ragwort	*S. erucifolius* (7–8)	fairly common on more calcareous soils
Saw-wort	* *Serratula tinctoria* (7–9)	rare, confined to a few damper sites in Brookmans Park to Barnet area
Pepper Saxifrage	* *Silaum silaus* (6–8)	occasional, mainly on clay soils
Devil's-bit Scabious	* *Succisa pratensis* (6–10)	occasional on damper soils
Dandelions	*Taraxacum* spp.	common and widespread with several micro-species
Goat's-beard	* *Tragopogon pratensis* (6–7)	on more calcareous soils
Red Clover	*Trifolium pratense* (5–9)	common
White Clover	*T. repens* (6–9)	common, especially on clay soils
Lesser Trefoil	*T. dubium* (5–10)	common. especially in drier places
Alsike Clover	*T. hybridum* (6–9)	introduced, commonly cultivated; more frequent on less calcareous soils

Hare's-foot Clover	* *T. arvense* (6–9)	scarce and declining on light sandy soils
Hop Trefoil	*T. campestre* (6–9)	reasonably common on open drier soils and in bare places
Strawberry Clover	* *T. fragiferum* (7–9)	scarce, in a few sites on Boulder Clay near Weston and Walkern and on river gravels between London Colney and Hertford
Zigzag Clover	*T. medium* (6–9)	mainly on clay soils in south of county
Slender Trefoil	*T. micranthum* (6–7)	scarce in short turf on less calcareous soils
Sulphur Clover	* *T. ochroleucon* (6–7)	very rare on Boulder Clay, much declined; reasonable populations now remain only at Norton Common and the golf course, Letchworth
Knotted Clover	* *T. striatum* (5–7)	scarce on dry open soils mainly around Hertford
Stinging Nettle	*Urtica dioica* (6–8)	frequent, often indicative of neglect and poor management
Common Valerian	*Valeriana officinalis* (6–8)	occasional in ungrazed places on both damp and dry soils
Germander Speedwell	* *Veronica chamaedrys* (3–7)	common
Thyme-leaved Speedwell	* *V. serpyllifolia* (3–10)	fairly common on less calcareous soils
Tufted Vetch	* *Vicia cracca* (6–8)	frequent except on Clay-with-Flints and decalcified Boulder Clay
Hairy Tare	*V. hirsuta* (5–8)	common on drier less calcareous soils
Smooth Tare	*V. tetrasperma* (5–8)	similar distribution to Hairy Tare but noticeably less frequent
Common Vetch	*V. sativa* (5–9)	fairly common in less well-managed places with two subspecies; ssp. *nigra* is native and most frequent on less calcareous soils; spp. *sativa,* cultivated as fodder, is more widespread, often as escape
Bush Vetch	*V. sepium* (5–8)	common in field margins and hedges, except on highly calcareous soils
Hairy Violet	*Viola hirta* (4–5)	occasional in short turf on calcareous soils

1.7 Checklist of Characteristic Wild Flowers of Unimproved Wet Grasslands

NB *See also neutral grasslands*

Perennial Rye-grass	*Lolium perenne* (5–8)	often co-dominant
Crested Dog's-tail	*Cynosaurus cristatus* (6–8)	often co-dominant
Creeping Bent	*Agrostis stolonifera* (7–8)	common
Meadow Foxtail	*Alopecurus pratensis* (5–7)	common
Marsh Foxtail	*A. geniculatus* (6–7)	fairly common on neutral to slightly acidic soils
Yorkshire Fog	*Holcus lanatus* (6–9)	common
Tufted Hair-grass	*Deschampsia cespitosa* (6–8)	common
Red Fescue	*Festuca rubra* (5–7)	common
Sweet Vernal-grass	*Anthoxanthum odoratum* (4–6)	frequent on less calcareous soils
Smooth Meadow-grass	*Poa pratensis* (5–7)	common
Spreading Meadow-grass	*P. subcaerulea* (5–7)	very rare, only four recent records
Smooth Brome	*Bromus racemosus* (6)	once frequent, now very rare with a single recent record from near Bayford
Reed-grass	*Phalaris arundinacea* (6–7)	in more permanently wet places, once important in meadows on alluvial soils
Common Reed	*Phragmites australis* (8–9)	in permanently wet places and may spread if management neglected
Floating Sweet-grass	*Glyceria fluitans* (5–8)	common in slow-moving waters and pond margins
Small Sweet-grass	*G. declinata* (6–9)	less common, in more or less permanently wet places and pond margins
Plicate Sweet-grass	*G. plicata* (5–6)	fairly frequent in streams, ditches and swampy places
Hairy Sweet-grass	*G. × pedicillata* (6–7)	this hybrid between *fluitans* and *plicata* has been found at a number of sites without either parent species being noted
Soft Rush	*Juncus effusus* (6–8)	common, especially in less calcareous conditions
Hard Rush	*J. inflexus* (6–8)	common, although less frequent away from basic or neutral soils
Compact Rush	*J. conglomeratus* (5–7)	frequent, prefers acidic soils
Jointed Rush	*J. articulatus* (6–9)	frequent, prefers acidic soils in more open sites
Toad Rush	*J. bufonius* (5–9)	common in less calcareous and open areas, especially along tracks and around ponds
Glaucous Sedge	*Carex flacca* (5–6)	common
Spiked Sedge	*C. spicata* (6–7)	occasional on less basic soils
Grey Sedge	*C. divulsa* (6–7)	similar situations to Spiked Sedge

Hairy Sedge	*C. hirta* (5–6)	common
False Fox-sedge	*C. otrubae* (6–7)	fairly frequent on clay soils
Brown Sedge	*C. distichia* (7–8)	occasional on more basic soils
Carnation-grass	*C. panicea* (5–6)	more restricted to sites on the Boulder Clay, often in association with Glaucous Sedge
Bristle Club-rush	*Isolepis setacea* (5–7)	scarce, known from about eight sites scattered across the county
Adder's-tongue	*Ophioglossum vulgatum*	a fern of more basic soils, frequent
Marsh Marigold	*Caltha palustris* (3–7)	declining, most frequent in mineral flushes on calcareous soils, stream and pond margins
Lesser Spearwort	*Ranunculus flammula* (5–9)	occasional, most frequent in south-east Herts on less calcareous soils
Cuckoo-flower or Ladies-smock	*Cardamine pratensis* (4–6)	fairly common
Ragged Robin	*Lychnis flos-cuculi* (5–8)	not uncommon in more permanently damp places; rare or absent in south-west Herts
Devil's-bit Scabious	*Succisa pratensis* (6–10)	occasional
Fleabane	*Pulicaria dysenterica* (8–9)	common
Brooklime	*Veronica beccabunga* (5–9)	common
Procumbent Pearlwort	*Sagina procumbens* (5–9)	common in bare and open places
Knotted Pearlwort	*S. nodosa* (7–9)	always rare possibly now extinct, the last record was from near Sandon in 1957
Water Mint	*Mentha aquatica* (7–10)	frequent in wetter places where management is low
Silverweed	*Potentilla anserina* (5–8)	common, especially where grazing and trampling levels are high
Tormentil	*P. erecta* (6–9)	occasional in more acid places
Creeping Jenny	*Lysimachia nummularia* (6–8)	occasional to frequent in wetter less-managed sites
Square-stemmed St John's-wort	*Hypericum tetrapterum* (6–9)	fairly frequent
Marsh Bedstraw	*Galium palustre* (6–7)	fairly frequent in wetter, less-managed places
Fen Bedstraw	*G. uliginosum* (7–8)	scarce, about 20 sites known, on basic to calcareous soils
Twayblade	*Listera ovata* (6–7)	occasional
Common Spotted-orchid	*Dactylorhiza fuchsii* (6–8)	occasional
Southern Marsh-orchid	*D. majalis* ssp. *praetermissa* (6–7)	scarce, mainly in wetter places
Early marsh-orchid	*D. incarnata* (5–8)	very rare in wetter calcareous sites, recent records from just five sites

These three *Dactylorhiza* orchids have great tendencies to hybridise and at a few sites, where they occur together, hybrids between all three may be found

Frog Orchid	*Coeloglossum viride* (6–8)	very rare, a single Boulder Clay site with less than five plants
Great Hairy Willowherb	*Epilobium hirsutum* (7–8)	common in wetter places where management levels are low
Redshank	*Polygonum persicaria* (6–10)	common
Common Bistort	*P. bistorta* (6–8)	rare, with recent records from Weston, Purwell near Hitchin, and Therfield
Great Burnet	*Sanguisorba officinalis* (6–9)	rare, recent records from Rye Meads, Totteridge Green and near Barwick
Spiny Restharrow	*Ononis spinosa* (6–9)	rare, recent records from calcareous sites near Hitchin and on more acidic road verge at Hertford Heath
Marsh Valerian	*Valeriana dioica* (5–6)	rare at wetter calcareous sites near Hitchin, Stevenage, Norton Common at Letchworth, Sandon and Reed
Water Figwort	*Scrophularia auriculata* (6–9)	common in wetter places, along ditches and pond margins
Angelica	*Angelica sylvestris* (7–9)	fairly common in damper places with low management
Meadowsweet	*Filipendula ulmaria* (6–9)	frequent in wetter places, especially sites with lapsed management

1.8 Checklist of the Wild Flowers of Unimproved Acid Grasslands

Common Bent-grass	*Agrostis capillaris* (6–8)	frequent to dominant
Sweet Vernal-grass	*Anthoxanthum odoratum* (4–6)	frequent to dominant
Creeping Soft-grass	*Holcus mollis* (6–7)	frequent
Red Fescue	*Festuca rubra* (5–7)	frequent
Sheep's-fescue	*F. ovina* (5–7)	occasional in open places
Fine-leaved Sheep's-fescue	*F. tenuifolia* (5–6)	rare on sands in central Herts
Heath grass	*Danthonia decumbens* (7)	very rare, only five locations
Wavy Hair-grass	*Deschampsia flexuosa* (6–7)	occasional
Lesser Stitchwort	*Stellaria graminea* (5–8)	common
Tormentil	*Potentilla erecta* (5–9)	common

Creeping Cinquefoil	*P. reptans* (6–9)	very common
Hybrid between Tormentil and Creeping Cinquefoil	*P. × mixta*	not uncommon in central and south-east Herts
Hoary Cinquefoil	*P. argentea* (6–9)	rare in central Herts
Lady's Bedstraw	*Galium verum* (7–8)	common
Heath Bedstraw	*G. saxatile* (6–8)	occasional on more acid open soils
Betony	*Stachys officinalis* (6–9)	occasional
Sheep's Sorrel	*Rumex acetosella* (5–8)	common
Ribwort Plantain	*Plantago lanceolata* (4–8)	common
Common Bird's-foot-trefoil	*Lotus corniculatus* (6–9)	common
Yarrow	*Achillea millefolium* (6–8)	common
Sneezewort	*A. ptarmica* (7–8)	damper sites, mainly in south-east
Pignut	*Conopodium majus* (5–6)	common in central and south-east Herts
Centaury	*Centaurium erythraea* (6–9)	fairly common on more open soils
Harebell	*Campanula rotundifolia* (7–9)	occasional
Trailing St John's-wort	*Hypericum humifusum* (6–9)	rare
Cat's-ear	*Hypochoeris radicata* (6–9)	common
Mouse-ear Hawkweed	*Hieracium (Pilosella) pilosella* (5–10)	locally common on drier open soils
Ragwort	*Senecio jacobea* (6–10)	common especially at poorly managed and over-grazed sites
Saw-wort	*Serratula tinctoria* (7–9)	rare, confined to a few damp sites in the Brookmans Park to Potters Bar area
Autumnal Hawkbit	*Leontodon autumnalis* (6–10)	common
Selfheal	*Prunella vulgaris* (6–9)	common
Small-flowered Cranesbill	*Geranium pusillum* (6–9)	common
Sticky Mouse-ear Chickweed	*Cerastium glomeratum* (4–9)	very common in disturbed places
Wall Speedwell	*Veronica arvensis* (3–10)	frequent on bare patches
Thyme-leaved Speedwell	*V. serpyllifolia* (3–10)	frequent
Heath Speedwell	*V. officinalis* (5–8)	occasional
Musk Thistle	*Carduus nutans* (5–8)	occasional on dry disturbed soils
Dyer's Greenweed	*Genista tinctoria* (7–8)	rare, mainly in rough pastures on London Clay
Hare's-foot Clover	*Trifolium arvense* (6–9)	scarce and declining
Knotted Clover	*T. striatum* (6–7)	rare, about seven recent records from south-east Herts
Changing Forget-me-not	*Myosotis discolor* (5–9)	scarce on open gravelly soils
Field Wood-rush	*Luzula campestris* (3–6)	common
Heath Wood-rush	*L. multiflora* (4–6)	occasional on more acidic soils
Hairy Sedge	*Carex hirta* (5–6)	common on damper soils
Prickly Sedge	*C. muricata* (5–6)	very rare, only two records since 1970

1.9 Checklist of the Characteristic Wild Flowers of Swamps and Marshes

NB *See also neutral and wet grasslands*

Common Reed	*Phragmites australis* (8–9)	common in swampy or shallow, slow-flowing water of fens, ponds, lakes and river margins, often in dense stands; our tallest grass
Reed-grass	*Phalaris arundinacea* (6–7)	found in similar conditions to Common Reed but more acid-tolerant
Tufted Hair-grass	*Deschampsia caespitosa* (6–8)	common
Marsh Foxtail	*Alopecurus geniculatus* (6–7)	fairly common in less calcareous conditions
Purple Moor-grass	*Molinea caerulea* (6–8)	rare, seven locations in Herts, all on acid soils except that on Boulder Clay at Norton Common
Hard Rush	*Juncus inflexux* (6–8)	common on more basic soils
Soft Rush	*J. effusus* (6–8)	common on less basic soils
Compact Rush	*J. conglomeratus* (5–7)	frequent on less basic soils
Jointed Rush	*J. articulatus* (6–9)	reasonably common on acidic soils
Blunt-flowered Rush	*J. subnodulosus* (7–9)	scarce, a fen species recorded from about 15 sites
Sharp-flowered Rush	*J. acutiflorus* (7–9)	occasional on more acidic soils
Toad Rush	*J. bufonius* (5–9)	common on open, neutral to acidic soils
Glaucous Sedge	*Carex flacca* (5–6)	common
Brown Sedge	*C. disticha* (7–8)	occasional on basic soils
Spiked Sedge	*C. spicata* (6–7)	occasional on less basic soils
False Fox-sedge	*C. otrubae* (6–7)	common
Hairy Sedge	*C. hirta* (5–6)	common
Greater Tussock-sedge	*C. paniculata* (5–6)	scarce, mainly a feature of carr and swampy woods
Carnation-grass	*C. panicea* (5–6)	scarce, 16 sites mainly on Boulder Clay
Distant Sedge	*C. distans* (5–6)	rare, only recent records from Ickleford, Norton Common, Sandon, near Ardeley and Claypits Meadow
Tufted Sedge	*C. elata* (5–6)	very rare, only known from Braughing Mead
Tawny Sedge	*C. hostiana* (6)	very rare, only recent record is from a calcareous flush at Foulwells near Brickendon
Yellow Sedge	*C. lepidocarpa* (6–7)	very rare, only recent record from Norton Common
Beaked or Bottle Sedge	*C. rostrata* (6–7)	very rare, only known from Purwell Meadow near Hitchin

Bladder Sedge	*C. vesicaria* (6)	rare, three recent reports from Oughtonhead Common, Knebworth Park and Braughing Meads in swampy conditions
Tufted or Graceful Sedge	*C. acuta* (5–7)	very rare, only recent records from margin of Tring Reservoir and wet flush near Ardeley
Common Sedge	*C. nigra* (6–8)	occasional, mainly on less calcareous soils
Common Spike-rush	*Eleocharis palustris* (5–7)	frequent in marshes, pondsides and ditches
Few-flowered Spike-rush	*E. quinqueflora* (7–8)	very rare, only known from base-rich peat near Sandon and Foulwells
Bristle Club-rush	*Isolepis setacea* (5–7)	rare; recent records from five sites including Claypits Meadow and Colney Heath
Marsh Marigold	*Caltha palustris* (3–7)	fairly common, mainly in calcareous situations along flush lines, stream and pond margins
Lesser Spearwort	*Ranunculus flammula* (5–9)	occasional, mostly in south-east Herts
Cuckoo-flower or Ladies-Smock	*Cardamine pratensis* (4–6)	common
Ragged Robin	*Lychnis flos-cuculi* (5–8)	common
Creeping Jenny	*Lysimachia nummularia* (6–8)	common
Marsh Thistle	*Cirsium palustre* (7–9)	common
Tormentil	*Potentilla erecta* (6–9)	occasional, usually in more acid situations
Greater Bird's-foot-trefoil	*Lotus uliginosus* (6–8)	most often on acidic clay soils
Water Figwort	*Scrophularia auriculata* (6–9)	common
Brooklime	*Veronica beccabunga* (5–9)	common
Water Mint	*Mentha aquatica* (7–10)	common
Fen Bedstraw	*Galium uliginosum* (7–8)	restricted to about 20 sites on basic soils
Marsh Bedstraw	*G. palustre* (6–7)	common
Fleabane	*Pulicaria dysenterica* (8–9)	common
Marsh Valerian	*Valeriana dioica* (5–6)	rare in base-rich sites at Norton Common, near Hitchin, Stevenage, Sandon and Reed
Devil's-bit Scabious	*Succisa pratensis* (6–10)	occasional
Twayblade	*Listera ovata* (6–7)	reasonably common on neutral to basic soils
Common Spotted-orchid	*Dactylorhiza fuchsii* (6–8)	occasional
Southern Marsh-orchid	*D. majalis* ssp. *praetermissa* (6–7)	occasional
Early Marsh-orchid	*D. incarnata* (5–8)	rare, five sites near Sandon, Ardeley, Hoddesdon, Cheshunt and Tring

Dactylorhiza species are known to hybridise readily and, at sites where the above occur together, gradations of hybridisation between all three are not infrequent

Marsh Fragrant Orchid	*Gymnadenia conopsea* ssp. *densiflora* (6–7)	very rare, perhaps 20 plants at a single locality in central Herts
Marsh Helleborine	*Epipactis palustris* (6–8)	very rare, one site in central Hertfordshire with population that has ranged from over 100 plants in 1978 to just one in 1980
Great Hairy Willowherb	*Epilobium hirsutum* (7–8)	common, often abundant in unmanaged and drying sites
Hoary or Small-flowered Hairy Willowherb	*E. parviflorum* (7–8)	common
Short-fruited Willowherb	*E. obscurum* (7–8)	occasional
Marsh Willowherb	*E. palustre* (7–8)	rare, a calcifuge with recent reports from Purwell Meadows, Patmore Heath and Tyttenhanger
Marsh Ragwort	*Senecio aquaticus* (7–8)	occasional and declining, recent records from a dozen scattered sites
Marsh Pennywort	*Hydrocotyle vulgaris* (6–8)	scarce, with five sites at Norton Common, near Barkway, Hertford Heath, Croxley Common Moor and near Aldenham Reservoir
Parsley Water-dropwort	*Oenanthe lachenalii* (6–9)	very rare, the sole locality on peat over Boulder Clay at Norton Common
Angelica	*Angelica sylvestris* (7–9)	fairly common in swamps and unmanaged marshes
Tufted Forget-me-not	*Myosotis laxa* ssp. *caespitosa* (5–8)	occasional on acidic soils
Water Chickweed	*Myosoton aquaticum* (7–8)	fairly common on acid soils
Marsh Arrow-grass	*Triglochin palustris* (6–8)	very rare, the only post-1974 sightings are from Foulwells, Lemsford, Archers Green and Purwell Meadows
Brookweed	*Samolus valerandi* (6–8)	always very rare, now possibly extinct although small colony found in ditchside north of Ashwell in 1980
Meadowsweet	*Filipendula ulmaria* (6–9)	common, especially in unmanaged sites
Water Avens	*Geum rivale* (5–9)	always very rare, possibly extinct, a recent report from Patmore Heath may have been an introduction

Common Meadow-rue	*Thalictrum flavum* (7–8)	scarce, mainly in swampy river margins at a few sites by Rivers Colne, Lea and Stort
Golden-rod	*Solidago gigantea* (8–10)	occasional as a garden escape
Michaelmas Daisy	*Aster nova-belgae* (8–9)	occasional as a garden escape
Hemp Agrimony	*Eupatorium cannabinum* (7–9)	occasional in unmanaged and drying sites
Field Milk-thistle	*Sonchus arvensis* (7–10)	common in unmanaged sites
Stinging Nettle	*Urtica dioica* (6–8)	common in unmanaged and drying sites
Adder's-tongue	*Ophioglossum vulgatum*	a fern not uncommon in less heavily managed sites on basic soils
Great Horsetail	*Equisetum telmateia*	scarce, also by ponds and streams
Marsh Horsetail	*E. palustre*	scarce, also by ponds and ditches

1.10 Checklist of Characteristic Wild Flowers of Headwaters

Aquatic and emergent species

Chalk-stream Water-crowfoot	*Ranunculus penicillatus* var. *calcareus* (5–8)	typical of good-quality calcareous streams
Common Water-crowfoot	*R. aquatilis* (5–6)	rare, has been found in spring pool at Lemsford
Pond Water-crowfoot	*R. peltatus* (5–8)	occasional, most records from south-east of county
Ivy-leaved Crowfoot	*R. hederaceus* (6–9)	rare, only five sites reported in last decade, with muddy non-calcareous substrates mainly in southern Herts (A site near Stevenage was destroyed in 1989)
Common Water-starwort	*Callitriche stagnalis* (5–9)	the most common and widespread species found in streams, ponds and wet woodland rides
Blunt-fruited Water-starwort	*C. obtusangula* (5–9)	local with recent records from Rivers Mimram, Hiz, Purwell and Rhee
Intermediate Water-starwort	*C. hamulata* (5–9)	scarce, mainly by ponds and gravel pits, but has been recorded from the upper reaches of River Mimram
Various-leaved Water-starwort	*C. platycarpa* (5–9)	apparently once not uncommon, but now seriously declined, the only recent report from River Lea in 1980

211

Opposite-leaved Pondweed	*Groenlandia densa* (5–9)	occasional
Green or Summer Watercress	*Nasturtium officinale* (5–10)	common, often abundant, in calcareous waters
One-rowed Watercress	*N. microphyllum* (6–10)	common, but less frequent, in highly calcareous waters
Brown or Winter Watercress	*N. microphyllum* × *officinale* (5–10)	a hybrid frequent where both parents are present
Fool's Watercress	*Apium nodiflorum* (7–8)	frequent
Narrow-leaved Water-parsnip	*Berula erecta* (7–9)	local
Spiked Water-milfoil	*Myriophyllum spicatum* (6–7)	scarce, although locally frequent along River Chess

Marginal species

Plicate Sweet-grass	*Glyceria plicata* (5–6)	frequent
Floating Sweet-grass	*G. fluitans* (5–8)	occasional, more often by slow-moving water or ponds
Small Sweet-grass	*G. declinata* (6–9)	scarce, more often by ponds
Hybrid Sweet-grass	*G.* × *pedicillata* (6–7)	scarce, a hybrid between *fluitans* and *plicata*, it may be found in sites without either parent
Hard Rush	*Juncus inflexus* (6–8)	common
Soft Rush	*J. effusus* (6–8)	common
Marsh Marigold	*Caltha palustris* (3–7)	most frequent in calcareous flushes, declining
Water Mint	*Menta aquatica* (7–10)	frequent
Brooklime	*Veronica beccabunga* (5–8)	common
Angelica	*Angelica sylvestris* (7–9)	common in overgrown places
Water Chickweed	*Myosoton aquaticum* (7–8)	occasional
Marsh Thistle	*Cirsium palustre* (7–9)	common
Ragged Robin	*Lychnis flos-cuculi* (5–8)	occasional
Water Figwort	*Scrophularia auriculata* (6–9)	common
Great Hairy Willowherb	*Epilobium hirsutum* (7–8)	common to abundant
Square-stemmed Willowherb	*E. tetragonum* (7–8)	occasional
Blue Water-speedwell	*Veronica anagallis-aquatica* (6–8)	occasional but more widespread than *catenata*
Pink Water-speedwell	*V. catenata* (6–8)	occasional, mainly in less calcareous places
Hybrid of Blue and Pink Water-speedwell	*V. anagallis-aquatica* × *catenata*	rare, although sometimes locally abundant, most recent records are from Lemsford and Kings Meads, Hertford
Common Skullcap	*Scutellaria galericulata* (6–9)	occasional, mainly by less calcareous waters in south Herts
Celery-leaved Crowfoot	*Ranunculus sceleratus* (5–9)	occasional
Purple Willow	*Salix purpurea* (3–4)	scarce, about ten locations
Common Osier	*S. viminalis* (2–4)	fairly common

Goat Willow	*S. caprea* (3–4)	common
Grey Willow	*S. cinerea* (3–4)	common
Alder	*Alnus glutinosa* (2–3)	common
Guelder Rose	*Viburnum opulus* (6–7)	occasional
Bittersweet or Woody Nightshade	*Solanum dulcamara* (6–9)	common
Hop	*Humulus lupulus* (7–8)	occasional
Hemlock	*Conium maculatum* (6–7)	common in central and east Herts
Giant Hogweed	*Heracleum mantegazzianum* (6–7)	not uncommon in northern Herts, spreading
Wild Teasel	*Dipsacus fullonum* ssp. *fullonum* (7–8)	fairly common

1.11 Checklist of Characteristic Wild Flowers of Middle-course Rivers

Aquatic and emergent

Broad-leaved Pondweed	*Potamogeton natans* (5–9)	occasional in silted places
Curled Pondweed	*P. crispus* (5–10)	occasional
Fennel Pondweed	*P. pectinatus* (5–9)	occasional in base-rich rivers, recorded from Hiz, Rib, Mimram, Lea, Gade and Chess
Perfoliate Pondweed	*P. perfoliatus* (6–9)	scarce, recent records from Rib, Colne and lower Lea
Canadian Waterweed	*Elodea canadensis* (5–10)	introduced into Britain in 1842, reached Herts c. 1856 and spread rapidly; common to abundant in clear water
Nuttall's Waterweed	*E. nuttallii*	introduced, first noted in Lea in 1976, spreading
Water-plantain	*Alisma plantago-aquatica* (6–8)	fairly common in shallow and silty places
Narrow-leaved Water-plantain	*A. lanceolatum* (6–8)	scarce, only recent records from running waters are a ditch at Knebworth Woods and by the Colne at Colney Heath
Mare's-tail	*Hippuris vulgaris* (6–7)	occasional in shallow silty places
Common Reed	*Phragmites australis* (8–9)	common in swampy margins
Reed-grass	*Phalaris arundinacea* (6–7)	common in swampy places
Reed Sweet-grass	*Glyceria maxima* (7–8)	common
Water Whorl-grass	*Catabrosa aquatica* (6–8)	local, by Mimram, scarce elsewhere with recent records from Rye Meads, Tring Reservoirs and Ickleford

213

Marsh Foxtail	*Alopecurus geniculatus* (6–7)	fairly common in less calcareous areas
Lesser Pond-sedge	*Carex acutiformis* (6–7)	common in base-rich areas
Greater Pond-sedge	*C. riparia* (5–6)	common
Greater Tussock-sedge	*C. paniculata* (5–6)	scarce
Green or Summer Watercress	*Nasturtium officinale* (5–10)	common in shallows
One-rowed Watercress	*N. microphyllum* (6–10)	common in shallows of less calcareous waters
Brown or Winter Watercress	*N. microphyllum* × *officinale* (5–10)	often found where both parents are present
Fool's Watercress	*Apium nodiflorum* (7–8)	common in shallows
Yellow Iris or Yellow Flag	*Iris pseudocorus* (5–7)	fairly common, some introductions probable
Branched Bur-reed	*Sparganium erectum* (6–8)	fairly common
Unbranched Bur-reed	*S. emersum* (6–7)	scarce
Water Dock	*Rumex hydrolapathum* (7–9)	local
Golden Dock	*R. maritimus* (6–9)	scarce, recent records from Upper Lea
Marsh Dock	*R. palustris* (6–9)	rare, only record, in last 20 years, from Berkhamsted
River Water-dropwort	*Oenanthe fluviatilis* (7–9)	very local in lower Beane and Ash, also by Colne near Watford and in Lea Navigation
Celery-leaved Buttercup	*Ranunculus sceleratus* (5–9)	occasional

Marginal

Hemp Agrimony	*Eupatorium cannabinum* (7–9)	common
Meadowsweet	*Filipendula ulmaria* (6–9)	common
Great Hairy Willowherb	*Epilobium hirsutum* (7–8)	common
Brooklime	*Veronica beccabunga* (5–9)	common
Water Mint	*Mentha aquatica* (7–10)	common
Blue Water-speedwell	*Veronica anagallis-aquatica* (6–8)	occasional
Purple-loosestrife	*Lythrum salicaria* (6–8)	occasional
Marsh Woundwort	*Stachys palustris* (7–9)	rare in north of county, but reasonably common in south
Gypsywort	*Lycopus europaeus* (6–9)	common in south of county, occasional in north
Indian Balsam	*Impatiens glandulifera* (7–10)	introduced, occasional to common
Orange Balsam	*I. capensis* (6–8)	introduced, local, by Lea near Stanstead Abbots, Gade and Colne between Rickmansworth and Watford, near Tring and Berkhamsted
Monkeyflower	*Mimulus* spp. (7–9)	introduced, naturalised, especially by Mimram near Welwyn Garden City;

		guttatus has been recorded but other species may be present
Water Forget-me-not	*Myosotis scorpioides* (5–9)	common in south of county, occasional elsewhere
Nodding Bur-Marigold	*Bidens cernua* (7–9)	local to more readily drained situations in south Herts
Common Marsh Yellow-cress	*Rorippa palustris* (6–9)	occasional to frequent in south Herts
Greater Yellow-cress	*R. amphibia* (6–8)	rare, by Lea, Stort and Gade
Wood Bitter-cress	*Cardamine flexuosa* (4–9)	occasional to common in shady places, mainly in south-east Herts
Large Bitter-cress	*C. amara* (4–6)	very rare, only 3 records this century, the latest from near Stockers Lake in 1981
Butterbur	*Petasites hybridus* (3–5)	fairly common and widely distributed, most frequent in central and south-west Herts
Alder	*Alnus glutinosa* (2–3)	common
Goat Willow	*Salix caprea* (3–4)	common
Grey Willow	*S. cinerea* (3–4)	common
Crack Willow	*S. fragilis* (4–5)	common
White Willow	*S. alba* (4–5)	frequent
'Cricket-bat' Willow	*S. alba* var. *caerulea* (4–5)	occasional, mainly planted for timber
White Poplar	*Populus alba* (2–3)	introduced, occasional
Grey Poplar	*P.* × *canescens* (3)	a hybrid between White Poplar and Aspen; introduced and occasional
Balm of Gilead	*P. candicans* (3)	introduced, very rare, recent records from Lemsford (planted) and Stanborough (also near Cuffley and Barkway)
Black Poplar	*P. nigra* (3–4)	very rare native, probably less than 20 trees mainly by ditches or rivers, recent records from near Willian, Ickleford and Codicote
Guelder Rose	*Viburnum opulus* (6–7)	occasional
Black Currant	*Ribes nigrum* (6–7)	occasional

1.12 Checklist of Characteristic Wild Flowers of Lower-course Rivers and Canals

Submerged aquatics

Grassy Pondweed	*Potamogeton obtusifolius* (6–9)	very rare, only recent record from Broad Colney

Perfoliate Pondweed	*P. perfoliatus* (6–9)	scarce, recent reports from Colne, lower Lea and Rib
Fennel Pondweed	*P. pectinatus* (5–9)	occasional in base-rich rivers, recorded from Lea, Mimram, Rib, Gade, Chess and Hiz
Curled Pondweed	*P. crispus* (5–10)	occasional
Canadian Waterweed	*Elodea canadensis* (5–10)	common to abundant in clear water
Nuttall's Waterweed	*E. nuttallii*	first noted in Lea in 1976, probably spreading
Chalk-stream Water-crowfoot	*Ranunculus pencillatus* var. *calcareus* (5–8)	occasional in shallows with clear calcareous water
Common Water-starwort	*Callitriche stagnalis* (5–9)	common in shallow, faster flowing places
Various-leaved Water-starwort	*C. platycarpa* (5–9)	once fairly common, now rare, the only recent report from River Lea in 1980
Rigid Hornwort	*Ceratophyllum demersum* (7–9)	common
Spiked Water-milfoil	*Myriophyllum spicatum* (6–7)	scarce, recent records from River Lea and Grand Union Canal; locally frequent along River Chess
'Tapegrass'	*Vallisneria spiralis* (6–10)	introduced into River Lea and Lea Navigation, survives mainly by warm water outfalls

Floating aquatics

Common Duckweed or Duck's-meat	*Lemna minor* (6–7)	common and widespread
Fat Duckweed	*L. gibba*	rare, recent records from River Lea, also pond at Brickendon and Rye House moat
Ivy-leaved Duckweed	*L. trisulca* (5–7)	reasonably common, probably under-recorded for it is only at surface when flowering
Least Duckweed	*L. minuscula*	rare, first noted in Herts from Grand Union Canal near Croxley Green in 1981, since noted in the Colne near Watford, moat at Rye House and in pit near Cheshunt
Water Fern	*Azolla filiculoides*	introduced fern from tropical America, occasional. especially in warm summers, and most frequent in south Herts

White Water-lily	*Nymphaea alba* (6–8)	native although introductions probably quite frequent, declining and now only occasional
Yellow Water-lily	*Nuphar lutea* (6–8)	native, prefers calcareous water, most frequent in Colne, Stort and Lea, occasional in lower reaches of Beane, Rib and Ash, also noted in Grand Union Canal
Fringed Water-lily	*Nymphoides peltata* (7–8)	introduced; most records from pits and ponds, but has been seen in Grand Union Canal near Berkhamsted
Shining Pondweed	*Potamogeton lucens* (6–9)	rare and declining; recent records from the Lea and a gravel pit near Cheshunt
Flat-stalked Pondweed	*P. friesii* (6–8)	rare and declining, most recent record from the Lea in 1981; was known in Grand Union Canal and Tring Reservoirs up to 1960s
Broad-leaved Pondweed	*P. natans* (5–9)	occasional

Emergent and marginal

Common Reed	*Phragmites australis* (8–9)	common
Reed-grass	*Phalaris arundinacea* (6–7)	common
Reed Sweet-grass	*Glyceria maxima* (7–8)	common
Bulrush or Cat's-tail	*Typha latifolia* (6–7)	common
Lesser Bulrush	*T. angustifolia* (6–7)	scarce, only recent records from Grand Union Canal near Northchurch and gravel pit near Amwell
Common Club-rush	*Schoenoplectus lacustris* (6–7)	occasional
Greater Pond-sedge	*Carex riparia* (5–6)	common
Lesser Pond-sedge	*C. acutiformis* (6–7)	common
Greater Tussock-sedge	*C. paniculata* (5–6)	occasional in swamp and carr
Branched Bur-reed	*Sparganium erectum* (6–8)	common
Unbranched Bur-reed	*S. emersum* (6–7)	occasional
Yellow Iris or Yellow Flag	*Iris pseudocorus* (5–7)	fairly common
Sweet Flag	*Acorus calamus* (5–7)	introduced, scarce, recent records from Grand Union Canal near Berkhamsted, the Stort near Bishops Stortford, lower Lea and in Broad Colney and Stockers Lakes
Water-plantain	*Alisma plantago-aquatica* (6–8)	fairly common

Narrow-leaved Water-plantain	*A. lanceolatum* (6–8)	scarce, recent record from Colne at Colney Heath
Flowering Rush	*Butomus umbellatus* (7–9)	scarce and declining, along lower Lea and Colne, also by Gade at Cassiobury Park, Watford
Arrowhead	*Sagittaria sagittifolia* (7–8)	scarce and declining in Lea and Colne, in drought year of 1976 reports were made from Grand Union Canal near Northchurch, Kings Langley and Barwick Ford
Watercress	*Nasturtium* spp.	common, especially in shallows
Fool's Watercress	*Apium nodiflorum* (7–8)	common in shallows
Water Mint	*Mentha aquatica* (7–10)	common
Water Forget-me-not	*Myosotis scorpioides* (5–9)	common
Amphibious Bistort	*Polygonum amphibium* (7–9)	fairly common
Water Pepper	*P. hydropiper* (7–9)	occasional
Greater Yellow-cress	*Rorippa amphibia* (6–9)	rare by Lea, Stort and Gade
Brooklime	*Veronica beccabunga* (5–9)	common
River Water-dropwort	*Oenanthe fluviatilis* (7–9)	local in Colne near Watford, Lea Navigation, also in Lower Beane and Ash
Hemlock Water-dropwort	*O. crocata* (6–7)	rare, possibly extinct in Colne and Lea (although recent record from Waltham Abbey just outside county), confirmed in 1986 from gravel pit at Cheshunt
Celery-leaved Crowfoot	*Ranunculus sceleratus* (5–9)	occasional
Gypsywort	*Lycopus europaeus* (6–9)	common
Marsh Woundwort	*Stachys palustris* (7–9)	reasonably common
Common Skullcap	*Scutellaria galericulata* (6–9)	occasional
Indian Balsam	*Impatiens glandulifera* (7–10)	introduced, common
Orange Balsam	*I. capensis* (6–8)	introduced, local by Lea near Stanstead Abbots, by Gade and Colne between Rickmansworth and Watford, near Tring and Berkhamsted
Angelica	*Angelica sylvestris* (7–9)	common
Hemlock	*Conium maculatum* (6–7)	common
Giant Hogweed	*Heracleum mantegazzianum* (6–7)	occasional
Wild Teasel	*Dipsacus fullonum* ssp. *fullonum* (7–8)	common
Purple-loosestrife	*Lythrum salicaria* (6–8)	fairly common
Yellow Loosestrife	*Lysimachia vulgaris* (7–8)	rare, mainly restricted to lower Colne
Dotted Loosestrife	*L. punctata* (7–10)	introduced, scarce, mainly in waste places

Marsh Thistle	*Cirsium palustre* (7–9)	common
Water Figwort	*Scrophularia auriculata* (6–9)	common
Great Hairy Willowherb	*Epilobium hirsutum* (7–8)	common
Tufted Hair-grass	*Deschampsia caespitosa* (6–8)	common
Meadowsweet	*Filipendula ulmaria* (6–9)	common
Water Chickweed	*Myosoton aquaticum* (7–8)	occasional
Soft Rush	*Juncus effusus* (6–8)	common
Hard Rush	*J. inflexus* (6–8)	fairly common
Compact Rush	*J. conglomeratus* (5–7)	common
Jointed Rush	*J. articulatus* (6–9)	fairly common
Sharp-flowered Rush	*J. acutiflorus* (7–9)	occasional
Nodding Bur-Marigold	*Bidens cernua* (7–9)	occasional
Tripartite Bur-Marigold	*B. tripartita* (7–9)	locally common by Stort and Lea
Beggarticks or Stick Tight	*B. frondosa* (7–10)	scarce, recorded from Lea near Hoddesdon and Grand Union Canal near Berkhamsted and Rickmansworth
Bur-marigold	*B. connata*	rare and as yet without a full vernacular name, first recognised in Britain in 1977, small colonies found by Grand Union Canal and pits near Rickmansworth in 1978, no further records
Butterbur	*Petasites hybridus* (3–5)	occasional
Hemp Agrimony	*Eupatorium cannabinum* (7–9)	common
Common Comfrey	*Symphytum officinale* (5–6)	reasonably common
Russian Comfrey	*S. × uplandicum* (6–8)	occasional on drier banks
Rough Comfrey	*S. aspersum* (6–7)	scarce, recent records by Lea Navigation near Ware and near Watford
Wild Turnip or Bargeman's Cabbage	*Brassica rapa* ssp. *sylvestris* (5–8)	once more or less restricted to lower Stort and Lea now more widespread in disturbed pits and dumps

Tree and shrub species are similar to those noted for higher reaches of the rivers, swamps and alder woods.

1.13 *Checklist of Characteristic Wild Flowers of Ponds and Lakes*

Marginal

Soft Rush	*Juncus effusus* (6–8)	common; more frequent on acidic soils
Hard Rush	*J. inflexus* (6–8)	common, more frequent on basic soils

Jointed Rush	*J. articulatus* (6–9)	fairly common
Orange Foxtail	*Alopecurus aequalis* (5–7)	very rare, possibly extinct as pond-edge plant
Marsh Foxtail	*A. geniculatus* (6–7)	more frequent on less calcareous soils
Water Figwort	*Scrophularia auriculata* (6–9)	common
Meadowsweet	*Filipendula ulmaria* (6–9)	common
Great Hairy Willowherb	*Epilobium hirsutum* (7–8)	common
Brooklime	*Veronica beccabunga* (5–9)	common
Marsh Speedwell	*V. scutellata* (6–8)	scarce, mainly on acid soils
Blue Water-speedwell	*V. anagallis-aquatica* (6–8)	occasional
Pink Water-speedwell	*V. catenata* (6–8)	occasional, mainly on less calcareous soils, less widepread than *angallis-aquatica*
Water Forget-me-not	*Myosotis scorpioides* (5–9)	occasional, mainly in south of county
Tufted Forget-me-not	*M. laxa* ssp. *caespitosa* (5–8)	occasional on less calcareous soils
Common Marsh Yellow-cress	*Rorippa palustris* (6–9)	occasional to locally frequent in south Herts
Cuckoo-flower or Ladies-smock	*Cardamine pratensis* (4–6)	occasional
Ragged Robin	*Lychnis flos-cuculi* (5–8)	occasional
Marsh Bedstraw	*Galium palustre* (6–7)	fairly common
Water Mint	*Mentha aquatica* (7–10)	common
Gypsywort	*Lycopus europaeus* (6–9)	common in south Herts
Lesser Spearwort	*Ranunculus flammula* (5–9)	occasional, most often on less calcareous soils of south Herts
Greater Spearwort	*R. lingua* (6–9)	scarce, status doubtful, possibly introduced at all sites, recent records from Reed, Westland Green, Ickleford, Aston, Chorleywood Common and pits near Smallford
Common Skullcap	*Scutellaria galericulata* (6–9)	occasional in south Herts
Nodding Bur-marigold	*Bidens cernua* (7–9)	occasional on acid soils
Tripartite Bur-marigold	*B. tripartita* (7–9)	occasional on acid soils
Water Horsetail	*Equisetum fluviatile*	scarce

Marginal trees and shrubs may include a wide variety of wetland and drier habitat species, largely relating to the topography of individual pond margins and banks.

Emergent

Common Reed	*Phragmites australis* (8–9)	common in swampy margins
Reed-grass	*Phalaris arundinacea* (6–7)	common in swampy margins
Bulrush or Cat's-tail	*Typha latifolia* (6–7)	common in swampy margins
Small Sweet-grass	*Glyceria declinata* (6–9)	occasional
Floating Sweet-grass	*G. fluitans* (5–8)	common

Plicate Sweet-grass	*G. plicata* (5–6)	occasional
Hairy Sweet-grass	*G.* × *pedicillata* (6–7)	this hybrid between *fluitans* and *plicata* is scarce but may be found in sites without either parent
Greater Pond-sedge	*Carex riparia* (6–7)	common
Lesser Pond-sedge	*C. acutiformis* (6–7)	common
Bladder Sedge	*C. vesicaria* (6)	rare, only three recent records from Oughtonhead Common, Knebworth Park and Braughing Meads in swampy conditions
False Fox-sedge	*C. otrubae* (6–7)	common
Cyperus Sedge	*C. pseudocyperus* (5–6)	scarce, mainly on more acid soils
Common Spike-rush	*Eleocharis palustris* (5–7)	common
Sweet Galingale	*Cyperus longus* (8–9)	very rare, limited to single site near Albury, where it has been 'known for many years'
Branched Bur-reed	*Sparganium erectum* (6–8)	common
Unbranched Bur-reed	*S. emersum* (6–7)	occasional
Common Water-crowfoot	*Ranunculus aquatilis* (5–6)	rare, recent records from ponds near Langley and Weston, and in spring pool at Lemsford
Pond Water-crowfoot	*R. peltatus* (5–8)	scarce, mainly on acidic soils
Thread-leaved Water-crowfoot	*R. trichophyllos* (5–6)	scarce, about a dozen sites, mainly on calcareous clay soils
Ivy-leaved Crowfoot	*R. hederaceus* (6–9)	scarce, about five sites on muddy, less calcareous soils
Celery-leaved Crowfoot	*R. sceleratus* (5–9)	common
Marsh Marigold	*Caltha palustris* (3–7)	occasional where calcareous flushes, sometimes planted
Yellow Iris	*Iris pseudocorus* (5–7)	fairly common, often planted
Water Plantain	*Alisma plantago-aquatica* (6–8)	common
Water Dock	*Rumex hydrolapathum* (7–9)	scarce
Mare's-tail	*Hippuris vulgaris* (6–7)	occasional
Lesser Marshwort	*Apium inundatum* (6–8)	very rare, single site at Hadley Green
Water-violet	*Hottonia palustris* (5–6)	rare, recent records from near Stevenage, Welham Green, South Mimms, Hertford Heath, Manifold Ditch at Kings Meads, Hertford and gravel pit at Rye Meads
Tubular Water-dropwort	*Oenanthe fistulosa* (7–9)	rare, recent reports near Hitchin, Knebworth Park and Kings Meads, near Hertford

Appendix 1.13

Fine-leaved Water-dropwort	*O. aquatica* (6–9)	very rare, only recent record from near Stevenage
Common Water-starwort	*Callitriche stagnalis* ((5–9)	common
Intermediate Water-starwort	*C. hamulata* (5–9)	scarce, mainly in central Herts
Bogbean	*Menyanthes trifoliata* (5–7)	once not uncommon in peaty marshes; recent reports from ponds at Bayford and Brickendon Green may relate to introductions; also noted from Wormley Wood in 1970 – a possible native site
Australian Pigmyweed	*Crassula helmsii* (8–9)	introduction, first noted at Hadley Highstone in 1976, further recent reports from Batchworth Heath, Hoddesdon Power Station and Meesden; grows very vigorously and can present conservation problems
Greater Bladderwort	*Utricularia vulgaris* (7–8)	very rare, only site at Balls Park in acidic water

Submerged aquatic

Canadian Waterweed	*Elodea canadensis* (5–10)	common in clear water
Rigid Hornwort	*Ceratophyllum demersum* (7–9)	common
Whorled Water-milfoil	*Myriophyllum verticillatum* (7–8)	rare, recent records from Norton Green near Stevenage, Brickendon Green, pool at Hoddesdon Power Station, Rye Meads and gravel pit at Amwell
Alternate-flowered Water-milfoil	*M. alterniflorum* (5–8)	very rare, only site at Hadley Green
Horned Pondweed	*Zannichellia palustris* (5–8)	occasional
Curly Water-thyme	*Lagarosiphon major*	introduced, scarce, recent records from Hadley Green, by Cowheath Wood and Potten End
Broad-leaved Pondweed	*Potamogeton natans* (5–9)	occasional
Curled Pondweed	*P. crispus* (5–10)	occasional

Floating aquatic

Common Duckweed or Duck's-meat	*Lemna minor* (6–7)	common to abundant
Fat Duckweed	*L. gibba*	very rare, only recent records from Brickendon Green and Rye House Moat
Ivy-leaved Duckweed	*L. trisulca* (5–7)	fairly common, probably under-recorded for it is only at surface when flowering

Greater Duckweed	*L. polyrhiza*	rare, possibly under-recorded, most recent records from Hadley Green
Least Duckweed	*L. miniscula*	Rye House Moat, also pit near Cheshunt, Colne near Watford and Grand Union Canal near Croxley Green
White Water-lily	*Nymphaea alba* (6–8)	occasional and most probably introduced
Yellow Water-lily	*Nuphar lutea* (6–8)	sometimes found as introduction
Fringed Water-lily	*Nymphoides peltata* (7–8)	introduced, scarce
Water Soldier	*Stratiotes aloides* (6–8)	rare, probably introduced although long established at Meesden Green; other reports from Hadley Common in 1979, Hitchin in early 1980s; can present conservation problems if allowed to spread
Frogbit	*Hydrocharis morsus-ranae* (7–8)	once rare native, now only as introduction, recent reports from Broad Colney pit in 1975, moat at Batlers Green in 1982 and Devitt's Lake, Northaw in 1984
Water Fern	*Azolla filiculoides*	introduced; occasional and sporadic, sometimes locally abundant in warm summers
Sphagnum moss	*Sphagnum* spp.	scarce around ponds with more acidic waters

1.14 Checklist of Characteristic Wild Flowers of Hedges

Trees and woody shrubs

Field Maple	*Acer campestre* (5–6)	common in older hedges, except on Chalk
Sycamore	*A. pseudoplatanus* (4–6)	introduced in the 15th or 16th century, naturalised and sometimes planted, often invades unmanaged hedges
Blackthorn	*Prunus spinosa* (3–5)	common to abundant
Wild Plum or Bullace	*P. domestica* ssp. (4–5)	formerly cultivated, common, especially near past and present habitation
Cherry Plum	*P. cerasifera* (3–4)	introduced, formerly planted, found mainly in south-east, scarce elsewhere

Wild Cherry or Gean	*P. avium* (4–5)	frequent on Clay-with-Flints and decalcified Boulder Clay, occasional elsewhere
Dwarf or Sour Cherry	*P. cerasus* (4–5)	introduced, very rare with only one recent record in hedge near Great Offley where known since at least 1914
Common Hawthorn	*Crataegus monogyna* (5–6)	abundant, especially in later-enclosure hedges
Midland Hawthorn	*C. laevigata* (5–6)	rare in hedges on clay soils, good indicator of former woods, assarts and ancient hedges
Beech	*Fagus sylvatica* (4–5)	not uncommon in west and north, especially on Chalk, sometimes planted
Spindle	*Euonymus europaeus* (5–6)	occasional to frequent on calcareous soils, especially Boulder Clay
Dogwood	*Cornus sanguinea* (6–7)	common on calcareous soils
Holly	*Ilex aquifolium* (5–8)	absent or infrequent on highly calcareous soils, elsewhere common
English Elm	*Ulmus procera* (2–3)	once abundant, decimated by Dutch Elm disease, still quite common as suckering saplings which may last for a few years until disease reinfects
Smooth Elm	*U. minor* (2–3)	occasional in north and east, also affected by Dutch Elm disease
Wych Elm	*U. glabra* (2–3)	occasional on calcareous soils
Walnut	*Juglans regia* (6)	introduced, scarce in hedges and usually near habitation, at times planted or bird-sown
Hornbeam	*Carpinus betulus* (4–5)	common on less calcareous soils in southern portion of county
Hazel	*Corylus avellana* (1–4)	common
Crab Apple	*Malus sylvestris* (5)	occasional to frequent
Apple	*M. domestica* (5)	occasional as escape from gardens
Ash	*Fraxinus excelsior* (4–5)	common
Pedunculate Oak	*Quercus robor* (4–5)	common
Sessile Oak	*Q. petraea* (4–5)	occasional on more acid soils
Goat Willow	*Salix caprea* (3–4)	fairly common on damper soils
Grey Willow	*S. cinerea* (3–4)	fairly common on damper soils
Whitebeam	*Sorbus aria* (5–6)	scarce, only on highly calcareous soils, mainly in south-west

Wayfaring Tree	*Viburnum lantana* (5–6)	frequent on calcareous soils
Guelder Rose	*V. opulus* (6–7)	occasional on damper soils
Buckthorn	*Rhamnus catharticus* (5–6)	common on Chalk and Chalky Boulder Clay
Wild Privet	*Ligustrum vulgare* (6–7)	occasional to frequent on Chalk
Elder	*Sambucus nigra* (6–7)	common
Danewort or Dwarf Elder	*S. ebulus* (7–8)	very rare, only two recent records from Stevenage and near Brickendon
Dog Rose	*Rosa canina* (6–7)	abundant
Field Rose	*R. arvensis* (6–7)	common except on highly calcareous soils
Wild Pear	*Pyrus pyraster* (4–5)	very rare, only two recent records from hedges, at Barnet Gate and near Totteridge
Gooseberry	*Ribes uva-crispa* (3–5)	occasional
Barberry	*Berberis vulgaris* (5–6)	introduced and formerly frequent in hedges but selectively removed when found to harbour wheat rust; now very rare, only two recent records from Hoddesdon and White Hill, Berkhamsted
Duke of Argyll's Tea-plant	*Lycium barbarum* (6–9)	introduced and naturalised, scarce, sometimes locally abundant and usually near habitation

Woody climbers and scramblers

Wild Clematis	*Clematis vitalba* (7–8)	common to abundant on more calcareous soils
Brambles or Blackberry	*Rubus fruticosus* agg. (5–9)	often abundant and includes many species
Dewberry	*R. caesius* (6–9)	frequent on Chalk and Boulder Clay, scarce elsewhere
Honeysuckle	*Lonicera periclymenum* (6–9)	frequent except on highly calcareous soils
Hop	*Humulus lupulus* (7–8)	native, but often as past escape from cultivation, fairly common on damper soils
Bittersweet or Woody Nightshade	*Solanum dulcamara* (6–9)	common
Wild Liquorice	*Astragalus glycyphyllos* (7–8)	rare on Chalk in Holwell and Pirton area

Herbs

NB *In many older hedges, according to soils, aspects of woodland ground flora may be found (see relevant checklists); only a few such species are noted here; also, in more recent hedges, some relics of former habitats may still be present.*

225

Appendix 1.14

Dog's Mercury	*Mercurialis perennis* (2–4)	common, especially in older hedges, but capable of quite rapid spread
Bluebell	*Hyacinthoides non-scriptus* (4–6)	occasional to common in older hedges, absent or scarce from Chalk and Pebble Gravels
Greater Stitchwort	*Stellaria holostea* (4–6)	frequent, especially in older hedges, but absent from Chalk
Wood Anemone	*Anemone nemorosa* (3–5)	scarce in hedges; a good indicator of antiquity
Lesser Celandine	*Ranunculus ficaria* (3–5)	occasional to frequent
Goldilocks	*R. auricomus* (4–5)	scarce in older hedges on damper calcareous soils
Yellow Archangel	*Lamiastrum galeobdolon* (5-6)	common in older hedges on Clay-with-Flints
Common Dog-violet	*Viola riviniana* (4–6)	common in older hedges
Early Dog-violet	*V. reichenbachiana* (3–5)	occasional in older hedges
Sweet Violet	*V. odorata* (2–4)	occasional on calcareous soils
Lords-and-Ladies	*Arum maculatum* (4–5)	common
Garlic Mustard	*Alliaria petiolata* (4–8)	common, often referred to as Hedge Garlic or Jack-by-the-Hedge
Ground Ivy	*Glechoma hederacea* (3–5)	common to abundant
Red Campion	*Silene dioica* (5–6)	common on more acidic soils
Black Horehound	*Ballota nigra* ssp. *foetida* (6–10)	common
Hedge Woundwort	*Stachys sylvatica* (7–8)	common
Bush Vetch	*Vicia sepium* (5–8)	common except on Chalk
Tufted Vetch	*V. cracca* (6–8)	mainly absent from Clay-with-Flints and decalcified Boulder Clay, not infrequent elsewhere
Narrow-leaved Everlasting-pea	*Lathyrus sylvestris* (6–8)	very rare, only 7 records since 1970
Tuberous Pea	*L. tuberosus* (7)	introduction, very rare; most recent records from Kings Langley and Croxley Moor are probably of casuals
Broad-leaved Everlasting-pea	*L. latifolius* (6–8)	introduced, scarce and usually casual
Common Figwort	*Scrophularia nodosa* (6–9)	frequent in shady older hedges
Herb Bennet	*Geum urbanum* (6–8)	common in shady places
Ivy	*Hedera helix* (9–11)	common to abundant
Rough Chervil	*Chaerophyllum temulentum* (6–7)	common
Cow Parsley or Keck	*Anthriscus sylvestris* (4–6)	common to abundant
Upright Hedge-parsley	*Torilis japonica* (7–8)	common to abundant
Hogweed or Cow Parsnip	*Heracleum sphondylium* (6–9)	common to abundant
White or Red Bryony	*Bryonia cretica* ssp. *dioica* (5–9)	common

Common or Stinging Nettle	*Urtica dioica* (6–8)	common to abundant
Red-veined Dock	*Rumex sanguineus* (6–8)	frequent
Sharp Dock	*R. conglomeratus* (7–8)	frequent on damper soils
Broad-leaved Dock	*R. obtusifolius* (6–10)	common
Common Sorrel	*R. acetosa* (5–6)	common
Hedge Bindweed	*Calystegia sepium* ssp. *sepium*(7–9)	common
American Bindweed	*C. sepium* ssp. *pulchra* (7–9)	recent introduction, scarce, usually near habitation
Great Bindweed	*C. sepium* ssp. *silvatica* (7–9)	introduced, naturalised and fairly widespread
Black Bryony	*Tamus communis* (5–7)	frequent, especially in older hedges
Great Burdock	*Arctium lappa* (7–9)	scarce on damper soils, notably Boulder Clay
Lesser Burdock	*A. minus* (7–9)	frequent
Babington's Burdock	*A. pubens* (7–9)	occasional in central and south Herts
Greater Periwinkle	*Vinca major* (4–6)	introduced, occasional as escape from gardens
Perforate St John's-wort	*Hypericum perforatum* (6–9)	occasional on calcareous soils
Hairy St John's-wort	*H. hirsutum* (7–8)	occasional on Boulder Clay
Tutsan	*H. androsaemum* (6–8)	scarce; about ten recent records mainly from woods, but includes hedge near Weston where possibility of garden escape cannot be ruled out
Moschatel or Town-hall Clock	*Adoxa moschatellina* (4–5)	rare, a good indicator of antiquity, for example in hedge bank of Icknield Way near Lilley
Toothwort	*Lathraea squamaria* (4–5)	rare, mainly on Clay-with-Flints
Bats-in-the-Belfry or Nettle-leaved Bellflower	*Campanula trachelium* (7–8)	scarce on Boulder Clay
Creeping Bellfower	*C. rapunculoides* (7–9)	introduced, very rare in wood edges and hedges near Pirton; about five other recent reports
Red Dead-nettle	*Lamium purpureum* (3–10)	common
White Dead-nettle	*L. album* (5–12)	common
Goosegrass or Cleavers	*Galium aparine* (6–8)	common to abundant
Hedge Bedstraw	*G. mollugo* (6–9)	common on calcareous soils
Crosswort	*Cruciata laevipes* (4–7)	rare, about 11 sites, mainly near Ashwell and between Potters Bar and London Colney
Germander Speedwell	*Veronica chamaedrys* (3–7)	common
Grey Sedge	*Carex divulsa* (6–7)	occasional on drier soils
Lesser Spiked-sedge	*C. muricata* (6–7)	rare on acidic soils
Spiked Sedge	*C. spicata* (6–7)	occasional in older hedges
Annual Meadow-grass	*Poa annua* (1–12)	common

Wood Meadow-grass	*P. nemoralis* (6–7)	common on shady more acidic soils
Cock's-foot	*Dactylis glomerata* (5–8)	common to abundant
Hairy Brome	*Bromus ramosus* (7–8)	common
Barren Brome	*B. sterilis* (5–7)	common to abundant
Wood False-brome	*Brachypodium sylvaticum* (7–8)	common
Bearded Couch	*Elymus caninus* (7)	occasional on damper calcareous soils
Couch-grass or Twitch	*E. repens* (6–9)	common to abundant
False Oat-grass	*Arrhenatherum elatius* (6–7)	common to abundant
Yorkshire Fog	*Holcus lanatus* (6–9)	common
Creeping Soft-grass	*H. mollis* (6–7)	common on acidic soils
Giant Fescue	*Festuca gigantea* (6–7)	frequent in shady places
Tall Fescue	*F. arundinacea* (6–8)	occasional on damper soils
Bracken	*Pteridium aquilinum*	a fern, common on acidic soils

1.15 Checklist of Characteristic Wild Flowers of Arable Fields (mainly margins)

NB *See also the checklist of arable rarities.*

Common or Field Poppy	*Papaver rhoeas* (6–10)	frequent to locally abundant
Long-headed Poppy	*P. dubium* (5–7)	scarce, mainly on lighter soils, notably glacial sands and gravels and, occasionally, Chalk
Prickly or Long Prickly-headed Poppy	*P. argemone* (5–7)	rare, similar distribution to *dubium*, recent records from near Royston, Pirton, Datchworth, Hertford and St Albans
Rough or Round Prickly-headed Poppy	*P. hybridum* (5–8)	scarce, more or less restricted to Chalk between Hexton and Royston
Opium Poppy	*P. somniferum* (7–8)	occasional as an escape
Common Fumitory	*Fumaria officinalis* (5–10)	much declined, but still quite common and widespread on lighter calcareous soils
Fine-leaved Fumitory	*F. parviflora* (6–9)	rare, mainly on Chalk in north of county
Dense-flowered Fumitory	*F. densiflora* (6–10)	as *parviflora*
Rape, Oil-seed Rape or Coleseed	*Brassica napus* ssp. *oleifera* (5–8)	often common as crop and survivor of cultivation in field margins and verges
Charlock or Wild Mustard	*Sinapis arvensis* (5–7)	common and widespread, especially on Chalk and Boulder Clay

White Mustard	*S. alba* (6–8)	once common as crop on calcareous soils, survives as weed mainly in north and west Herts
Wild Radish	*Raphanus raphanistrum* (5–9)	common except on highly calcareous soils
Treacle Mustard	*Erysimum cheiranthoides* (6–8)	relatively widespread on London Clay, elsewhere rather local, for example around Hitchin
Field Pennycress	*Thlaspi arvense* (5–7)	much declined from central and west Herts, most recent records are from the south-east on disturbed gravels
Shepherd's Purse	*Capsella bursa-pastoris* (1–12)	ubiquitous and often abundant
'Shepherd's Purse'	*C. rubella*	this alien from the Mediterranean was recorded as a casual from near Boxmoor in 1976
Swine-cress	*Coronopus squamatus* (6–9)	common, especially in northern and eastern Herts
Lesser Swine-cress	*C. didymus* (7–9)	scarce in south Herts
Wild Mignonette	*Reseda lutea* (6–8)	common on Chalk and Chalky Boulder Clay
Weld or Dyer's Rocket	*R. luteola* (6–8)	occasional in field margins in southern Herts
Field Pansy or Heart's-ease	*Viola arvensis* (4–10)	common and widespread except on acid soils
Chickweed	*Stellaria media* (1–12)	common and ubiquitous
Thyme-leaved Sandwort	*Arenaria serpyllifolia* ssp. *serpyllifolia* (6–8)	common and widespread
Slender Sandwort	*A. serpyllifolia* ssp. *leptoclados* (6–8)	fairly common on calcareous soils
Annual Knawel	*Scleranthus annuus* (6–8)	not uncommon on dry, open sandy and gravelly soils in central and south Herts
Corn Spurrey	*Spergula arvensis* (6–8)	much declined, occasionally on acidic soils
White Campion	*Silene latifolia* ssp. *alba* (5–9)	common on calcareous and light sandy soils
Hybrid between White and Red Campion (often called Pink Campion)	*S. dioica* × *latifolia* (6–8)	not uncommon in south and east Herts
Night-flowering Catchfly	*S. noctiflora* (7–9)	much declined, now rare on Chalk and Chalky Boulder Clay; only eight records in last decade, from between Letchworth and Sandon, and near Benington
Bladder Campion	*S. vulgaris* (5–9)	common and widespread
Fat Hen	*Chenopodium album* (7–10)	common and widespread
Many-seeded Goosefoot or All-seed	*C. polyspermum* (7–10)	frequent on damper acid soils in south Herts

Red Goosefoot	*C. rubrum* (7–9)	most frequent on damp, neutral soils, scarce elsewhere
Fig-leaved Goosefoot	*C. ficifolium* (7–9)	less frequent but with similar distribution to *rubrum*, also often on manure heaps
Good-King-Henry	*C. bonus-henricus* (5–7)	much declined and now rare with less than ten records in the last 20 years, all from the southern portion of the county
Common Orache or Iron-root	*Atriplex patula* (8–10)	frequent and well distributed
Spear-leaved Orache	*A. prostrata* (7–9)	most frequent on acid soils, occasional elsewhere
Lucerne or Alfalfa	*Medicago sativa* ssp. *sativa* (6–7)	introduced as fodder crop, naturalised and persists, especially on dry calcareous soils
Sickle Medick	*M. sativa* ssp. *falcata* (6–7)	introduced, very rare, records from Baldock, Albury, Great Amwell and Brookmans Park
Spotted Medick	*M. arabica* (4–8)	rare, generally short-lived, most recent reports from around Hoddesdon, near Holwell, Hitchin, around Stevenage, Baldock and Newnham
Parsley-piert	*Aphanes arvensis* (4–10)	common except on heavier soils of Chalk Marl, London Clay and Boulder Clay
Slender Parsley-piert	*A. microcarpa* (4–10)	apparently declining but also probably under-recorded; most frequent on acid soils of central Herts, often with *arvensis*
Fool's Parsley	*Aethusa cynapium* (7–8)	common and widespread, sometimes abundant
Cow Parsley or Keck	*Anthriscus sylvestris* (4–6)	common
Rough Chervil	*Chaerophyllum temulentum* (6–7)	common
Stone Parsley	*Sison ammonum* (7–9)	occasional in field margins on London Clay, scarce elsewhere
Petty Spurge	*Euphorbia peplus* (4–11)	common to abundant
Sun Spurge	*E. helioscopia* (5–10)	common and well distributed, although scarce or absent on acidic soils
Dwarf Spurge	*E. exigua* (6–10)	common on calcareous soils, scarce elsewhere
Broad-leaved Spurge	*E. platyphyllos* (6–10)	declining from Boulder Clay, always scarce and, in past decade, only noted from near Letchworth, Brent Pelham and Hadham Ford

Leafy Spurge	*E. esula* (5–7)	introduced but perennial and sometimes persistent; recent records from Wallington to Ashwell area, and gravel pits near Radlett and in south-east Herts
Sharp Dock	*Rumex conglomeratus* (7–8)	common on damper soils
Broad-leaved Dock	*R. obtusifolius* (6–10)	common
Red-veined Dock	*R. sanguineus* (6–8)	occasional
Curled Dock	*R. crispus* (6–10)	common
Sheep's Sorrel	*R. acetosella* (5–8)	common on acidic soils
Knotgrass	*Polygonum aviculare* (7–10)	common and widespread
Equal-leaved Knotgrass	*P. arenastrum* (7–11)	common on trampled ground such as field entrances and tracks; probably under-recorded
Redshank	*P. persicaria* (6–10)	common and widespread except on driest soils
Pale Persicaria	*P. lapathifolium* (6–10)	occasional to frequent on acidic soils
Black Bindweed	*Fallopia convolvulus* (7–10)	common and widespread
Buckwheat	*Fagopyrum esculentum* (7–8)	introduced and once cultivated as fodder crop; scarce survivor, although in places sown along field margins as food for game birds
Small Nettle	*Urtica urens* (6–8)	frequent on lighter soils of north-west and south-east of county, occasional elsewhere
Scarlet Pimpernel	*Anagallis arvensis* (6–8)	common
Blue Pimpernel	*A. arvensis* ssp. *foemina* (6–8)	very rare; only recent reports are from near Little Hadham
Field Forget-me-not	*Myosotis arvensis* (4–9)	common
Early Forget-me-not	*M. ramosissima* (4–6)	local; main distribution centred upon glacial gravels between Hitchin and Hertford and terrace gravels between Potters Bar and lower Stort valley, mainly in pits but occasionally in field margins
Borage	*Borago officinalis* (6–8)	occasionally cultivated as crop, sometimes persists for a few years
Viper's-bugloss	*Echium vulgare* (6–9)	scarce on open, light dry soils
Bugloss	*Anchusa arvensis* (6–9)	scarce, on Chalk and light sandy soils of central and south-east Herts
Corn Gromwell	*Lithospermum arvense* (5–7)	occasional to frequent on Chalk and Chalky Boulder Clay
Field Bindweed	*Convolvulus arvensis* (6–9)	common and widespread

Black Nightshade	*Solanum nigrum* (7–9)	common
Deadly Nightshade	*Atropa belladonna* (6–8)	once cultivated for use in drug distilleries; very rare as arable weed survivor, but occasional in hedges or waste places; most recent reports from near Hitchin, Berkhamsted, Rickmansworth and Watford
Henbane	*Hyoscyamus niger* (6–8)	also once cultivated for drugs; rare on lighter soils, also waste tips
Thorn Apple	*Datura stramonium* (7–10)	introduced drug plant, once cultivated, now found occasionally in waste places very rarely in arable fields, usually in hot summers
Common Toadflax	*Linaria vulgaris* (7–10)	common except on wetter heavier parts of Boulder Clay and London Clay
Small Toadflax	*Chaenorhinum minus* (5–10)	considerable declines, scarce to occasional on Chalk and some glacial and terrace gravels
Sharp-leaved Fluellen	*Kicksia elatine* (7–10)	declining, occasional on Chalk and Boulder Clay, scarce elsewhere
Round-leaved Fluellen	*K. spuria* (7–10)	similar to *elatine*, perhaps slightly more frequent
Germander Speedwell	*Veronica chamaedrys* (3–7)	common
Ivy-leaved Speedwell	*V. hederifolia* (3–8)	common
Common Speedwell	*V. persica* (1–12)	introduced into Britain in 1825, now abundant and widespread
Grey Speedwell	*V. polita* (1–12)	occasional, scarce or absent from much of terrace gravels, Boulder Clay and Clay-with-Flints
Green Field-speedwell	*V. agrestis* (1–12)	similar distribution to *polita* but less frequent in north of county
Thyme-leaved Speedwell	*V. serpyllifolia* (3–10)	common and well distributed on all but the driest of soils
Wall Speedwell	*V. arvensis* (3–10)	common and widespread on open dry soils
Red Dead-nettle	*Lamium purpureum* (3–10)	common and widespread
Cut-leaved Dead-nettle	*L. hybridum* (3–10)	scarce but probably underrecorded, recent records from Boulder Clay area and near Berkhamsted, Little Berkhampstead and Hoddesdon
Henbit Dead-nettle	*L. amplexicaule* (4–8)	locally frequent on Chalk of north Herts, occasional on light dry gravel soils

Common Hemp-nettle	*Galeopsis tetrahit* (7–9)	occasional to common on all but heavy clays
Lesser Hemp-nettle	*G. bifida* (7–9)	similar to above, but distribution uncertain
Red Hemp-nettle	*G. angustifolia* (7–10)	rare; recent records from dry or stony soils at Therfield, Hitchin, Rickmansworth, Knebworth, Peters Green, St Albans and Cuffley
Basil Thyme	*Acinos arvensis* (5–9)	scarce, few recent records from Chalk between Hexton and Therfield and Welwyn Garden City and Benington
Corn Mint	*Mentha arvensis* (5–10)	occasional on Boulder Clay and London Clay, scarce or absent elsewhere
Venus's-looking-glass	*Legousia hybrida* (5–8)	occasional on Chalk and dry stony Chalky Boulder Clay
Creeping Bellflower	*Campanula rapunculoides* (7–9)	rare; known for many years near Pirton; most other records are of garden escapes
Goosegrass	*Galium aparine* (6–8)	common to abundant
Field Madder	*Sherardia arvensis* (5–10)	declining, local to scarce on highly calcareous soils and rare on sandy soils in central Herts
Common Cornsalad or Lamb's Lettuce	*Valerianella locusta* (4–6)	local to frequent on chalky or gravelly soils near Hitchin and Hertford, around St Albans, Watford and Berkhamsted
Narrow-fruited Cornsalad	*V. dentata* (6–7)	rare, confined to cornfields on Chalk between Lilley and Hitchin, near Ashwell and Benington
Groundsel	*Senecio vulgaris* (1–12)	common to abundant
Stinking Groundsel	*S. viscosus* (7–9)	occasional on gravelly soils in central and south Herts, more frequent in waste places, tracks, railway banks and disturbed soils
Scentless Mayweed	*Tripleurospermum inodorum* (7–9)	common, often abundant and widespread
Stinking Mayweed	*Anthemis cotula* (7–9)	scarce and local on heavy, basic soils in central and south-east Herts
Corn Chamomile	*A. arvensis* (6–7)	always very rare, possibly now extinct; most recent record near Potters Bar in 1970
Wild Chamomile	*Matricaria recutita* (6–7)	occasional to frequent on sandy soils, particularly in south-east Herts

Appendix 1.15

Pineappleweed or Rayless Mayweed	*M. matricarioides* (6–7)	introduced; first noted in Herts in 1907, now common and widespread
Mugwort	*Artemisia vulgaris* (7–9)	occasional in relatively un-disturbed field margins, common in verges and waste places
Verlot's or Chinese Mugwort	*A. verlotiorum* (10–11)	introduced, occasional as casual in waste areas, may possibly spread to arable margins
Wormwood	*A. absinthium* (7–8)	scarce, usually on verges or waste places near habita-tion, may possibly spread into field margins
Marsh or Wayside Cudweed	*Gnaphalium uliginosum* (7–9)	frequent on damper acidic soils in central and south-east Herts, especially by field entrances and on tracks
Creeping Thistle	*Cirsium arvense* (7–9)	generally widespread and abundant, although less so on sands and gravels
Spear Thistle	*C. vulgare* (7–10)	similar distribution to *arvense*, but slightly less abundant
Musk Thistle	*Carduus nutans* (5–8)	occasional on Chalk or light, dry sandy soils
Welted Thistle	*C. acanthoides* (6–8)	occasional on calcareous soils, more often typical of verges and waste places
Smooth Milk- or Sow-Thistle	*Sonchus oleraceus* (6–8)	common and widespread
Prickly Milk- or Sow-Thistle	*S. asper* (6–8)	common and widespread
Perennial or Field Milk-Thistle	*S. arvensis* (7–10)	common, more frequent on damper soils
Nipplewort	*Lapsana communis* (6–10)	common and widespread
Chicory	*Cichorium intybus* (7–10)	once common pernicious weed of cornfields, now scarce, but occasional on verges
Wild-oat (also called Spring or Common Wild-oat)	*Avena fatua* (7–9)	common, particularly on Boulder Clay
Winter Wild-oat	*A. sterilis* ssp. *ludoviciana* (7–8)	introduced; first noted for county in 1945; appears to be increasing and fairly widespread but probably very under-recorded
Cultivated Oat	*A. sativa*	common as survivor of cultivation
Barren Brome	*Bromus sterilis* (5–7)	common often abundant, particularly on well-drained soil

Black Grass or Black Twitch	*Alopecurus myosuroides* (6–7)	common to abundant
False Oat-grass	*Arrhenatherum elatius* (6–7)	common
Annual Meadow-grass	*Poa annua* (1–12)	common
Rough Meadow-grass	*P. trivialis* (6)	common on damper soils
Couch-grass or Twitch	*Elymus repens* (6–9)	common to abundant
Black Bent	*Agrostis gigantea* (6–8)	frequent on lighter soils
Creeping Bent	*A. stolonifera* (7–8)	common

Amongst the wide number of herbs, usually more characteristic of other habitats, that may also be found in arable fields and sometimes quite commonly are the following:

Cut-leaved Cranesbill, Black Medick, Tall and Ribbed Melilot, Sainfoin, Hairy and Smooth Tare, clovers, Small Broomrape, Common Nettle, Red Bartsia, Field Scabious, Ragwort, hawkbits, dandelions, Bristly Oxtongue, Coltsfoot, Daisy, plantains, Self-heal, Hogweed, Wild Carrot, Wild Parsnip, willowherbs, Common Mallow, Silverweed, Creeping Cinquefoil, mousears, Creeping and Bulbous Buttercups.

1.16 Checklist of Hertfordshire's Rarest Arable Weeds

NB (i) *This list is based on data available up to 1987; a few of these species may now be extinct (although former sites are still worth investigating very carefully) and some may occur as introductions, casual or otherwise*

    (ii) *Species marked * are nationally rare and included in the* British Red Data Book *(Perring and Farrell, 1983).*

Corn Crowfoot or Corn Buttercup *Ranunculus arvensis* (6–7)

In 19th century a common weed of cornfields on calcareous soils, particularly Boulder Clay where it was still reasonably frequent up to the 1950s. Since 1978 only five records, from waste areas at Rickmansworth and near Ickleford, from the Broad Baulk at Rothamsted in 1979 with a few plants, from Patmore Heath (no precise date) and in arable just north of Letchworth in 1984

Pheasant's Eye *Adonis annua* (7)

First noted in the county in the late 19th century; an introduction from southern Europe and Asia never apparently particularly common. The most recent records both in 1979, with single plants in a cornfield margin just north of Barley and in the churchyard at Ridge

Mouse-tail *Myosurus minimus* (6–7)

Never common, although easily overlooked, and preferring damp, sandy or gravelly soils, notably where water stands on arable or open grassland during winter. The most recent records from north-east of Codicote, near Westland Green and north of South Mimms

Few-flowered Fumitory *Fumaria vaillantii* (6–9)

Very rare, only recent record from soil disturbed by fallen beech trees near Therfield, 1989

Appendix 1.16

Wild Candytuft *Iberis amara* (7–8)
Restricted to the Chalk and always local. (*See* Chapter 9.1.) Apparently not infrequent along arable margins. No recent reports from arable land although a few plants seen in a fallow field just outside the county boundary near Pirton in 1978

* **Corn Cockle** *Agrostemma githago* (6–8)
Once a widespread and pernicious weed of cereal crops but drastically reduced by improved seed-screening techniques and herbicides in early decades of this century. Last wild occurrences a few plants in the late 1940s or early 1950s; subsequent sightings almost certainly related to attempted introductions of this attractive plant now included in some 'wild flower seed mixes'. In garden cultivation at Baldock, Letchworth, Hitchin and Ashwell in the late 1970s – the record from the 'edge of a wheat field' near Little Hadham in 1984 likely to be from sown seed

Yellow Vetchling *Lathyrus aphaca* (6–8)
Always rare; a colonist of dry soils not recorded from arable fields for decades, but records from 'dumps' at Park Street and Hitchin in 1968 and waste ground near Wormley in 1985. Sightings, as yet unconfirmed, reported 'by path' near Pirton in 1982

Shepherd's Needle *Scandix pecten-veneris* (4–7)
Once common and well distributed, especially on calcareous soils. Even in 1960s not uncommon but has since suffered considerable declines which should be regarded with concern. Records, since 1976, from Westfield Common near Clothall, Claybush Hill near Ashwell, Bramfield, the Broad Baulk at Rothamsted, near Pirton and Sandridge. Some conservation measures implemented at one of these sites

Spreading Hedge-parsley *Torilis arvensis* (7–9)
A widely distributed and most troublesome weed in the 19th century, particularly on the lighter, neutral to calcareous soils. Dony (1967) noted considerable and continuing decline. Since 1980 only reports from Broad Baulk, Rothamsted and near Pirton, both with rather small numbers of plants

Knotted Hedge-parsley *T. nodosa* (5–7)
Although recorded very occasionally on dry soils in other parts of the county, a species mainly of bare dry Chalk soils, where 19th century botanists found it to be 'common'. Only two reports since 1970, from road verge near Wallington, where is still survives, and garden at Berkhamsted. A small thriving colony also just across the county border near Hexton

Corn Parsley *Petroselinum segetum* (8–9)
Also known as Corn Caraway; generally scarce and found on open banks as well as field margins on calcareous soils, reported as a 'quite common' plant of Hitchin area in early decades of this century; still to be found near Pirton, Purwell and, possibly, Cadwell. No other sightings reported since 1980, although sites near London Colney, Kings Langley, Abbots Langley and Bragbury End, Stevenage, where plants seen in the 1970s, worth searching

Longleaf *Falcaria vulgaris* (7–9)
Introduced and naturalised, never more than scarce and more or less limited to Chalk soils. Since 1960s, Longleaf present in relatively small, but varying, quantities, in banks

236

south of Ashwell. Former locations – near Reed (two plants found 1978), White Hall near Aston, east of Lilley and near Pirton – perhaps worth searching

* Great Pignut *Bunium bulbocastanum* (6-7)
First discovered as British species by W. H. Coleman, co-author of first Herts county flora; now more or less confined to road or track verges at about ten locations on Middle Chalk in north of county. Once, apparently, not uncommon as arable weed although no reports of such occurrences for at least 50 years. North Herts still at centre of plant's national distribution and some spread possible if herbicide spraying relaxed and set-aside regimes introduced into nearby fields

Field Woundwort *Stachys arvensis* (4–11)
Always rare, now possibly extinct, from light sandy and Chalk soils. Last sightings in 1970 near Ridge and 1973 near Rickmansworth. Between 1958 and 1961, Field Woundwort seen at Therfield, Harmer Green, east of Bull's Green and near Ardeley

Ground Pine *Ajuga chamaepitys* (5–11)
An inconspicuous plant, always rare and more or less limited to disturbed stony Chalk soils or shallow calcareous gravels, perhaps now extinct from Herts, although recent reports from within yards of county boundary near Hexton; many old records made in disturbed field margins around Hexton, Pirton, Baldock and Ashwell – old sites well worth checking. Germination often restrained until autumn by modern cultivation methods, flowers sometimes still present well into November

Rough Corn Bedstraw *Galium tricornutum* (6–9)
Up to early decades of this century, a widespread weed of cereal fields on calcareous soils, but declined very rapidly presumably as more potent herbicides developed. Just a handful of records in 1950s and 60s. Subsequently only seen in untreated experimental plot at the Broad Baulk, Rothamsted during 1980/81 and in 1984, when 20 plants counted

Cornflower or Bluebottle *Centaurea cyanus* (6–8)
Virtually eradicated from cornfields by modern seed-screening, this most attractive species was particularly abundant in corn fields on more calcareous soils in the 19th century. Still present in a few areas until early post-Second World War years, particularly just east of Baldock. Most recent records from waste tips, presumably of garden throwouts. Possible relict occurrences from field near Radlett with records in 1963 and 1981, from Purwell area in the 1970s, from Essendon in 1973, from near Pirton in 1981, and on disturbed soil by the M 25 neat Radlett in 1986. The species frequently marketed in wild flower mixes and so any future records should be regarded with care

Corn Marigold *Chrysanthemum segetum* (6–8)
Once a common and troublesome weed of arable fields on sandy soils, decline attributed to improved seed-screening and reductions in soil acidity from applications of lime. Few recent records, although near St. Ippollitts in 1978 and near Clothall in 1982 large colonies seen in cornfields, presumably from imported poorly screened grain stocks. Casual occurrences possibly due to its frequent inclusion in wild flower mixes and wild bird food

Cudweed *Filago vulgaris* (7–8)
Always rather scarce and restricted to dry acid soils derived from terrace gravels in east

and central Herts, now very rare or possibly extinct; only recent record made near Wheathampstead in 1985, on old railway track

Meadow Brome *Bromus commutatus* (6)
Never common and once found in meadows as well as being an occasional arable weed, now disappeared from most of its former haunts, mainly in north of the county; only recent records from Eastwick Meads and by a field path near Hinxworth, both in 1984

1.17 Checklist of Some Characteristic Wild Flowers of Open Road Verges

NB *As noted in the text, many sites will have aspects of the flora of grasslands, heaths, hedges, arable land and waste areas. (See relevant checklists.)*

Field Horsetail	*Equisetum arvense*	common and widespread, especially in disturbed places
Bracken	*Pteridium aquilinum*	a fern, frequent on acid soils
Bulbous Buttercup	*Ranunculus bulbosus* (5–6)	common on dry calcareous soils
Creeping Buttercup	*R. repens* (5–8)	abundant
Meadow Buttercup	*R. acris* (5–7)	common on damper neutral to calcareous soils
Lesser Celandine	*R. ficaria* (3–5)	common in shadier places and on moist, but not acidic, soils
Lesser Meadow-rue	*Thalictrum minus* (6–8)	limited to Chalk, at Therfield Heath and one verge site near Sandon where known since about 1848 (Sawford, 1974)
Field or Common Poppy	*Papaver rhoeas* (6–10)	common in disturbed places on calcareous soils
Long Prickly-headed or Prickly Poppy	*P. argemone* (4–6)	occasional in disturbed places on light soils
Long-headed Poppy	*P. dubium* (5–7)	scarce in disturbed places on light soils
Round Prickly-headed or Rough Prickly Poppy	*P. hybridum* (5–8)	rare on Chalk
Wild Clematis	*Clematis vitalba* (7–8)	common and increasing on calcareous soils
Greater Celandine	*Chelidonium majus* (5–8)	fairly common, especially in south of county, mainly in shady places and often close to habitation
Rape	*Brassica napus* (5–8)	common on disturbed soils
Charlock	*Sinapis arvensis* (5–7)	common and widespread on disturbed soils

White Mustard	*S. alba* (6–8)	fairly frequent but declining on disturbed calcareous soils
Wild Radish	*Raphanus raphanistrum* (5–9)	common on less calcareous, disturbed soils
Dittander	*Lepidium latifolium* (6–7)	mainly a coastal species and rare in Herts; a long-known colony by A505 at Baldock
Hoary Cress	*Cardaria draba* (5–6)	introduced and common in disturbed places
Shepherd's-purse	*Capsella bursa-pastoris* (1–12)	abundant on disturbed soils
Horse-radish	*Armoracia rusticana* (5–6)	common in disturbed places
Winter Cress	*Barbarea vulgaris* (5–8)	common on damper soils
Dame's-violet	*Hesperis matronalis* (5–7)	occasional, mainly in central and south Herts
Hedge Garlic	*Alliaria petiolata* (4–6)	common and widespread, indicates phosphate-rich soils
Hedge Mustard	*Sisymbrium officinale* (6–7)	common
Wild Mignonette	*Reseda lutea* (6–8)	abundant on Chalk and Chalky Boulder Clay, common on other dry neutral calcareous soils, scarce elsewhere
Dyer's Rocket or Weld	*R. luteola* (6–8)	locally common on disturbed dry soils
Sweet Violet	*Viola odorata* (2–4)	occasional to common on calcareous soils
Red Campion	*Silene dioica* (5–6)	common in shadier places on more acidic soils of south and east Herts
White Campion	*S. latifolia* ssp. *alba* (5–9)	common and widespread, especially on more neutral soils
Hybrid between White and Red Campion	*S. dioica* × *latifolia*	occasional in central southern Herts, often called Pink Campion
Bladder Campion	*S. vulgaris* (6–8)	common and widespread
Field Mouse-ear Chickweed	*Cerastium arvense* (4–8)	rare on dry calcareous or slightly acid sandy soils; recent records from near Sandon, and Barley
Dusty Miller or Snow-in-Summer	*C. tomentosum* (5–8)	introduced, occasional as garden escape
Common Mouse-ear Chickweed	*C. fontanum* (4–9)	common
Sticky Mouse-ear Chickweed	*C. glomeratum* (4–9)	common in disturbed places, except on calcareous and wet soils
Chickweed	*Stellaria media* (1–12)	common to abundant in disturbed places
Fine-leaved Sandwort	*Minuartia hybrida* (5–6)	very rare on open Chalk, recent records from Bygrave and Sandon

Appendix 1.17

Soapwort	*Saponaria officinalis* (7–9)	introduced, occasional, mainly near habitation
Musk Mallow	*Malva moscata* (7–8)	occasional on more fertile, less calcareous soils, mainly in south Herts
Dwarf Mallow	*M. neglecta* (6–9)	occasional in disturbed places
Small Mallow	*M. pusilla* (6–9)	introduced, very rare, only recent record from near Pirton in 1980
Common Mallow	*M. sylvestris* (6–9)	common and widespread, although apparently scarcer in south-west Herts
Meadow Crane's-bill	*Geranium pratense* (6–9)	local, declined from west Herts, most records from around Hitchin, Hertford and Ware areas
Cut-leaved Crane's-bill	*G. dissectum* (5–8)	common in disturbed areas
Dove's-foot Crane's-bill	*G. molle* (4–9)	common on dry soils
Dusky Crane's-bill	*G. phaeum* (5–6)	introduced; colonies at Clothall and Wallington almost certainly garden escapes, although long-established, also recorded near Sopwell Mill in 1985
Small-flowered Crane's-bill	*G. pusillum* (6–9)	occasional in dry disturbed soils
Hedgerow Crane's-bill	*G. pyrenaicum* (6–8)	occasional, mainly on drier calcareous soils, largely absent from clays and acidic soils
Herb Robert	*G. robertianum* (5–9)	common and widespread on shady or scrubby verges
Gorse	*Ulex europaeus* (3–6)	increasing on light acid soils
Broom	*Cytisus scoparius* (5–6)	common in heathy places
Hairy Tare	*Vicia hirsuta* (5–8)	common on less calcareous soils
Smooth Tare	*V. tetrasperma* (5–8)	similar to *hirsuta*, but less frequent
Common Vetch	*V. sativa* (5–9)	common and widespread; ssp. *sativa* – the cultivated forage plant seems to be more frequent on acidic soils whilst ssp. *nigra* – the native plant occurs more frequently on drier calcareous soils
Tufted Vetch	*V. cracca* (6–8)	common except on the Clay-with-Flints
Bush Vetch	*V. sepium* (5–8)	common except on Chalk
Meadow Vetchling	*Lathyrus pratensis* (5–8)	common and widespread
Ribbed Melilot	*Melilotus officinalis* (7–9)	introduced, naturalised; occasional in disturbed places
Tall Melilot	*M. altissima* (6–8)	introduced, naturalised and occasional, most frequent on Boulder Clay

Lucerne	*Medicago sativa* (6–7)	occasional in open or disturbed places, mainly as an escape from cultivation as ssp. *sativa*
Spotted Medick	*M. arabica* (5–9)	very rare as native; only recent record near Baldock, although also noted from waste dumps
White Clover	*Trifolium repens* (6–9)	abundant
Red Clover	*T. pratense* (5–9)	abundant
Hare's-foot Clover	*T. arvense* (6–9)	rare, declining from dry sandy soils, only recent verge records from Hertford in 1980 and Rye Meads in 1984
Hop Trefoil	*T. campestre* (6–9)	occasional to common on dry calcareous soils
Lesser Trefoil	*T. dubium* (5–10)	common on dry soils
Alsike Clover	*T. hybridum* (6–9)	introduced and common
Zigzag Clover	*T. medium* (6–9)	local, more frequent on acidic soils of south Herts
Knotted Clover	*T. striatum* (5–7)	rare on open dry sandy soils; only recent verge record from Hertford in 1978
Bird's-foot Trefoil	*Lotus corniculatus* (6–9)	common and widespread
Narrow-leaved Bird's-foot-trefoil	*L. tenuis* (6–8)	very rare on dry soils, only recent verge record from Slip End near Ashwell in 1983
Kidney Vetch	*Anthyllis vulneraria* (6–9)	local on dry, open, mainly Chalk soils, much declined but sometimes flourishing for a while in disturbded places
Sainfoin	*Onobrychis viciifolia* (6–8)	introduced, sometimes cultivated and locally common in disturbed places on Chalk
Blackberry or Bramble	*Rubus fruticosus* agg.	common to abundant
Dewberry	*R. caesius* (6–9)	common on basic soils
Silverweed	*Potentilla anserina* (6–8)	common and widespread, especially in open and disturbed places
Creeping Cinquefoil	*P. reptans* (6–9)	abundant
Sulphur Cinquefoil	*P. recta* (6–7)	introduced, a few records mainly from the Hatfield and Hertford areas
Herb Bennett	*Geum urbanum* (6–8)	common in shady places
Agrimony	*Agrimonia eupatoria* (6–8)	common and widespread especially on calcareous soils
Salad Burnet	*Sanguisorba minor* ssp. *minor* (5–8)	common on calcareous soils
Orpine or Livelong	*Sedum telephium* (7–9)	scarce, mainly a species of woods and hedges in

		central and south Herts, declining but was noted from a verge near Standon in 1980 which was subsequently cleared
Wall-pepper or Biting Stonecrop	*S. acre* (6–7)	occasionally on dry open acidic soils, also noted from kerbsides
Rosebay Willowherb	*Chamaenerion angustifolium* (7–9)	common to abundant in disturbed and burnt places
Rough Chervil	*Chaerophyllum temulentum* (6–7)	common and widespread
Cow Parsley or Keck	*Anthriscus sylvestris* (4–6)	common to abundant, often dominant
Bur Chervil	*A. caucalis* (5–6)	very rare, most recent verge records from near Stevenage in 1971 and near Ware in 1977
Alexanders	*Smyrnium olusatrum* (4–6)	a maritime plant, probably introduced, with recent records from roadsides at Pirton, Hertford, Weston and near Baldock, where it has been known for over 20 years
Great Pignut	*Bunium bulbocastanum* (6–7)	nationally rare, but not uncommon on relict Chalk grassland verges in North Herts apparently extinct from the west of the county
Pignut	*Conopodium majus* (5–6)	common on acid soils
Burnet-saxifrage	*Pimpinella saxifraga* (7–8)	common on dry soils
Greater Burnet-saxifrage	*P. major* (6–7)	occasional, mainly on clay soils in north-east Herts but also recorded sparingly from south and west
Hemlock	*Conium maculatum* (6–7)	fairly common and increasing on damper and disturbed soils
Stone Parsley	*Sison amomum* (7–9)	occasional, mainly on acidic soils
Wild Parsnip	*Pastinaca sativa* (7–8)	locally common on calcareous soils
Hogweed or Cow Parsnip	*Heracleum sphondylium* (6–9)	common and widespread
Giant Hogweed	*H. mantegazzianum* (6–7)	introduced, naturalised and increasing especially in north-east Herts
Upright Hedge-parsley	*Torilis japonica* (7–8)	common and widespread
Spreading Hedge-parsley	*T. arvensis* (7–9)	rare and declining arable weed, recorded from verges near Hitchin in 1976, near Bygrave in 1977 and Pirton in 1981

Knotted Hedge-parsley	*T. nodosa* (5–7)	very rare arable weed, still present (1989) on verge near Wallington
Wild Carrot	*Daucus carota* (6–8)	common on chalky soils
Birthwort	*Aristolochia clematitis* (6–9)	introduced, only known from verge in Walkern
Leafy Spurge	*Euphorbia esula* (5–7)	rare; on chalky verges in Sandon and Ashwell area, also around gravel pits in south-east
Sheep's Sorrel	*Rumex acetosella* (5–8)	common on open heathy verges on acid soils in southern half of Herts
Common Sorrel	*R. acetosa* (5–6)	common and widespread
Sharp Dock	*R. conglomeratus* (7–8)	common and widespread, especially in damper soils
Curled Dock	*R. crispus* (6–10)	common and widespread
Broad-leaved Dock	*R. obtusifolius* (6–10)	common and widespread
Red-veined Dock	*R. sanguineus* (6–8)	common, especially in shady places
Common or Stinging Nettle	*Urtica dioica* (6–8)	common and widespread, especially in disturbed and eutrophic places
Walnut	*Juglans regia* (6)	occasional, mainly introduced by birds or mammals transporting nuts
Japanese Knotweed	*Reynoutria japonica* (8–9)	introduced, escaped from cultivation and spreading, especially in south Herts around old gravel pits
Giant Knotweed	*R. sachalinensis* (8–9)	introduced, less common than *R. japonica* but apparently increasing in south of county, known from near Berkhamsted for about 30 years
Cowslip	*Primula veris* (8–9)	occasional and declining on calcareous soils mainly in north-east and south-west Herts
Buddleia	*Buddleja davidii* (6–10)	introduced, naturalised with some notable recent increases on disturbed or new verges on Chalk
Scarlet Pimpernel	*Anagallis arvensis* (6–8)	common on disturbed soils
Rough Comfrey	*Symphytum asperum* (6–7)	introduced fodder crop, rare, recent verge records from near Batchworth and Hamper Mill near Watford
Common Comfrey	*S. officinale* (5–6)	occasional in damper places mainly in south and east Herts
White Comfrey	*S. orientale* (4–5)	introduced; rare, recent records from Ickleford and Barley

Russian Comfrey	*S.* × *uplandicum* (6–8)	occasional to frequent, hybrid of *asperum* and *officinale*
Alkanet	*Pentaglottis sempervirens* (5–6)	introduced, occasional often as garden escape
Field Bindweed	*Convolvulus arvensis* (6–9)	common and widespread on disturbed soils
Hedge Bindweed or Belbine	*Calystegia sepium* ssp. *sepium* (7–9)	common and widespread, especially in overgrown and damper places; the introduced ssp. *silvatica* has also been found to be common and well distributed, whilst ssp. *pulchra*, also introduced, is rare with recent reports from Ashwell and Harmer Green
Dark Mullein	*Verbascum nigrum* (6–10)	occasional on open, usually calcareous soils
Great Mullein or Aaron's Rod	*V. thapsus* (6–8)	common on open dry soils
Purple Toadflax	*Linaria purpurea* (6–8)	introduced, occasional as garden escape
Common Toadflax	*L. vulgaris* (7–10)	common on drier soils, rather infrequent on Boulder Clay
Germander Speedwell	*Veronica chamaedrys* (3–7)	common
Wall Speedwell	*V. arvensis* (3–10)	common in disturbed places on dry soils
Red Bartsia	*Odontites verna* (6–7)	common in open and disturbed places on calcareous soils; ssp. *serotina* probably most frequent, but ssp. *verna* also noted
Tall or Knapweed Broomrape	*Orobanche elatior* (6–7)	not uncommon on chalky verges in north Herts, scarce elsewhere, no recent records from south-west Herts
Small Broomrape	*O. minor* (6–9)	scarce, most recent verge records from Chalk in north of county
Marjoram	*Origanum vulgare* (7–9)	occasional on more calcareous soils
Large Thyme	*Thymus pulegioides* (7–8)	scarce on relict downland verges, mainly in north Herts
Wild Thyme	*T. praecox* (5–8)	very rare, only verge records from relict downland near Sandon and Clothall
Common Calamint	*Calamintha sylvatica* ssp. *ascendens* (7–9)	scarce and declining on dry usually calcareous soils, recent verge records mainly from the Hitchin to Ashwell area
Wild Basil	*Clinopodium vulgare* (7–9)	common on dry usually calcareous soils

Wild Clary	*Salvia verbenaca* (5–8)	rare, recent records from dry soils at Ashwell, Holwell and Windmill Hill, Hitchin
Hedge Woundwort	*Stachys sylvatica* (7–8)	common and widespread in shady places
Black Horehound	*Ballota nigra* ssp. *foetida* (6–10)	common and widespread
White Dead-nettle	*Lamium album* (5–12)	common and widespread
Red Dead-nettle	*L. purpureum* (3–10)	common and widespread in open and disturbed places
Spotted Dead-nettle	*L. maculatum* (5–10)	introduced, occasional as garden escape
Henbit Dead-nettle	*L. amplexicaule* (4–8)	occasional on dry disturbed soils, mainly on Chalk
Cut-leaved Dead-nettle	*L. hybridum* (3–10)	rare and declining; most recent verge record from Little Berkhamsted in 1976
Common Hemp-nettle	*Galeopsis tetrahit* (7–9)	occasional on less calcareous soils, especially Clay-with-Flints
Cat-mint	*Nepeta cataria* (7–9)	rare and declining on calcareous soils; most recent records from verges near Pirton, Clothall and Puckeridge
Greater Plantain	*Plantago major* (5–9)	common and widespread in open and disturbed places
Ribwort Plantain	*P. lanceolata* (4–8)	common and widespread especially on basic and neutral soils
Hoary Plantain	*P. media* (5–8)	common on more basic soils
Clustered Bellflower	*Campanula glomerata* (5–9)	occasional, mainly on relict downland verges
Harebell	*C. rotundifolia* (7–9)	occasional on dry open soils
Bats-in-the-Belfry or Nettle-leaved Bellflower	*Campanula trachelium* (7–9)	scarce on Boulder Clay, recent verge records from Rushden and Sandon area
Crosswort	*Cruciata laevipes* (4–7)	rare, mainly on calcareous soils with recent records from path side near Bovingdon and green lane near Ashwell; also noted at Colney Heath, Tyttenhanger gravel pits, Mimmshall Brook and near Pirton
Goosegrass	*Galium aparine* (6–8)	widespread; often abundant
Hedge-bedstraw	*G. mollugo sensu lato* (6–9)	common and well distributed on richer more basic soils; two species *mollugo* and *album* may be present but taxonomy is awaiting further research
Lady's Bedstraw	*G. verum* (7–8)	common on basic to slightly acidic soils

Wild Teasel	*Dipsacus fullonum* (7–8)	common on disturbed damper soils
Field Scabious	*Knautia arvensis* (7–9)	common on dry basic soils, especially Chalk and Chalky Boulder Clay, scarce in south-east Herts
Small Scabious	*Scabiosa columbaria* (7–8)	scarce on a few relict downland verges, mainly in north Herts
Ragwort	*Senecio jacobea* (6–10)	common and widespread in disturbed and rank places
Hoary Ragwort	*S. erucifolius* (7–8)	common on Chalk, Boulder Clay and London Clay
Groundsel	*S. vulgaris* (1–12)	common to abundant on disturbed open soils
Coltsfoot	*Tussilago farfara* (3–4)	common on recently disturbed soils, especially clays
Winter Heliotrope	*Petasites fragrans* (1–3)	introduced, an occasional escape from gardens; most recent record from near Walkern
Ploughman's Spikenard	*Inula conyza* (7–9)	occasional on recently disturbed calcareous soils, especially Chalk
Michaelmas Daisy	*Aster novi-belgae* (8–9)	introduced, not uncommon as garden escape in open places
Blue Fleabane	*Erigeron acer* (7–8)	local on dry soils, most frequent on gravels across south of county and around Hitchin
Canadian Fleabane	*Conyza canadensis* (8–9)	introduced, increasing on disturbed light soils especially in south Herts
Daisy	*Bellis perennis* (3–10)	common but declining except in close-mown verges
Yarrow	*Achillea millefolium* (6–8)	common and widespread
Oxeye Daisy	*Leucanthemum vulgare* (6–8)	common and well distributed, a feature of recently disturbed Chalk verges
Mugwort	*Artemesia vulgaris* (7–9)	common and widespread particularly in disturbed, rank and eutrophic sites
Wormwood	*A. absinthium* (7–8)	now scarce; only recent verge records from Berkhamsted and near Baldock where it has been known for about 20 years
Lesser Burdock	*Arctium minus* 'group' (7–9)	this group contains three variable species of which two, at least, occur in the county; *minus* appears to be the most frequent and is well distributed, whilst

		pubens is scarcer and found more often on less calcareous drier soils
Great Burdock	*A. lappa* (7–9)	local to occasional on damper soils, mainly in east of county; recognised by solid leaf stalks
Welted Thistle	*Carduus acanthoides* (6–8)	common on more calcareous soils, scarce and even absent on drier acid soils of southern Herts
Musk Thistle	*C. nutans* (5–8)	occasional on dry, open and disturbed calcareous soils
Spear Thistle	*Cirsium vulgare* (7–10)	common and widespread
Marsh Thistle	*C. palustre* (7–9)	occasional, sometimes common on damp verges
Creeping Thistle	*C. arvense* (7–9)	common and widepread, often abundant in disturbed places
Stemless Thistle	*C. acaule* (7–9)	occasional on relict downland
Melancholy Thistle	*C. helenioides* (7–8)	only site is at Meesden Green where plants have been introduced
Milk Thistle	*Silybum marianum* (6–8)	introduced and rare casual; verge records were made at Stevenage in 1971 and by green lane at Purwell near Hitchin in 1984
Scotch Thistle	*Onopordum acanthium* (7–9)	scarce, usually in disturbed or open verges as a garden escape
Hardheads or Lesser Knapweed	*Centaurea nigra* (6–9)	common and widespread
Greater Knapweed	*C. scabiosa* (7–9)	common on more open chalky verges, occasional on other calcareous soils, scarce or absent elsewhere
Cornflower	*C. cyanus* (6–8)	once frequent cornfield weed, now rare as casual; recorded in 1986 by M25 near London Colney
Chicory	*Cichorium intybus* (7–10)	occasional, well distributed, mainly on calcareous soils
Nipplewort	*Lapsana communis* (6–10)	common and widespread
Cat's-ear	*Hypochoeris radicata* (6–9)	common and widespread although rather scarce on the more calcareous soils
Autumnal Hawkbit	*Leontodon autumnalis* (6–10)	common and widespread, often abundant on close-mown verges
Rough Hawkbit	*L. hispidus* (6–9)	common on open more calcareous soils
Bristly Oxtongue	*Picris echioides* (6–10)	occasional to frequent on calcareous clay soils. especially Boulder Clay

Hawkweed Oxtongue	*P. hieracioides* (7–9)	occasional on dry calcareous soils
Goat's-beard	*Tragopogon pratensis* (6–7)	common and widespread in more open verges
Salsify	*T. porrifolius* (6–8)	introduced; only recent record is of about 100 plants on a roundabout on the A414 at Hertingfordbury in 1985
Prickly Lettuce	*Lactuca serriola* (7–9)	occasional in disturbed dry soils
Great Lettuce	*L. virosa* (7–9)	scarce in disturbed dry sandy and calcareous soils
Field Milk-Thistle	*Sonchus arvensis* (7–10)	common and widespread in open and disturbed places and on damper soils
Milk- or Sow-Thistle	*S. oleraceus* (6–8)	common and widespread in open and disturbed places
Spiny Milk- or Sow-Thistle	*S. asper* (6–8)	common and widespread in open and disturbed places
Blue Sowthistle	*Cicerbita macrophylla* (7–9)	introduced, scarce; recent records, probably originating from garden escapes, from near Cuffley, near Wallington, Rabley Heath and near Knebworth
Mouse-ear Hawkweed	*Hieracium pilosella* (5–10)	common on open, light, dry soils
Hawkweeds	*Hieracium* spp.	in most of this genus seeds are frequently produced apomictically, ie, without fertilisation of the ovum by pollen, so that rather closed groups of plants can result from one individual, giving many true breeding lines and hence many 'species'; identification and taxonomy are complex and there are many 'species' in Herts
Dandelions	*Taraxacum* spp.	like *Hieracium*, this is an apomictic genus, with groups of microspecies of which some may be widespread and abundant on close-mown verges
Smooth Hawk's-beard	*Crepis capillaris* (6–9)	common and widespread
Beaked Hawk's-beard	*C. vesicaria* (5–7)	common on drier, open more calcareous soils
Rough Hawk's-beard	*C. biennis* (6–7)	scarce, mainly on calcareous soils; long-established colony on Chalk verge near Sandon, also recorded from verge at Cheshunt in 1985

Drooping Star-of-Bethlehem	*Ornithogalum nutans* (4–5)	introduced, naturalised, and known from verge near Little Hadham since the 19th century
Crow Garlic	*Allium vineale* (6–7)	introduced, occasional to common in grassy verges, mainly on Boulder Clay
Daffodil	*Narcissus* sp.	increasingly, cultivated varieties are occurring as garden throwouts or are being planted on some rural verges; native Wild Daffodil may occur occasionally on verges close to its main sites. (*See* Chapter 7.2.)
Stinking Iris or Gladdon	*Iris foetidissima* (5–7)	scarce on shady verges on calcareous soils; recent records from near Brickendon, Widford and Clothall
Twayblade	*Listera ovata* (6–7)	occasional on damper calcareous soils
Bee Orchid	*Ophrys apifera* (6–7)	occasional, sometimes well established on open verges, especially on Chalk; recent verge records from near Radwell, Reed and Stevenage
Common Spotted-orchid	*Dactylorhiza fuchsii* (6–8)	rare on calcareous soils
Lords-and-Ladies	*Arum maculatum* (7–8)	common in shady places
Tall Fescue	*Festuca arundinacea* (6–8)	common on damper calcareous soils
Giant Fescue	*F. gigantea* (6–7)	common and widespread in shadier places
Sheep's-fescue	*F. ovina* (5–7)	occasional on open, dry Chalk and sandy soils
Meadow Fescue	*F. pratensis* (6)	occasional to common, most frequent on clay soils
Red Fescue	*F. rubra* (5–7)	common and widespread
Rye-grass	*Lolium perenne* (5–8)	common to abundant
Italian Rye-grass	*L. multiflorum* (5–9)	introduced, common and widespread
Fern-grass	*Desmazeria rigida* (5–6)	scarce in dry, open places, more usually on calcareous soils
Annual Meadow-grass	*Poa annua* (1–12)	common and widespread
Wood Meadow-grass	*P. nemoralis* (6–7)	occasional in shadier places on more acidic soils mainly in southern Herts
Rough Meadow-grass	*P. trivialis* (6–9)	common and widespread
Reflexed Saltmarsh-grass	*Puccinellia distans* (6–7)	noted along major roads where winter salting occurs, full distribution uncertain

Appendix 1.17

Crested Dog'-tail	*Cynosaurus cristatus* (6–8)	common and widespread especially in better unimproved sites
Quaking-grass	*Briza media* (6–7)	occasional in relict downland and better unimproved sites on basic and acidic soils
Wood Melick	*Melica uniflora* (5–6)	occasional in shadier places on acidic soils
Upright Brome	*Bromus erectus* (6–7)	occasional on dry calcareous soils, especially downland relicts
Lop-grass	*B. hordeaceus* (6–8)	common and widespread
Slender Soft-brome	*B. lepidus* (6–8)	apparently scarce on verges but possibly under-recorded; recent records from Ashwell and Berkhamsted
Hybrid between *B. hordeaceus* and *lepidus*	*B. × pseudothominii*	has been recorded from a few verges
Hairy Brome	*B. ramosus* (7–8)	common and widespread in shady places
Barren Brome	*B. sterilis* (5–7)	common and widespread, often abundant in disturbed and eutrophic places
False-brome	*Brachypodium sylvaticum* (7)	common and widespread in shady places
Wall Barley	*Hordeum murinum* (6–7)	common and widespread in dry, open, disturbed places
Meadow Barley	*H. secalinum* (6–7)	scarce in verges, mainly on better sites on Boulder Clay and London Clay
Couch-grass or Twitch	*Elymus repens* (6–9)	common and widespread, especially in disturbed places
Bearded Couch	*E. caninus* (7)	occasional in shady places on damper calcareous soils
Wild Oat	*Avena fatua* (7–9)	introduced; common in disturbed places on Boulder Clay, occasional elsewhere
Downy Oat-grass	*Avenula pubescens* (6–7)	occasional on calcareous soils
False Oat-grass	*Arrhenatherum elatius* (6–7)	common and widespread, often abundant and dominant
Crested Hair-grass	*Koeleria macrantha* (6–7)	occasional on light, usually calcareous soils, most often as a downland relict
Yellow Oat-grass	*Trisetum flavescens* (5–6)	fairly common and widespread, particularly on dry, more open calcareous soils
Tufted Hair-grass	*Deschampsia caespitosa* (6–8)	occasional to frequent on wetter clay soils
Wavy hair-grass	*D. flexuosa* (6–7)	scarce in acid heathy places; most recent verge record from near Berkhamsted

250

Sweet Vernal-grass	*Anthoxanthum odoratum* (4–6)	common and well distributed except on the more calcareous soils of Chalk and Boulder Clay
Yorkshire Fog	*Holcus lanatus* (6–9)	common and widespread
Creeping Soft-grass	*H. mollis* (6–7)	occasional to common in shady places on more acid soils, especially in south-east Herts
Brown Bent-grass	*Agrostis canina* (6–7)	scarce on damper acid soils, mainly in central and south-east Herts
Common Bent-grass	*A. capillaris* (6–8)	common on open acidic soils in southern Herts
Black Bent-grass	*A. gigantea* (6–8)	occasional to frequent on lighter acidic soils, more often in shady places
Creeping Bent	*A. stolonifera* (7–8)	common and widespread, especially in disturbed places
Timothy	*Phleum pratense* ssp. *pratense* (7)	common and well distributed
Smaller Cat's-tail	*P. pratense* ssp. *bertolonii* (7)	common and widespread in less rank places
Purple-stemmed Cat's-tail	*P. phleoides* (6–7)	a national rarity, only known from thin dry sandy soil over Chalk at Wilbury Hill near Letchworth
Meadow Foxtail	*Alopecurus pratensis* (4–6)	common and widespread
Black-grass	*A. myosuroides* (6–7)	common in disturbed places on calcareous soils

1.18 Checklist of Some of the More Interesting Wild Flowers of Railways

NB *As indicated in the text, railway floras, like road verges, may contain elements of many other habitats and so a great many species not listed here may be recorded in railway habitats. (See other checklists, especially for road verges, hedges and walls.)*

Ferns

Hart's-tongue Fern	*Asplenium scolopendrium*	occasional on shady, damp walls
Black Spleenwort	*A. adiantum-nigrum*	occasional on shady, damp walls
Wall-rue	*A. ruta-muraria*	occasional
Maidenhair Spleenwort	*A. trichomanes*	scarce, most recent record from shady wall at Berkhamsted Station car park in 1985

251

Appendix 1.18

Rustyback Fern	*A. ceterach*	scarce on calcareous substrate; noted from Royston Station (just in Cambs)
Oak Fern	*Gymnocarpium dryopteris*	very rare; most recent record from bridge near Radlett Station in 1968

Wild Flowers

Green Hellebore	*Helleborus viridis* (3–4)	scarce; long established near Knebworth Station
Wall-rocket	*Diplotaxis muralis* (6–9)	introduced; local in south Herts and between Hitchin and Royston
Early Scurvy-grass	*Cochleria danica* (1–6)	always scarce, now declined; most recent record from railway near Kings Langley in 1979
Pepperwort	*Lepidium campestre* (5–8)	scarce and apparently declining; most recent record from near Brookmans Park Station in 1977
Wild Candytuft	*Iberis amara* (7–8)	scarce; still occurs on banks between Letchworth and Baldock Stations
Warty Cabbage	*Bunias orientalis* (5–8)	introduced, scarce; seen near Baldock Station in 1981
Thale Cress	*Arabidopsis thaliana* (4–5)	occasional in central and south Herts on dry banks and walls
Flixweed	*Descurania sophia* (6–8)	scarce and local, a feature of banks south of Hitchin Station
Dyer's Rocket or Weld	*Reseda luteola* (6–8)	more frequent in south Herts and a feature of sidings and tracksides, especially on calcareous substrata
Wild Mignonette	*R. lutea* (6–8)	common to abundant on calcareous railsides
Common Annual Pearlwort	*Sagina apetala* (5–8)	fairly common and widespread on walls and in sidings
Hedgerow Crane's-bill	*Geranium pyrenaicum* (6–8)	occasional
Herb Robert	*G. robertianum* (5–9)	often common on ballast
Goat's-rue	*Galega officinalis* (6–7)	introduced, occasional in sidings
Bladder Senna	*Colutea arborescens* (5–7)	introduced, scarce; most recent record from near St Albans Station in 1983
Crown Vetch	*Coronilla varia* (7–8)	introduced; known from sidings at Hitchin for at least 30 years

Orpine or Livelong	*Sedum telephium* (7–9)	much declined; most recent record from old railway at Croxley Common Moor about 1980
White Stonecrop	*S. album* (6–8)	scarce; recorded from bank at Woolmer Green in 1977
Wall Pepper or Biting Stonecrop	*S. acre* (6–7)	occasional on walls and calcareous tracksides
Reflexed Stonecrop	*S. reflexum* (6–8)	rare; noted from bank at Woolmer Green in 1979 and Berkhamsted Station car park in 1985
Rosebay Willowherb	*Chamaenerion angustifolium* (7–9)	common to abundant by tracksides
Spear-leaved Willowherb	*Epilobium lanceolatum* (7–9)	very rare; records only from Elstree and Bragbury End near Stevenage
Evening Primrose	*Oenothera* spp. (6–9)	this group has not been studied in detail in Herts and several species may be involved as casuals or somewhat more permanent features of tracksides and sidings; species so far most frequently noted are *biennis*, *erythrosepala* and *parviflora*
Corn Parsley	*Petroselinum segetum* (8–9)	rare; recorded from bank at Bragbury End in 1979
Hemp	*Cannabis sativa* (7–9)	scarce as casual or bird-seed alien; several plants on banks south of Hitchin Station in 1978 probably being illegally cultivated as source of marijuana
Buddleia	*Buddleja davidii* (6–10)	introduced (*c.* 1890), common and spreading on open banks and sidings
Deadly Nightshade	*Atropa belladonna* (6–8)	local, not uncommon about Hitchin sidings
Dark Mullein	*Verbascum nigrum* (6–10)	occasional on open calcareous banks
Great Mullein or Aaron's Rod	*V. thapsus* (6–8)	common on open banks and in sidings with chalky soils
Common Toadflax	*Linaria vulgaris* (7–10)	common on open banks and on calcareous ballast
Pale Toadflax	*L. repens* (6–9)	scarce; only recent records from ballast of abandoned lines near Bishop's Stortford, east of Wheathampstead and near Watford
Small Toadflax	*Chaenorhinum minus* (5–10)	occasional along tracksides
Ivy-leaved Toadflax	*Cymbalaria muralis* (5–9)	occasional on old walls and brickwork

Whorled Clary	*Salvia verticilliata* (6–8)	only recent railside records at Hitchin in 1978 and Kings Langley in 1974
Lamb's Lettuce or Cornsalad	*Valerianella locusta* (4–6)	occasional to common along tracksides
Oxford Ragwort	*Senecio squalidus* (5–12)	common along tracksides, in sidings and on old walls
Stinking Groundsel	*S. viscosus* (7–9)	common
Groundsel	*S. vulgaris* (1–12)	common
Coltsfoot	*Tussilago farfara* (3–4)	common in disturbed and open places
Canadian Fleabane	*Conyza canadensis* (8–9)	common and spreading, especially in sidings and along tracksides
Oxeye Daisy	*Leucanthemum vulgare* (6–8)	still frequent but much declined due to overgrowth
Feverfew	*Tanacetum parthenium* (7–9)	occasional in sidings and on old brickwork
Great Lettuce	*Lactuca virosa* (7–9)	occasional on open banks, in sidings and on old walls
Bee Orchid	*Ophrys apifera* (6–7)	scarce, but has been recorded from old lines near Bishop's Stortford and Cole Green
Common Spotted-orchid	*Dactylorhiza fuchsii* (6–8)	rare, record from Berkhamsted Station car park in 1981
Squirrel-tail Fescue	*Vulpia bromoides* (5–7)	occasional on open, dry sandy ground and walls
Rat's-tail Fescue	*V. myuros* (5–7)	scarce, in similar habitats to *bromoides*, recent records from near Hitchin, Watford and Berkhamsted
Fern-grass	*Desmazeria rigida* (5–6)	occasional on dry banks and walls
Flattened Meadow-grass	*Poa compressa* (6–8)	occasional on dry banks and walls
Narrow-leaved Meadow-grass	*P. angustifolia* (5–7)	occasional on dry banks and walls
Wall Barley	*Hordeum murinum* (6–7)	common in dry open places and on walls
False Oat-grass	*Arrhenatherum elatius* (6–7)	common, often abundant in more open places

1.19 *Checklist of Some Urban Wild Flowers*

NB *See also the checklists for arable fields, walls and waste areas.*

Trees, often aliens and ornamental varieties, frequently used in street or park plantings

Common Lime	*Tilia* × *europaea* (7)	pollution-tolerant hybrid between *cordata* and *platyphyllos*
Large-leaved Lime	*T. platyphyllos* (6, before × *europaea* and *cordata*)	
Small-leaved Lime	*T. cordata* (7)	
Sycamore	*Acer pseudoplatanus* (4–6)	
Norway Maple	*A. platanoides* (4–5)	
Horse-chestnut	*Aesculus hippocastanum* (5–6)	
Red Chestnut	*A. carnea* (5–6)	
Rowan	*Sorbus aucuparia* (5–6)	
Swedish Whitebeam	*S. intermedia* (5)	
Turkey Oak	*Quercus cerris* (5)	
Evergreen or Holm Oak	*Q. ilex* (5)	
Southern Beech	*Nothofagus* spp.	
Black Italian Poplar	*Populus* × *canadensis* (3–4)	
Lombardy Poplar	*P. nigra* var. *italica* (3–4)	
Balm of Gilead	*P. candicans* (3)	only female plants known in Britain
London Plane	*Platanus hybrida* (5)	pollution-tolerant
Japanese Cherry	*Prunus serratula* (4–5)	often double-flowered varieties

Herbs and shrubs

Welsh Poppy	*Mecanopsis cambrica* (6–8)	introduced, native to south-west England and Wales, not infrequent escape from gardens into damp shady places
Greater Celandine	*Chelidonium majus* (5–8)	fairly common and widespread, seldom far from habitation
Shepherd's-purse	*Capsella bursa-pastoris* (1–12)	common to abundant
Hairy Bitter-cress	*Cardamine hirsuta* (4–8)	frequent on bare ground and walls in south Herts, occasional elsewhere
Creeping Yellow-cress	*Rorippa sylvestris* (6–8)	occasional as weed on damper acid soils, mainly in south and central Herts
Common Annual Pearlwort	*Sagina apetala* (5–8)	common on open ground and in lawns on better drained, less calcareous, soils
Procumbent Pearlwort	*S. procumbens* (5–9)	common and well distributed on bare soils, short turf, trampled places and gardens

Fat Hen	*Chenopodium album* (7–10)	common in waste places and on disturbed soils
Dusky Crane's-bill	*Geranium phaeum* (5–6)	introduced as garden plant, naturalised on road bank at Clothall, where it has been known since 1915; other recent records from bank of lane at Benington and wood edge near Sopwell Mill
Laburnum	*Laburnum anagyroides* (5–6)	introduced, often planted and readily colonises waste ground close by
White Clover	*Trifolium repens* (6–9)	common to abundant in close-mown swards
Slender Trefoil	*T. micranthum* (6–7)	rather scarce in open grassy places on sandy and gravelly soils
Black Medick	*Medicago lupulina* (5–9)	common in verges and lawns
Bramble	*Rubus fruticosus* agg. (5–9)	common with many species, hybrids and apomicts
Rosebay Willowherb	*Chamaenerion angustifolium* (7–9)	common and widespread, especially in waste places
Ground Elder or Goutweed	*Aegopodium podagraria* (5–7)	introduced, a persistent weed of gardens and common in waste places
Fool's Parsley	*Aethusa cynapium* (7–8)	common and widespread in cultivated ground
Annual Mercury	*Mercurialis annua* (7–10)	doubtfully native, local in waste places and as garden and allotment weed, mainly in southern Herts and around Baldock
Caper Spurge	*Euphorbia lathyrus* (6–7)	scarce as a garden escape
Sun Spurge	*E. helioscopia* (5–10)	common on cultivated and disturbed ground
Petty Spurge	*E. peplus* (4–11)	very common in waste places and on cultivated ground
Fiddle Dock	*Rumex pulcher* (6–7)	scarce in dry soils and apparently declining; has been known from Windmill Hill at Hitchin for many years, other recent records from Baldock and Ashwell roadside
Stinging Nettle	*Urtica dioica* (6–8)	common, especially where rubble and litter accumulate
Small Nettle	*U. urens* (6–9)	common in gardens, allotments and waste places on light soils, scarce to absent on clays
Mind-your-own-business	*Soleirolia soleirolia* (5–10)	introduced, scarce as naturalised escape near gardens and greenhouses

Japanese Knotweed	*Reynoutria japonica* (8–9)	introduced and increasing as a pernicious escape from cultivation into waste places
Giant Knotweed	*R. sachalinensis* (8–9)	similar to *japonica* but, as yet, less frequent
Dotted Loosestrife	*Lysimachia punctata* (7–10)	introduced, often planted in garden ponds; occasional escapes may occur in wet or marshy places
Scarlet Pimpernel	*Anagallis arvensis* (6–8)	common in cultivated soils
Buddleia	*Buddleja davidii* (6–10)	introduced, commonly grown in gardens and increasingly recorded as escape, especially on drier calcareous soils in waste places
Garden Privet	*Ligustrum ovalifolium* (7)	introduced, commonly planted as garden hedge and not infrequent as escape
Greater Periwinkle	*Vinca major* (4–6)	introduced and occasionally escaping from gardens to copses, hedges and waste places
Lungwort	*Pulmonaria officinalis* (3–5)	introduced, recorded as garden escape near Stevenage
Alkanet	*Pentaglottis sempervirens* (5–6)	introduced and occasionally found as escape from gardens and in churchyards
Duke of Argyll's Tea-plant	*Lychium barbarum* (6–9)	introduced; occasional as an escape in hedges and waste places; the closely related *L. chinense* may also occur
Black Nightshade	*Solanum nigrum* (7–9)	common as weed of gardens and waste places on lighter soils, scarce on clays
Bittersweet or Woody Nightshade	*S. dulcamara* (6–9)	common and widespread in hedges and waste places
Germander Speedwell	*Veronica chamaedrys* (3–7)	very common in grassland and disturbed soils
Thyme-leaved Speedwell	*V. serpyllifolia* (3–10)	common in damper grassland
Slender Speedwell	*V. filiformis* (4–6)	introduced, fairly common and increasing, especially in close-mown grassland
Balm	*Melissa officinalis* (8–9)	introduced; a few records of garden escapes
Selfheal	*Prunella vulgaris* (6–9)	common, sometimes abundant in close-mown grass
White Dead-nettle	*Lamium album* (5–12)	common in waste places and along hedgerows and overgrown verges
Red Dead-nettle	*L. purpureum* (3–10)	common in cultivated and waste areas
Spotted Dead-nettle	*L. maculatum* (5–10)	introduced; occasional as garden escape

Ground Ivy	*Glechoma hederacea* (3–5)	common and widespread
Greater Plantain	*Plantago major* (5–9)	common in cultivated and waste ground, also often in close-mown lawns
Ribwort Plantain	*P. lanceolata* (4–8)	common in grassland and waste places, especially on more calcareous soils
Hoary Plantain	*P. media* (5–8)	fairly common in less improved, although often short-swarded, grassland on calcareous soils; a feature of some churchyards on Chalk and Boulder Clay
Elder	*Sambucus nigra* (6–7)	often common in waste places with disturbed nutrient-rich, neutral to basic soils
Gallant Soldier	*Galinsoga parviflora* (5–10)	introduced; occasional and spreading in waste places mainly in south Herts
Shaggy Soldier	*G. ciliata* (5–10)	introduced and local in waste places mainly in south Herts; also known from Baldock for several years
Ragwort	*Senecio jacobea* (6–10)	common in waste places
Oxford Ragwort	*S. squalidus* (5–12)	introduced; common in waste places and on derelict buildings, most frequent in south Herts
Groundsel	*S. vulgaris* (1–12)	common, often abundant in disturbed soils
Winter Heliotrope	*Petasites fragrans* (1–3)	introduced, occasional as garden escape on banks and verges in shady places
Creamy Butterbur	*P. japonicus* (3–4)	introduced; scarce as garden escape, mainly on banks of ponds, apparently only male plants are found
Daisy	*Bellis perennis* (3–10)	common to abundant in short-mown grass
Yarrow	*Achillea millefolium* (6–8)	often common in short-mown grass and waste places except on the most acid soils
Wall Lettuce	*Mycelis muralis* (7–9)	occasional in waste places
Annual Meadow-grass	*Poa annua* (1–12)	common in waste places, gardens and grassland
Cock's-foot	*Dactylis glomerata* (5–8)	common in waste places
Couch-grass or Twitch	*Elymus repens* (6–9)	common to abundant in waste places and cultivated ground, frequent and difficult to control in gardens
Wall Barley	*Hordeum murinum* (6–7)	common in waste places
False Oat-grass	*Arrhenatherum elatius* (6–7)	common and widespread in waste and overgrown places

| Creeping Bent or Fiorin | *Agrostis stolonifera* (7–8) | common in grassy and waste places |

1.20 Checklist of Characteristic Wild Flowers of Old Walls, Roofs and Bridges

Ferns

Hart's-tongue Fern	*Asplenium scolopendrium*	not infrequent on shaded structures by rivers or lakes, occasional on damp, older brickwork elsewhere
Black Spleenwort	*A. adiantum-nigrum*	scarce on shady walls, recent records from Norton School at Letchworth, Potters Bar, Broxbourne churchyard and railway bridge near Cadwell
Wall-rue	*A. ruta-muraria*	occasional on basic brickwork and mortar in shady situations
Maidenhair Spleenwort	*A. trichomanes*	scarce on basic substrates in shaded places; recent reports from wall at Berkhamsted Station and St Mary's Square at Hitchin
Rustyback Fern	*A. ceterach*	scarce, usually on limy mortar in shady places; recent reports from High Street at Standon, bridge at Woodhall Park, Kings Langley, and Hadham Towers
Broad Buckler-fern	*Dryopteris dilatata*	occasional in shady places
Male Fern	*D. filix-mas*	occasional in shady places
Hard Shield-fern	*Polystichium aculeatum*	rare; found growing from wall by River Hiz at St Mary's Square, Hitchin in 1976
Soft Shield-fern	*P. setiferum*	rare; noted on a wall by Great Amwell church in 1986
Polypody	*Polypodium vulgare*	appears to have declined considerably since 1960s when several records made from tree trunks and old walls; no recent records in urban situations

Appendix 1.20

Herbs and Shrubs

Yellow Corydalis	*Corydalis lutea* (5–8)	introduced, fairly frequent on old walls in towns and villages
Wall-rocket	*Diplotaxis muralis* (6–9)	introduced, local on limy substrates mainly in south Herts and between Hitchin and Royston but declining
Perennial Wall-rocket	*D. tenuifolia* (5–9)	probably introduced, on old walls and waste places, scarce and declining; no recent wall records, but noted from dump at Hoddesdon in 1986
Shepherd's-purse	*Capsella bursa-pastoris* (1–12)	common and widespread
Common Whitlow-grass	*Erophila verna* (4–6)	occasional to frequent in dry open conditions, usually on a basic substrate; it is possible that *E. majuscula* and *E. glabrescens* may also occur, although not recorded to date, and specimens should be checked for the superficially similar Wall Whitlow-grass *Draba muralis* last recorded from Loudwater, Markyate Cell and Nettleden in 1960s
Wallflower	*Cheiranthus cheiri* (4–6)	introduced; survives on walls about Hertford Castle where it has been known for centuries; *Cheiranthus* cultivars may occasionally occur on walls and in waste places
Common Annual Pearlwort	*Sagina apetala* (5–8)	common on and around bases of walls; two subspecies whose relative status in Herts have not been determined
Procumbent Pearlwort	*S. procumbens* (5–9)	occasional on old walls in damper situations
Fine-leaved Sandwort	*Minuartia hybrida* (5–6)	very rare on dry calcareous substrates; only recent wall records from bridge over canal at Hunton Bridge in 1969 and base of wall at Little Hadham in 1979
Thyme-leaved Sandwort	*Arenaria serpyllifolia* ssp. *serpyllifolia* (6–8)	common and widespread
Slender Sandwort	*A. serpyllifolia* ssp. *leptoclados* (6–8)	less frequent than ssp. *serpyllifolia*, but often found

		with it and, apparently, preferring calcareous substrates
Shining Crane's-bill	*Geranium lucidum* (5–8)	rare, on or by calcareous walls; most recent records from Baldock, Kings Langley, Bayford and Sandon
Herb Robert	*G. robertianum* (5–9)	common
Cotoneaster	*Cotoneaster* spp. (5–7)	several introduced species noted as garden escapes, casually, or sometimes more permanently, established on walls and waste places
Wall Pepper or Biting Stonecrop	*Sedum acre* (6–7)	frequent on basic substrates
White Stonecrop	*S. album* (6–8)	introduced, scarce; recent records from roof at Baldock and walls at Braughing, Ashwell and Ardeley
Thick-leaved Stonecrop	*S. dasyphyllum* (6–7)	introduced; only recent record from Much Hadham in 1979
Reflexed Stonecrop	*S. reflexum* (6–8)	introduced, scarce as garden escape; recent records from Totteridge churchyard and Berkhamsted Station car park
Houseleek	*Sempervivum tectorum* (6–7)	introduced and in past frequently planted on old walls and roofs; apparently much declined, only recent record from Langley in 1980
Rue-leaved Saxifrage	*Saxifraga tridactylites* (4–6)	much declined, now scarce on old walls and roofs although at a few sites quite abundant, such as walls near River Lea at Ware and one roof in The Arcade at Hitchin; other recent records from The Priory at Hitchin, Charlton, Rickmansworth, Bayford House, Hoddesdon and Ashwell
Ivy	*Hedera helix* (9–11)	common
Rosebay Willowherb	*Chamaenerion angustifolium* (7–9)	common
Pellitory-of-the-wall	*Parietaria judaica* (6–10)	occasional, a feature of some churchyards but scarce or absent from much of south Herts

Mind-your-own-business	*Soleirolia soleirolii* (5–10)	introduced, scarce as garden escape on and around damp shady walls
Hop	*Humulus lupulus* (7–8)	occasional as survivor from cultivation or near old malting sites
Buddleia	*Buddleja davidii* (6–10)	introduced and naturalised; increasing, especially on basic substrates
Snapdragon	*Antirrhinum majus* (7–9)	introduced and naturalised; still occurs as garden escape, mainly in waste places, and has been known on walls at Hertford Castle since the early 19th century
Ivy-leaved Toadflax	*Cymbalaria muralis* (5–9)	introduced in 17th century, frequent on railway brickwork and occasional elsewhere
Red Valerian	*Centranthus ruber* (6–8)	introduced, often escaping from gardens, sometimes naturalising; recent wall records from Hoddesdon, Astonbury near Stevenage and Ashwell
Oxford Ragwort	*Senecio squalidus* (5–12)	introduced, most frequent in south Herts, occasional elsewhere. (*See* railway flora.)
Stinking Groundsel	*S. viscosus* (7–9)	occasional
Groundsel	*S. vulgaris* (1–12)	common
Feverfew	*Tanacetum parthenium* (7–8)	occasional
Wall Lettuce	*Mycelis muralis* (7–9)	occasional, most frequent in south-west Herts
Fern-grass	*Desmazeria rigida* (5–6)	occasional, mainly on dry calcareous substrate
Squirrel-tail Fescue	*Vulpia bromoides* (5–7)	scarce, mainly on more acidic substrates
Rat's-tail Fescue	*V. myuros* (5–7)	scarce to rare; records from railway brickwork near Watford, Berkhamsted and Hitchin, also old concrete from wartime airfield at Scales Park near Nuthampstead
Flattened Meadow-grass	*Poa compressa* (6–8)	scarce, recent records from walls by Baldock Church and Berkhamsted Station
Narrow-leaved Meadow-grass	*P. angustifolia* (5–7)	scarce, recent records from walls at High Street in Barnet and Baldock Church
Wall Barley	*Hordeum murinum* (6–7)	common

1.21 Checklist of some of the More Frequent Casual and Opportunist Wild Flowers that might be found in association with Rubbish Dumps and Waste Places

NB *As noted in the text, many species mentioned for virtually the whole range of semi-natural habitats might potentially occur in waste places, especially those of disturbed road verges, arable lands and urban areas. This list is far from complete and, because of the transient nature of most sites and species, little will be said of status and distribution, many are non-native species.*

Larkspur	*Consolida ambigua* (6–8)	occasional as garden escape
Field Poppy	*Papaver rhoeas* (6–10)	common and widespread
Opium Poppy	*P. somniferum* (7–8)	fairly common
Common Fumitory	*Fumaria officinalis* (5–10)	common on lighter soils
Rape	*Brassica napus* (5–8)	common and increasing
Charlock	*Sinapis arvensis* (5–7)	common, but appears to be declining
White Mustard	*S. alba* (6–8)	occasional and declining
Radish	*Raphanus sativus* (6–8)	fairly common as a garden throw-out
Narrow-leaved Pepperwort	*Lepidium ruderale* (5–7)	local in south Herts
Garden Cress	*L. sativum* (5–8)	occasional
Shepherd's-purse	*Capsella bursa-pastoris* (1–12)	common and widespread
Field Penny-cress	*Thlaspi arvense* (5–7)	occasional
Warty Cabbage	*Bunias orientalis* (5–8)	scarce; has been a feature of the Cole Green and Baldock areas for several years
Honesty	*Lunaria annua* (4–6)	common as garden escape
Sweet Alison	*Lobularia maritima* (6–9)	occasional as garden throw-out
Horse-radish	*Armoracia rusticana* (5–6)	frequent
Intermediate Yellow Rocket	*Barbarea intermedia* (5–8)	scarce by dredged streams and margins of pits; most recent reports by canal at Berkhamsted and Amwell gravel pits
Tower Mustard	*Arabis glabra* (5–7)	scarce, found in the 1970s in pits about Hertford
Thale Cress	*Arabidopsis thaliana* (4–5)	fairly common on dry soils in south Herts
Tall Rocket	*Sisymbrium altissimum* (6–8)	occasional
Fale London-rocket	*S. loeselii* (6–8)	scarce
Hedge Mustard	*S. officinale* (6–7)	common
Eastern Rocket	*S. orientale* (6–8)	occasional
Weld or Dyer's Rocket	*Reseda luteola* (6–8)	common
Rose-of-Sharon	*Hypericum calycinum* (7–9)	occasional as garden throw-out

Maiden Pink	*Dianthus deltoides* (6–9)	rare, recorded from Mardley Heath and pit near Smallford in 1970s; most recent report from Ware tip in 1984/85, all probably garden throw-outs
Sweet William	*D. barbatus* (6–7)	occasional as garden escape
Sand-spurrey	*Spergularia rubra* (5–9)	scarce on open, acid sands and gravels in south Herts
Fat Hen	*Chenopodium album* (7–10)	common
Fig-leaved Goosefoot	*C. ficifolium* (7–9)	frequent
Oak-leaved or Glaucous Goosefoot	*C. glaucum* (6–9)	rare; most recent records from Rye House power station in 1981 and near Ware in 1984
Sowbane	*C. hybridum* (8–10)	rare; recorded from Ashwell in 1981 and from sewage works at Rye Meads in 1983
Nettle-leaved Goosefoot	*C. murale* (7–10)	rare; recorded from tips near St Albans and Ware in the 1970s
Many-seeded Goosefoot or Allseed	*C. polyspermum* (7–10)	common in south-east Herts, scarce elsewhere
Red Goosefoot	*C. rubrum* (7–9)	frequent
Hastate Orache	*Atriplex prostrata* (7–9)	frequent in south Herts, occasional elsewhere
Garden Orache	*A. hortensis* (8–9)	occasional
Common Orache	*A. patula* (8–10)	common
Dwarf Mallow	*Malva neglecta* (6–9)	fairly common
Flax	*Linum usitatissimum* (6–7)	occasional, sometimes cultivated
Slender Tare	*Vicia tenuissima* (6–8)	very rare; only recent records from Hexton Chalk Pit where it was introduced with dumped soil about 1977 and was still present in 1982
Yellow Vetchling	*Lathyrus aphaca* (6–8)	scarce, most recent record from 'waste' near Wormley in 1985
Broad-leaved Everlasting-pea	*L. latifolius* (6–8)	occasional
Narrow-leaved Everlasting-pea	*L. sylvestris* (6–8)	occasional
Sweet Pea	*L. odoratus* (6–8)	scarce
Goat's-rue or French Lilac	*Galega officinalis* (6–7)	occasional
Bladder Senna	*Colutea arborescens* (5–7)	scarce; most recent report from near Colney Heath in 1982
Crown Vetch	*Coronilla varia* (7–8)	scarce; recent records from Hitchin and Amwell gravel pit
American Willowherb	*Epilobium ciliatum* (6–8)	common

Rosebay Willowherb	*Chamaenerion angustifolium* (7–9)	common to abundant
Large-flowered Evening-primrose	*Oenothera erythrosepala* (6–9)	occasional
Common Evening-primrose	*O. biennis* (6–9)	occasional
Hemlock	*Conium maculatum* (6–7)	common
Fennel	*Foeniculum vulgare* (7–10)	occasional
Giant Hogweed	*Heracleum mantegazzianum* (6–7)	occasional and increasing
Coriander	*Coriandrum sativum* (6)	scarce
False Thorow-Wax	*Bupleurum subovatum* (6–10)	scarce; most recent records from Hitchin area
Dill	*Anethum graveolens* (7–8)	scarce
Annual Mercury	*Mercurialis annua* (7–10)	occasional on dry soils
Petty Spurge	*Euphorbia peplus* (4–11)	common
Sun Spurge	*E. helioscopia* (5–10)	common
Dwarf Spurge	*E. exigua* (6–10)	common
Knotgrass	*Polygonum aviculare* (7–10)	common
Pale Persicaria	*P. lapathifolium* (6–10)	common in south Herts, occasional elsewhere
Redshank	*P. persicaria* (6–10)	common
Black Bindweed	*Fallopia convolvulus* (7–10)	common
Buckwheat	*Fagopyrum esculentum* (7–8)	scarce
Japanese Knotweed	*Reynoutria japonica* (8–9)	fairly common in south Herts, occasional but increasing elsewhere
Giant Knotweed	*R. sachalinensis* (8–9)	occasional
Hemp	*Cannabis sativa* (7–9)	scarce
Buddleia	*Buddleja davidii* (6–10)	fairly common and increasing
Borage	*Borago officinalis* (6–8)	scarce
Bugloss	*Anchusa arvensis* (6-9)	scarce
Early Forget-me-not	*Myosotis ramosissima* (4–6)	occasional on open dry gravelly and sandy soils
Wood Forget-me-not	*M. sylvatica* (ssp. or cultivar) (5–6)	occasional as escape from gardens; ssp. *sylvatica* is native to woods in the Ash valley
Field Bindweed	*Convolvulus arvensis* (6–9)	common
Hedge Bindweed or Belbine	*Calystegia sepium* ssp. *sepium* (7–9)	common
Large Bindweed	*C. sepium* ssp. *silvatica* (7–9)	common
Dodder	*Cuscuta campestris* (7–9)	very rare; recorded from Rye Meads sewage works in 1976 and 1983
Henbane	*Hyoscyamus niger* (6–8)	scarce, most often in hot summers
Bittersweet	*Solanum dulcamara* (6–9)	common
Black Nightshade	*S. nigrum* (7–9)	common
'Potato'	*S. tuberosum*	frequent as throw-out
Thorn-apple	*Datura stramonium* (7–10)	scarce, most often in hot summers
Purple Toadflax	*Linaria purpurea* (6–8)	occasional

265

Vervain	*Verbena officinalis* (7–9)	rare
Peppermint	*Mentha* × *piperata* (7–9)	very rare; most recent record from Baldock in 1985
'Mint'	*M.* × *gentilis* (6–9)	rare; recent records from tips in Hertford and Ware area
'Mint'	*M.* × *villosa* (8–9)	rare
Goosegrass	*Galium aparine* (6–8)	common to abundant
Gallant Soldier	*Galinsoga parviflora* (5–10)	occasional
Shaggy Soldier	*G. ciliata* (5–10)	occasional
Ragwort	*Senecio jacobea* (6–10)	common and widespread
Hoary Ragwort	*S. erucifolius* (7–8)	common on heavier soils
Oxford Ragwort	*S. squalidus* (5–12)	common
Groundsel	*S. vulgaris* (1–12)	common and widespread
'Goldenrod'	*Solidago canadensis* (8–10)	frequent as garden escape
'Goldenrod'	*S. gigantea* (8–10)	occasional as garden escape
Blue Fleabane	*Erigeron acer* (7–8)	occasional on calcareous soils
Canadian Fleabane	*Conyza canadensis* (8–9)	occasional to common on light soils
Scentless Mayweed	*Tripleurospermum inoderum* (7–9)	common
Pineapple Weed	*Matricaria matricarioides* (6–7)	common
Shasta Daisy	*Leucanthemum maximum* (6–8)	scarce, a garden escape
Mugwort	*Artemesia vulgaris* (7–9)	common
Verlot's Mugwort	*A. verlotiorum* (10–11)	rare; no records since the 1970s
Spear Thistle	*Cirsium vulgare* (7–9)	common
Creeping Thistle	*C. arvense* (7–9)	common
Milk-Thistle	*Silybum marianum* (6–8)	rare; past records between Hitchin and Hertford, most recent at Purwell in 1984
Scotch Thistle	*Onopordum acanthium* (7–9)	occasional
Great Lettuce	*Lactuca virosa* (7–9)	occasional
Prickly Lettuce	*L. serriola* (7–9)	frequent
Garden Lettuce	*L. sativa* (7–8)	scarce
Michaelmas Daisy	*Aster* spp. (7–10)	fairly common as garden escapes and throw-outs, several species and hybrids involved
Barren Brome	*Bromus sterilis* (5–7)	common
Couch-grass or Twitch	*Elymus repens* (6–9)	common
Oat	*Avena sativa* (7–9)	frequent
False Oat-grass	*Arrhenatherum elatius* (6–7)	common
Creeping Bent or Fiorin	*Agrostis stolonifera* (7–8)	common
Black-grass	*Alopecurus myosuroides* (6–7)	common on neutral to calcareous soils
Canary Grass	*Phalaris canariensis* (6–7)	occasional
Green Bristle-grass	*Setaria viridis* (7–8)	scarce
Yellow Bristle-grass	*S. pumila* (7–8)	scarce
Foxtail Millet	*S. italica*	scarce, formerly occasional
Common Millet	*Panicum miliaceum*	scarce, formerly occasional

'Millet'	*P. capillare*	rare, recorded at Ware in 1985 and at Rye Meads sewage farm in 1982 and 1983
Cockspur or 'Barnyard Millet'	*Echinochloa crus-galli* (8–9)	scarce, recorded at Waterford tip in 1982 and at Ware in 1984 and 1985
Japanese Millet	*E. frumentacea* (8–9)	rare; recorded near Ware and at Rye Meads sewage works in 1983
Sorghum	*Sorghum halepense*	rare; recorded at Rye Meads sewage works in 1981 and 1984

1.22 Some Exotic Wild Flowers, Fruits and Vegetables recorded as Casuals from Tips in Hertfordshire during recent years, with their Areas of Origin

Hare's-ear Cabbage	*Conringia orientalis*	East Mediterranean and north Africa
Early-flowering Yellow Rocket or Land-cress	*Barbarea verna*	Western Mediterranean and western Pacific, also widely naturalised
Gold-of-pleasure	*Camelina sativa*	Eastern Europe and western Asia
'Amaranth'	*Amaranthus* spp.	Tropical and warm temperate regions
Chinese Jute	*Abutilon theophrasti*	Mediterranean
Hollyhock	*Althaea rosea*	China; forms and hybrids grown in gardens also may escape
Pink Oxalis	*Oxalis articulata*	Eastern (temperate) South America
Tree of Heaven	*Ailanthus altissima*	China
Grape-vine	*Vitis vinifera*	Warm temperate
Broad bean or Horse bean	*Vicia faba*	Mediterranean; also cultivated and may persist for a while in field margins
Soya	*Glycine maxima*	South-west Asia
Small Melilot	*Melilotus indica*	Southern Europe to India
Reversed Clover	*Trifolium resupinatum*	Asia
Spinach	*Spinacea oleracea*	Temperate regions
Sulphur Cinquefoil	*Potentilla recta*	Southern Europe and north Africa to central Asia
Japanese Rose	*Rosa rugosa*	Northern China and Japan; grown in gardens and may escape; planted at Amwell Gravel Pit and self-seeding

267

Syringa or Mock Orange	*Philadelphus coronarius*	South-east Europe and Caucasus
New Zealand Willowherb	*Epilobium brunnescens*	New Zealand
Cucumber	*Cucumis sativus*	Southern Asia; widely cultivated
Melon	*C. melo*	Originally tropical Africa; introduced into other subtropical and tropical regions
Marrows	*Cucurbita pepo* ssp.	America
Pumpkin	*C. maxima*	America
Watermelon	*Citrullus lanatus*	Tropical Africa
Squirting Cucumber	*Echballium elaterium*	Mediterranean
Himalayan Knotweed	*Polygonum polystachyum*	Himalayas
Tomato	*Lycopersicon esculentum*	South America
Potato	*Solanum tuberosum*	South America
Cape Gooseberry	*Physalis peruviana*	South America, later introduced to Cape of Good Hope area of South Africa
Apple-of-Peru	*Nicandra physalodes*	South America
Tobacco Plant	*Nicotiana* spp.	America
Star-Thistle	*Centaurea calcitrapa*	Southern Europe, north Africa and western Asia
Perennial Cornflower	*C. montana*	Southern and central Europe, often grown in gardens
Safflower	*Carthamus tinctorius*	Mediterranean
Niger	*Guizotia abyssinica*	East Africa and India
Sunflower	*Helianthus annua*	Western North America
Marigold	*Calendula arvensis*	Mediterranean
Asparagus	*Asparagus officinalis* ssp. *officinalis*	Europe; often cultivated
Garden Tulip	*Tulipa gesnerana*	Origin unknown but brought from Turkey in 16th century; many cultivars may occur as escapes
Spanish Bluebell	*Hyacinthoides hispanica*	Spain, Portugal; and north Africa, often cultivated in gardens and may escape
Grape Hyacinth	*Muscari* spp.	Various species from Europe, western Asia and north Africa occur as garden escapes or throw-outs; the native species *M. neglectum* of Breckland may also be cultivated and occur as an escape
Few-flowered Leek	*Allium paradoxum*	Caucasus to north Iran
'Daffodil' and 'Narcissus'	*Narcissus* spp.	Europe, north Africa and Asia; many hybrids cultivated in gardens and often found as throw-outs
Garden Iris	*Iris germanica*	Eastern Mediterranean
Siberian Iris	*I. sibirica*	South-eastern Europe
California Brome	*Bromus carinatus*	Western North America

Meadow Brome	*B. commutatus*	Much of central to southern Europe, north Africa and south-west Asia
Hare's-tail	*Lagarus ovatus*	Mediterranean region, Canary Islands and Madeira
'Millet'	*Panicum capillare*	North America
Maize	*Zea mays*	America

Appendix 2

Extinct Species

Notable wild flowers, ferns and a clubmoss considered to be now extinct in Hertfordshire, showing their former, broad habitat preferences and the date of their last recorded occurrences. Listed are 108 species, including a number of formerly established casuals, aliens and naturalised plants. Many exotics, short-term aliens and casuals are not listed.

Woodlands

Lesser Centaury	*Centaurium pulchellum*	1935
Crested Cow-wheat	*Melampyrum cristatum*	1961
Martagon Lily	*Lilium martagon*	*c.* 1955 (introduction)
Yellow Star-of-Bethlehem	*Gagea lutea*	1954
Purple Small-reed	*Calamagrostis canescens*	1843

Chalk downland

Moonwort	*Botrychium lunaria*	1882
Moon Carrot	*Seseli libanotis*	1976
Early Gentian	*Gentianella anglica*	1849
Slender Bedstraw	*Galium pumilum*	1964
Mountain Everlasting	*Antennaria dioica*	1947
Autumn Lady's-tresses	*Spiranthes spiralis*	1981
Lizard Orchid	*Himantoglossum hircinum*	1931
Military Orchid	*Orchis militaris*	1902
Man Orchid	*Aceras anthropophorum*	1931

Neutral grasslands and marshes

Knotted Pearlwort	*Sagina nodosa*	1957
Marsh Cinquefoil	*Potentilla palustris*	*c.* 1919
Grass-of-Parnassus	*Parnassia palustris*	1924
Round-leaved Sundew	*Drosera rotundifolia*	1914
Small Water-pepper	*Polygonum minus*	1964
Bog Pimpernel	*Anagallis tenella*	1965
Creeping Forget-me-not	*Myosotis secunda*	*c.* 1880
Marsh Lousewort	*Pedicularis palustris*	*c.* 1950
Common Butterwort	*Pinguicula vulgaris*	1880
Pennyroyal	*Mentha pulegium*	1926
Meadow Thistle	*Cirsium dissectum*	1980
Lesser Water-plantain	*Baldellia ranunculoides*	1845
Fen Pondweed	*Potamogeton coloratus*	1838
Lesser Butterfly-orchid	*Platanthera bifolia*	*c.* 1843
Wild Tulip	*Tulipa sylvestris*	*c.* 1940 (introduction)
Broader-leaved Cottongrass	*Eriophorum latifolium*	1849
Many-stalked Spike-rush	*Eleocharis multicaulis*	1839
Flat-sedge	*Blysmus compressus*	1955
Black Bog-rush	*Schoenus nigricans*	1843
Flea Sedge	*Carex pulicaris*	1838
Fibrous Tussock-sedge	*Carex appropinquata*	1885
Dioecious Sedge	*Carex dioica*	1878
Lesser Tussock-sedge	*Carex diandra*	1843

Acid grassland and heath

Stag's-horn Clubmoss	*Lycopodium clavatum*	1981
Shepherd's Cress	*Teesdalia nudicaulis*	*c.* 1940
Upright Chickweed	*Moenchia erecta*	1957
Subterranean Clover	*Trifolium subterraneum*	1913 (casuals recorded to 1973)
Fenugreek	*Trifolium ornithopoides*	*c.* 1848
Bilberry	*Vaccinium myrtillus*	1935
Chaffweed	*Anagallis minima*	1931
Dodder	*Cuscuta epithymum*	possibly into this century, with a few adventive records, last 1985
Sheep's-bit	*Jasione montana*	*c.* 1914
Small Fleabane	*Pulicaria vulgaris*	1923

Open waters and their margins

Reddish Pondweed	*Potamogeton alpinus*	1962
Sharp-leaved Pondweed	*Potamogeton acutifolius*	1841
Bog Pondweed	*Potamogeton polygonifolius*	1956
Grass-wrack Pondweed	*Potamogeton compressus*	1944
'Pondweed'	*Potamogeton* × *cooperi*	1959
Soft Hornwort	*Ceratophyllum submersum*	1956
Cowbane	*Cicuta virosa*	1929
Broad-leaved Ragwort	*Senecio fluviatilis*	*c.* 1960 (introduced)
Greater Butterwort	*Utricularia vulgaris*	*c.* 1960 (introduction survives at Balls Park)
Starfruit	*Damasonium alisma*	*c.* 1965
Frogbit	*Hydrocharis morsus ranae*	19th century (some recent introductions)
Mossy Stonecrop	*Crassula tillae*	*c.* 1945
Least Bur-reed	*Sparganium minimum*	1842
Floating Club-rush	*Eleogiton fluitans*	1962

Arable fields

Hairy Buttercup	*Ranunculus sardous*	1919 (casual 1960s)
Corncockle	*Agrostemma githago*	*c.* 1950 (*see* Chapter 11)
Small Bur-parsley	*Caucalis platycarpos*	1914
Thorow-wax	*Bupleurum rotundifolium*	1941
Green Hound's-tongue	*Cynoglossum germanicum*	1857
Field Cow-wheat	*Melampyrum arvense*	1840
Greater Yellow Rattle	*Rhinanthus angustifolius*	1925 (introduction *c.* 1980)
Annual Woundwort	*Stachys annua*	1956
Ground Pine	*Ajuga chamaepitys*	*c.* 1970 (*see* Chapter 11)
Lesser Snapdragon	*Misopates orontium*	1966
Broad-fruited Cornsalad	*Valerianella rimosa*	1965

Appendix 2

Red-tipped Cudweed	*Filago lutescens*	1919
Broad-leaved Cudweed	*Filago pyramidata*	1958
Narrow-leaved Cudweed	*Filago gallica*	1878
Small Cudweed	*Filago minima*	*c.* 1955
Lamb's Succory	*Arnoseris minima*	19th century
Darnel	*Lolium temulentum*	19th century (few recent casuals)
Interrupted Brome	*Bromus interruptus*	1849
Loose Silky-bent	*Apera spica-venti*	1960s
Annual Vernal-grass	*Anthoxanthum aristatum*	1930

Banks, verges, waste areas and urban

Brittle Bladder-fern	*Cystopteris fragilis*	1963
Oak Fern	*Gymnocarpium dryopteris*	1968
Crested Bunias	*Bunias erucago*	1930
London-rocket	*Sisymbrium irio*	1929
Wall Whitlow-grass	*Draba muralis*	1962
Curtis's Mouse-ear Chickweed	*Cerastium pumilum*	*c.* 1978
Strapwort	*Corrigiola littoralis*	1966
Least Mallow	*Malva parviflora*	1964
Greater Bur-parsley	*Caucalis latifolia*	1915
Cypress Spurge	*Euphorbia cyparissus*	1967 (garden escape)
Yarrow Broomrape	*Orobanche purpurea*	*c.* 1938
Copse Bindweed	*Fallopia dumetorum*	1875
Round-leaved Mint	*Mentha suaveolens*	1933
Wall Bedstraw	*Galium parisiense*	1860 (casual 1978)
Lesser Calamint	*Calamintha nepeta*	1955
Fuller's Teasel	*Dipsacus sativus*	1966 (casual 1985)
Elecampane	*Inula helenium*	1960s (garden relic)
Corn Chamomile	*Anthemis arvensis*	1970
Yellow Star-thistle	*Centaurea solstitialis*	1952
Maltese Star-thistle	*Centaurea melitensis*	*c.* 1916
Salsify	*Tragopogon porrifolius*	1951 (relic of cultivation; casuals recorded in 1985)
Field Garlic	*Allium oleraceum*	1950 (probably introduced)
Rough Dog's-tail	*Cynosaurus echinatus*	1939
Bristle Oat	*Avena strigosa*	1959
Annual Beard-grass	*Polypogon monspeliensis*	1961
Nit-grass	*Gastridium ventricosum*	1946
Rough Bristle-grass	*Setaria viridis*	1846

Appendix 3

Organisations concerned with wild flower studies and conservation

Because officers and addresses of some organisations may change they are omitted from the list below. The reader is best referred to local museums and libraries for up-to-date information on these, especially the

> Natural History Department,
> North Hertfordshire District Council Museums,
> Museums Resources Centre
> Bury Mead Road,
> Hitchin, Herts
> SG5 1RT
> *Telephone* Letchworth (0462) 686500 ext. 2384

where the major data files for Hertfordshire flora and the County Herbarium of preserved voucher specimens are housed.

Hertfordshire Natural History Society is the premier organisation for the study of natural history in the county. It organises a series of lectures and field meetings, promotes surveys and annually publishes the *Transactions,* which contains papers and articles related to all aspects of the natural sciences in Hertfordshire, including recent wild flower records.

London Natural History Society, whose area encompasses a twenty-mile radius of St Paul's Cathedral including a part of southern Hertfordshire, encourages fieldwork, research and publication of information relating to that region.

The British Naturalists' Association seeks 'to further the education of the general public in the study of natural history' and has an active Hertfordshire Branch which organises a full programme of meetings with many field excursions to all parts of the county.

Local natural history societies are based at Letchworth, Welwyn, Bishop's Stortford and Cheshunt. All have programmes covering many aspects of wildlife, with indoor and outdoor meetings, and often link with other organisations in the furtherance of studies and conservation activities.

The Nature Conservancy Council is the government body that promotes nature conservation in Britain. It gives advice on nature conservation to government and all whose activities affect our wildlife and wild places. It selects, establishes and manages national nature reserves and is responsible for the designation of Sites of Special Scientific Interest. The Assisiant Regional Officer is based at

> Archway House
> 7 Eastcheap
> Letchworth, Herts.
> SG6 3DC
> *Telephone* Letchworth (0462) 675830

The Hertfordshire and Middlesex Wildlife Trust is the major voluntary wildlife conservation organisation for the county. To date it owns or manages fifty nature reserves and promotes a wide range of associated events and activities. Several local groups have been established to support and publicise the aims of the Trust through field excursions, fund-raising, conservation tasks, nature reserve open days, talks and filmshows on wildlife, and surveys. The Trust can be contacted at

Grebe House
St Michaels Street
St Albans, Herts
AL3 4SN
Telephone St Albans (0727) 58901

WATCH is a national organisation with many local branches associated with the county wildlife conservation Trusts. Its aims are to encourage and teach children, between the ages of eight and fifteen, to appreciate the value and beauty of the environment. In Hertfordshire there are several local groups organising exciting and varied programmes of outdoor and indoor activities, including important studies of local and national interest. Further information is available from

WATCH (Herts and Middx Organiser)
Hudnall Park Environmental Studies Centre
Little Gaddesden
Berkhamsted, Herts.
Telephone Little Gaddesden (9584) 3400

WATCH Trust for Environmental Education Ltd
22 The Green
Witham Park
Lincoln
LN5 7JR
Telephone Lincoln (0522) 544400

The Botanical Society of the British Isles is the principal group for the study of British wild flowers and ferns. It is an association of amateur and professional botanists; publications deal with all aspects of the distribution, identification and taxonomy of British wild flowers and ferns. Indoor meetings, conferences, symposia and field meetings are organised, together with major surveys. The Society maintains a panel of referees to deal with the naming of difficult plant groups, a panel of specialists to deal with various scientific matters, a conservation committee to liaise over threats to rare native flora and a nation-wide network of Vice-County Recorders to co-ordinate local surveys, such as the Hertfordshire Flora Survey. The Society can be contacted as follows

BSBI
c/o Department of Botany
The Natural History Museum
Cromwell Road
London
SW7 5BD

The Vice-County 20 (Hertfordshire) Recorder can be contacted at the Natural History Department of North Hertfordshire District Council Museums (*see above*) to whom all offers of assistance in surveying the county's flora should be made and records sent.

The Farming and Wildlife Advisory Group has a branch in Hertfordshire and its objectives are 'to develop liaison between farming and conservation interests at a local level with a view to providing practical advice on the conservation of wildlife and landscape to farmers'. Study visits and advice and assistance in the preparation of conservation schemes are free from the local FWAG officer, who can be contacted at

> AIDAS
> Sovereign House
> Hale Road
> Hertford
> SG13 8EB
> *Telephone* Hertford (0992) 555250

Hertfordshire County Council's Planning and Estates Department operates a Countryside Management Service, which carries out practical conservation work in the county to care for the landscape and its wildlife habitats. It offers opportunities for volunteers to join with its professional workforce and welcomes requests for advice and assistance in local conservation and amenity projects. For further information contact

> The Countryside Management Service
> County Planning Department
> County Hall
> Hertford
> SG13 8DN
> *Telephone* Hertford (0992) 555250

Hertfordshire Environmental Records Centre is sponsored by local authorities and the Nature Conservancy Council. It gathers information on wildlife habitats and distribution in conjunction with the Hertfordshire Natural History Society and others. It supplies conservation advice to planners, wildlife groups and others concerned with the county's environment. The centre can be contacted at

> Museums Recources Centre
> Bury Mead Road
> Hitchin, Herts.
> SG5 1RT
> *Telephone* Hitchin (0462) 432454

Appendix 4

Some useful reference works, field guides and ancillary publications (See also Bibliography *on facing page.)*

BLAMEY, M. AND GREY-WILSON, C. (1989) *The Illustrated Flora of Britain and Northern Europe,* Hodder and Stoughton. Fully illustrated with keys to all major plant families; too bulky for the field but beautifully produced and would be a useful adjunct to this book

CLAPHAM, A.R. , TUTIN, T.G. AND MOORE, D.M. (1987) *Flora of the British Isles – 3rd edition,* Cambridge University Press. The standard work of reference

CLAPHAM, A.R. , TUTIN, T.G. AND WARBURG, E.F. (1981) *Excursion flora of the British Isles – 3rd edition,* Cambridge University Press. Handy, pocket-sized (and priced) field flora with taxonomic keys, but requires some botanical knowledge

FITTER, R., FITTER A. AND BLAMEY, M. (1985) *The Wild Flowers of Britain and Northern Europe – 4th edition,* Collins. One of the most useful field guides, particularly for beginners

HUBBARD, C.E. (1984) *Grasses – 3rd edition,* Penguin. With detailed keys to flowering and non-flowering grasses and detailed illustrations, a most useful publication

LOUSLEY, J.E. (1950) *Wild Flowers of Chalk and Limestone,* Collins (New Naturalist Series). Very readable account of the British flora associated with outcrops of calcareous rocks

PHILLIPS, R. (1977) *Wild Flowers of Britain,* PAN. A COLOUR-PHOTOGRAPHIC GUIDE SHOWING FRESH SPECIMENS, USEFUL IN CONJUNCTION WITH A FIELD GUIDE TO CONFIRM IDENTIFICATIONS

RICH, T.C.G. AND RICH, M.D.B. (1988) *Plant Crib,* Botanical Society of the British Isles. Very useful for the more advanced field botanists in dealing with critical determinations of difficult plant groups in the field

The Botanical Society of the British Isles has published a series of well illustrated guides to the identification of such rather difficult groups as willows and poplars, docks and knotweeds, umbellifers and sedges. Further titles will no doubt be added in due course

ROSE, F. (1981) *The Wild Flower Key – British Isles and N.W. Europe,* Warne. A very handy field book, combining easy to follow keys and nice illustrations, which has not had the popularity it deserves

As noted above, important papers, recent records and details of major sites relating to the flora of Hertfordshire are regularly published in *Transactions of the Hertfordshire Natural History Society.*

Local information regarding wild flowers can be obtained by contacting museums or natural history societies, which, together with other organisations, may produce a variety of guides and nature trails relating to specific sites or areas within Hertfordshire.

Bibliography

ARNOTT, J.G.L., BARTER, G.M., HENDERSON, A.C.B. AND NALL, J.L. (1978) *Survey of Rivers and Coast – Volume 4 – Hertfordshire,* Nature Conservancy Council, Wye.

BATEMAN, R. (1981) The Hertfordshire Orchidaceae. *Trans. Herts. Nat. Hist. Soc.* Vol. 28 Pt 4: 56–79.

BATEMAN, R. (1982) THE HERTFORDSHIRE ORCHIDACEAE – FURTHER RECORDS. *Trans. Herts. Nat. Hist Soc.* Vol. 28 Pt 6: 13–15.

BURLEIGH, G. AND SAWFORD, B. (1977) Hedges and Local History – Clothall. *Hertfordshire's Past* No 3: 18-20, Hertfordshire Archaeological Council and Hertfordshire Local History Council.

BURTON, R.M. (1983) *Flora of the London Area,* London Natural History Society.

CLAPHAM, A.R. , TUTIN, T.G. AND MOORE, D.M. (1987) *Flora of the British Isles – 3rd edition,* Cambridge University Press.

CANTOR, L. (ed) (1982) *The English Mediaeval Landscape,* Croom Helm, London.

DONY, J.G. (1967) *The Flora of Hertfordshire,* Hitchin Museum, Hitchin.

DONY, J.G., JURY, S.L. AND PERRING, F.H. (1986) *English Names of Wild Flowers. A List Recommended by the Botanical Society of the British Isles, Edition Two,* Botanical Society of the British Isles, London.

GODWIN, Sir H. (1975) *History of the British Flora – 2nd Edition,* Cambridge University Press.

HARRISON, S.G., MASEFIELD, G.B. AND WALLIS, M. (1969) *The Oxford Book of Food Plants,* Oxford University Press.

HARTING, J.E. (1881) Hertfordshire Deer Parks, *Trans. Herts. Nat. Hist. Soc.* Vol. 2: 97–111.

HERTFORDSHIRE COUNTY COUNCIL (1987) *Pond Report,* Hertford.

HERTFORDSHIRE COUNTY COUNCIL (1988) *Report of the Hertfordshire Grasslands Survey 1985-1987,* Hertford.

HEYWOOD, V.H. (1985) *Flowering Plants of the World,* Croom Helm, London.

HINTON, R. (ed.) (1978) *A Survey of Ancient Woodlands in Hertfordshire,* Hertfordshire and Middlesex Trust for Nature Conservation, St Albans.

MUNBY, L.M. (1977) *The Hertfordshire Landscape,* Hodder and Stoughton, London.

PERRING, F.H. AND FARRELL, L. (1983) *British Red Data Book: 1 – Vascular Plants,* The Royal Society for Nature Conservation, Lincoln.

PERRING, F.H. AND WALTERS, S.M. (1976) *Atlas of the British Flora – 2nd edition* EP Publishing for The Botanical Society of the British Isles, Wakefield.

PETERKEN, G.F. (1985) *Woodland Conservation and Management,* Chapman and Hall, London.

PRYOR, A. R. (1887) *Flora of Hertfordshire,* Stephen Austin and Sons, Hertford.

RACKHAM, O. (1986) *The History of the Countryside,* Dent, London.

RUTHERFORD DAVIS, K. (1973) *The Deserted Mediaeval Villages of Hertfordshire,* Phillimore for Hertfordshire Local History Council.

SAGE, B.L. (1959) *A History of the Birds of Hertfordshire,* Barrie and Rockliff, London.

SALISBURY, Sir E. (1961) *Weeds and Aliens,* Collins (New Naturalist Series), London.

SAWFORD, B. (1983) *Wildlife of the Letchworth Area,* Letchworth Naturalists Society, Letchworth.

Bibliography

SAWFORD, B. (1987) *The Butterflies of Hertfordshire,* Castlemead Publications, Ware.

SMITH, C.J. (1980) *Ecology of the English Chalk,* Academic Press, London.

STAMP, L.D. (1941) *Land Utilisation Survey of Hertfordshire,* Methuen, London.

WEBB, R.H. and COLEMAN, W.H. (1848-49) *Flora Hertfordiensis,* William Pamplin, London.

WILKINSON, G. *Trees in the wild and other trees and shrubs,* Stephen Hope, London.

Index and Glossary

Where definitions are to be found in the main text, relevant index entries are marked *. Certain other terms are defined below.

It should be noted that Appendices 1 and 2 are not indexed. In combination, these provide a comprehensive reference to Hertfordshire's wild flowers with both scientific and vernacular nomenclature.

Abbreviations used in the index; Chap. = Chapter, App. = Appendices, T. = Table. Page numbers in **bold** type =colour plate, page numbers in *italic* = figure.

calcifuge, 55*, 72, 79, 84
Callitriche hamulata, 120
C. platycarpa, 121
C. stagnalis, 120
Calluna spp., 15
Calluna vulgaris, 75, **97**
  distribution of, *78*
Caltha palustris, 14
Cam, River, 93, 95
Cambridge, 161
Camden, William, 99
Campanula spp., 15
Campion, Bladder, 127
  Red, 140
  White, 127
canals, 93, 100, *108*, 143, Chap. 10.7
  history of, Chap. 10.4, 161
  maintenance of levels in, 120
  wild flowers of, App. 1.12
Carex arenaria, 15
C. binervis, 84
C. demissa, 84
C. divulsa, 84
C. echinata, 84
C. flacca, 84
C. hirta, 84
C. maritimum, 15
C. nigra, 84
C. paniculata, 45, 92
C. pilulifera, 84
C. spicata, 84
Cannabis, *see* Hemp
Carpinus betulus, 16
carr, 91*, 95, 106, 110, 111, **117**, 120, 122, Chap. 10.2
  Alder, 91, 123
  natural succession of, 91
  willow, 91, 123
Carrot, Wild, 63, 175
carrots, 135
Cassiobury Park, Watford, 26, 109, 171
Castanea sativa, 47
casuals, 170, 177, 178, App. 1.21–22
Catchfly, Night-flowering, 144
catchments, river, 93, *94*
Cat's-ear, 81, 132
cattle, 24, 26, 66, 82, 126, 135, 141, 151, 153
  wild, 18, 19, 26
Cedar, Western Red, 50
Celandine, Greater, 128
  Lesser, 140
cemeteries, *see* churchyards
Centaurea cyanus, **176**

Centaurea spp., 15
Cerastium arvense, 14
C. pumilum, 165
cereals, 126–127, 135, 178
Chalk, 5*, 14, 39, 41, 52, 63, 73, 75, 89, 95, 104, 121, 177
Channel, English, 15, 16
charcoal, 113
Charlock, 127, 144
Chenies, Bucks, 81
Chenopodium rubrum, 121
Chequers Nature Reserve, Bucks, 65
Cherry, Wild, 20, 41, 42
Chervil, Rough, 44, 48, 158
Cheshunt, 8, 74, 81, 161
Chess, River, 71, 89, 93, *94*, 102, 103
Chestnut, Horse, 28, 47
  Sweet, 47
Chickweed, 127
  Curtis' Mouse-ear, 165
  Mouse-ear, 127, 174
  Sea or Dark-green Mouse-ear, 166
  Water, 121, 124
Chiltern Drift, 7
Chiltern Hills, 6, 63, 120
Chipperfield, 160
Chipperfield Common, 29, 74
chlorophyll, 58
Chorleywood, 160, 161
Chorleywood Common, *82*, 171
Church, the, 68, 133–134
Church Hill, Therfield, *53*
churchyards, 69, Chap. 14.2
  management of, 172
  tombstones in, 172
  walls of, 172
  wild flowers of, 172
Christmas tree, 50
Chrysanthemum segetum, **136**
Cinquefoil, Creeping, 81, 169
  Shrubby, 14
  Snowy, 14
cinquefoils, 81
Civil War, English, 138
Cladophora spp., 102
Claygate Beds, 6
Clay-with-Flints, 6*, 33, 39, 41, 66, 72, 73, 95
Claypits Meadow near Bayford, 79, 84, 85, 86
Clematis, Wild, 64, 139, 159, 164
climate, Chap. 4
  effects of . . . on flora, Chap. 4
  recent history of, Chap. 4
climates, palaeo-, Chap. 3.5

photodermatitis, 48*
photosynthesis (process within green plants whereby sugars are manufactured from water and carbon dioxide with the release of oxygen), 55, 109, 120
Phytolacca americana, 172
Picea abies, 50
P. sitchensis, 50
Pignut, 128
  Great, **76**, 144, 160
pigs, 24, 46, 126, 141, 151
Pimpernel, Bog, 88
  Scarlet, 128, 151, 169
  Yellow, 42
Pineappleweed, *146*, 168
pine/birch forest, 15, 16
Pine, Corsican, 49
  Scots, 15, 16, 47, 49
pines, uses of, 49–50
Pinus nigra ssp. *laricio*, 49
P. sylvestris, 15, 16, 49
Pinus spp., 15
Pirton, 61, 133, 141
pits, dry, 61, 83, 92, 112, 118, 150, 175
  history and ecology of, Chap. 15
  wild flowers of, Chap. 15, App. 1.21–22
  flooded, Chap. 10.10
    conservation of, 123
    history of, Chap. 10.10
    physical characteristics of, Chap. 10.10
    wild flowers of, Chap. 10.10
place names, 1
plague, bubonic, 25, 27, 129*, 134
Plantago maritima, 14
Plantago spp., 14
plantain, 14, 15, 159
Plantain, Hoary, 58, 158
  Great, 127, 168, 169
  Ribwort, 81, 127
  Sea, 14
plantations, 25, 28, Chap. 8
  conifer, 20, 46, 48–50, 74
  flora of, 47–50
  history of, Chap. 8
  Victorian, 47
Plashes Wood, Standon, 38
plashing, *45*, 138
Platanthera chlorantha, **36**
Pleistocene Period, 6–8*, 93, 122
plough, development of, 128, 131
podzol, 8, 73*
Pokeweed, 172

Polemonium caeruleum, 15
pollard, 21*, *22*, 25, 26, 30, 38, 92, 139
pollen (the mass of male spores produced by seed plants), 49
pollen (fossil), in sediments, 7, 14, 15, 16, 19, 20, 127
pollution, 2, 11, 123, 155, 168, 179
Polygala serpyllifolia, 81
P. vulgaris, **56**
Polygonum aviculare, 14
Pondbottom Wood, Nuthampstead, *35*
ponds, 70, 75, 83, 93, *115*, 112*
  ecology of, Chap. 10.8
  garden, 114, 169
  history of, 122, Chap. 10.8
  folklore of, 112
  loss and pollution of, 114–119, *119*, 122
  mill, 99, 111
  survey of Hertfordshire, 115–118
  wild flowers of, App. 1.13
  zonation of habitats in, 118
Pond-sedge, Lesser, 110, 124
  Greater, 110, 120, 124
Pondweed, Broad-leaved, 120, 123
  Curled, 120
  Fennel-leaved, 120
  Hair-like, 124
  Horned, 123
  Lesser, 124
  Shining, 120
  Small, 124
pondweeds, 106, 110, 119
poplars, 47
Poplars Green, *107*
Populus spp., 47
Populus tremula, 15
poppies, 144, 147
Poppy, Arctic, 14
  Field or Common, 125, 127, **156**, 159, 175
  Opium, 128
  Prickly-headed, 170
  Red, *see* Field Poppy
Potamogeton berchtoldii, 124
P. pusillus, 124
P. trichoides, 124
Potamogeton spp., 100
Potentilla anglica, 81
P. anserina, 14
P. erecta, 79
P. fruticosa, 14
P. nivea, 14
P. reptans, 79
P. × mixta, 79